DATE DUE			
Sep 12 '69			
Oct 9 69			
Mar 9 '71			
Dec 4 '71			
Oct 18 '82			

GAYLORD M-2   PRINTED IN U.S.A.

THE CHRISTIAN PHILOSOPHER

The
Christian Philosopher:

A Collection of
The Best Discoveries in Nature,
With Religious Improvements.

(1721)

BY

COTTON MATHER

A FACSIMILE REPRODUCTION

WITH AN INTRODUCTION

BY

JOSEPHINE K. PIERCY

GAINESVILLE, FLORIDA

SCHOLARS' FACSIMILES & REPRINTS

1968

SCHOLARS' FACSIMILES & REPRINTS

1605 N.W. 14TH AVENUE

GAINESVILLE, FLORIDA, 32601, U.S.A.

HARRY R. WARFEL, GENERAL EDITOR

L.C. CATALOG CARD NUMBER: 68-29082

MANUFACTURED IN THE U.S.A.

INTRODUCTION

The Improvement of Knowledge in the Works of Nature is a Thing whereby God, and his Christ is glorified. I may make a valuable Collection of many Curosities, which this Countrey has afforded; and present it unto the Royal Society. May the glorious Lord assist me, in this performance.

Cotton Mather's resolution, set down in his diary for July, 1711, was carried out; and in 1713 he was elected a member of the society in recognition of his contributions to knowledge. Ten years later he published *The Christian Philosopher*, a book on natural phenomena calculated to glorify God.

In December, 1711, he recorded a thought that he "often had in Mind. . . . The Light of *Reason* is the Work of God; the Law of *Reason* is the Law of God; the Voice of *Reason* is the Voice of God."

Unidentified as to its author, the last quotation might seem to have expressed the philosophy of the Deists or the theme of the Age of Reason. The fact is that the Puritans and the Deists were, in many respects, not poles apart.

There were many kinds of deists whose philosophy inspired them to work for the betterment of mankind: Franklin, the practical man of affairs; Paine, the revolutionist; Jefferson, the political idealist. All, however, impatient with orthodoxy, rejected revealed religion and hoped to substitute for it the religion of nature. There were several reasons why they did not succeed, one of the most important of which was that their philosophy, except for the rejection of revelation, was very much like that of the Puritans: Both believed in a First Cause, an ordered universe, the probability of a life hereafter, and an upright life in the present. They differed in these matters only in their interpretation of a First Cause. The Deists conceived an impersonal intelligence that planned and created the world, set it going, and then stepped aside to let it run its perfect course forever. The Puritans' First Cause was, of course, God, omniscient and omnipotent. They saw no paradox in their thinking that He had created a perfect whole that ran by itself, but that He was able to answer the prayers of the humblest Christian, or to reward and to punish the individual. Jonathan Edwards, caught in the cross currents of eighteenth century thought in America, attempted to reconcile this Christian paradox by declaring that God, having preordained everything, had preordained his own time to act or forebear to act in the affairs of man.

Anachronistically speaking, neither the Deists nor the Romanticists would have astonished Cotton Mather with the wonders of the natural world. He knew, as well as they, that God had created a perfect universe. He had looked at things of the earth and of the heavens, and he was filled with admiration and reverence. His attitude was, in a way, something new, because nature, in the hazardous days of early settlement, had seemed something antagonistic to man. Only a few, like Anne Bradstreet and Cotton Mather, saw it with a deeper meaning.

Yet the way had been prepared for Cotton Mather's thinking. According to Calvinist dogma, God had made man distinct from other animals by giving him intellect and reason. By using his powers of observation and reason, he could come to a greater understanding of God. Hence, the Puritans fostered the study of science and, indeed, became the scientists of their day. Although Harvard had been slow, after its founding in 1636, to reject the Ptolemaic system of the universe, by the middle of the century its students were eagerly examining the theories of Copernicus, Galileo, and Kepler, and later Newton. It was also in mid-century that advanced Harvard students and tutors began using empty pages in the almanacs that they issued for astronomical obstervations and theories. It is to be noted that, no matter how radical or new their ideas, not one finger of the Puritan faculty was raised against them. The almanac became, then, an important medium for the dissemination of advanced theories on astronomy. Nathaniel and Cotton Mather were among the contributors.

The acceptance by the Puritans of the theories of Copernicus, Galileo, Kepler, and Newton is a magnificent tribute to their rational thinking, because our world, for centuries thought to be center of the universe, was suddenly nothing but a small planet among probable millions. But this earth and those out there followed a fixed course, each in its own orbit, none calculated to deviate from its pattern of movement, not one endangering another. Men like Cotton Mather read the works of the scientists, and they became neither cynical nor disillusioned. They looked at the heavens and the earth, and they found their Creator, if possible, greater than ever.

The study of science had always fascinated Cotton Mather, whether it was about man or the heavens or the earth. He had wanted to be a physician; he championed the cause of smallpox inoculation at the risk of his life. He contributed many letters on the natural world of the colonies to the Royal Society. Among those with whom he corresponded most was Robert Boyle, one of the founders of that distinguished scientific body and author of *Usefulness of Experimental Natural Philosophy,* which undoubtedly inspired Cotton Mather to probe the natural phenomena of New England.* The minds of both men were sympathetically atuned to the wonder and beauty of the universe.

Cotton Mather's enthusiasms always found expression in writing, for he wished to share his convictions with others. Because of his tremendous influence in seventeenth century America, history remembers him best as a "Puritan priest," with all of the good and the less pleasant connotations of the term. He could equally have become, in his later life, a spokesman for eighteenth century rationalism had not he and Puritanism declined in influence after the witchcraft hysteria of 1692. *The Christian Philosopher* (1721) is a hymn to natural philosophy and, except for orthodoxy, a symbol of eighteenth century thought.

In his *Manuductio Ad Ministerium* (1726), he urges candidates for the ministry to spend more time on the study of Natural Philosophy. "Do it, with continual *Contemplations* and agreeable Acknowledgements of the Infinite GOD, whose Perfections are so display'd in His *Works* before you, that from them, you cannot but be perpetually ravished into the Acclamations of, *How Great is His Goodness and His Beauty!*"

After recommending for their reading in this study the *Philosophical Transactions* of the London Society, to which he contributed, and the "several Communications of our Illustrious Boyl, and of *Hook,* and of Grew, and *Cheyne* and *Keil* . . . *The Religious Philosopher,* of the Admirable *Nieuentyt;* . . . Industrious Ray and our In-

*See Samuel E. Morison, *Studies in the Intellectual Life of New England in the Seventeenth Century,* "Scientific Strivings," pp. 234-262.

genuous *Dexham,* who still nobly serve Religion as well as *Philosophy. . . . ,*" he hopes "it will be no Indecency for me to say so unto *you;* That if you desire to see the largest Collection, I have yet seen of the *Discoveries* which the last Age has made in *Philosophy,* adapted unto the general Capacity of Readers; and short Essays upon every Article, to Show and Raise those Dispositions of PIETY, wherein the *Works* of the Holy and Blessed GOD invite us to *Live* unto Him; together with the *First Claim* that I have ever yet seen so explicitly made on the behalf of a Glorious CHRIST, and the Consideration due to him in our *Philosophy;* you have this prepared for you in a Book Entituled, THE CHRISTIAN PHILO-SOPHER."

The divinity students' thorough pursuit of the subject will strengthen their faith in God. "Above all, I would have you see to it, that you be not, like some haughty, and short-sighted, and half-witted, *Smatterers in Philosophy,* seduced into the *Folly* of doubting the *Existence* or *Providence* of a Glorious GOD, by a Study, which, if well-pursued, would *Compel you to come in* to a *Strong Faith,* wherewith you would *give Glory* to Him, on all Occasions."

The Christian Philosopher is laden with quotations from the authors whom he recommended to his students and from others. If the work seems at times over-burdened with quotations, its author might be compared to other writers of the seventeenth century who felt that such use lent not only authority and conviction to their own words but learned decoration to their prose. Cotton Mather, however, denies that he is introducing names for mere learning's sake. Since he could not gather all scientific data by himself, he had to be in debt to others: "In introducing almost every article of it, the reader will continually find some author or other quoted.

This constant method of quoting, 'tis to be hoped, will not be censured, as proceeding from an ambition to intimate and boast a learning . . . But in these Quotations, there has been proposed, first, a due gratitude unto those, who have been my instructors; . . . it appears also but a piece of justice, that the names of those whom the great God has distinguished, by employing them to make those discoveries, which are here collected, should live and shine in every such collection."

Like a famous Englishman before him, Cotton Mather had taken all knowledge to be his province. Unshaken by revelations in the real world, he hoped to bring together in a book all knowledge of the physical universe to glorify God, who was the author of it all. In the introduction to his *Christian Philosopher,* he reiterates the thoughts expressed in his diary for 1711. "It is an Exercise highly becoming the *Christian Philosopher,* to fetch *Lessons of Piety f*rom the whole creation of GOD, and hear what *Maxims of Piety* all the creatures would, in the way of *Reflection* and *Similitude,* mind us of." And man alone can do this for he has the gift of reason, "The *Light of Reason, which enlightens every man that comes into the World;* every Man has all possible *Reason* to glorify *God."*

Piety and science sometimes made strange bedfellows. While accepting the premises of Halley and Newton and even accounting for comets in a reasonably scientific manner, he is so dazzled by their appearance that he is sure "that these frightful Bodies are the Ministers of *Divine Justice* . . . may bring about the great Catastrophe of our System . . . may be the Habitation of Animals in a State of *Punishment* . . . a Wicked World made a fiery *Oven in the Time* of the *Anger of God!"*

Of the earthquakes, too, he has both rational and spiritual explanations. However, when he points to the earthquakes of Sicily, his compassion for its inhabitants is greater than a lesson in piety or science. "No longer than t'other day what a rueful Spectacle was there exhibited in the Island of Sicily by an Earth quake, in which there perished the best part of two hundred thousand Souls!"

He is fascinated by revelations seen through the telescope, invented in the beginning of the seventeenth century and enlarged to eighty feet at the time of his writing, "whereby Objects of a mighty Distance are brought much nearer to us; is an instrument wherewith our GOOD GOD has in a singular manner favoured and enriched us: A *Messenger* that has brought in to us, from every distant Regions, most wonderful Discoveries."

He learns all he can on the stars, the sun, the comets, the rainbow, the air, this globe from the works by or about notable scientists most talked about in his day. From Newton he says " 'tis a difficult thing to dissent in anything that belongs to Philosophy."

Of the things of this earth, he has had more intimate contact. He finds sermons in stones. He is fascinated by the eyes and multi-legs of insects. He observes the commonwealth of bees and the city of ants. Oddly enough he makes no reference to the serpent in the Garden of Eden in his chapter on reptiles. His definition of them is charming: "A sort of Animals that rest one part of their Body on the Earth, while they advance the other part forward." He is aware of the use of their venom for medicinal purposes. He spends two and a half pages on a vivid, horrifying description of the dance of one bitten by a tarantula. He knows that the little fishes and the whales proclaim their creator. He is rapturous over "the feathered"', created by "the infinite God, who hath with so much Art contrived all Variety of *Birds,* and accomodated every part of them within and without after so rare a manner, that there is not so much as a *Feather* misplaced, redundant, or defective. . . ." He devotes twenty pages to the growth of vegetables and other plants, which he feels "cannot be wisely observed without admiration and astonishment."

His longest chapter of some eighty pages is on man, God's favorite creature. Having wanted to be a physician, he had devoured everything he could read about the body of man. His chapter, in part, is a short course in anatomy and physiology, whose wonderful structure and purposes are manifestly the creation of a divine planner. Indeed, "every Writer of *Anatomy* will offer enough to *trample Atheism under foot.*" But with this amazing structure alone, man would be no more wonderful than other animals. It is in this chapter that he emphasizes the "important thought he often had in mind" and that he declares in *Manuductio* and in the introduction to his book: that man has been given a soul and the faculty of reason, which he must use to understand himself and God.

The Christian Philosopher is more than a compilation of man's knowledge about himself, of the earth and its plants and animals, and of the stars. It does, indeed, glorify God, who created them all. For the most part, it is neither dull in statistics nor wearisome in religiosity. Cotton Mather had the gift of writing. Keenly aware of prose style, as his essay on the subject in *Manuductio Ad Ministerium* indicates, he always adapts his own to his purpose, from the varied biographies of his *Magnalia Christi Americana* to the sharp satirical prose of Political Fables. In *The Christian Philosopher* he has the gift of choosing the most pertinent material from others, and the best expressed.

When Cotton Mather turns from authentic references to his own observations, he speaks alone in often rhapsodic prose, befitting the author who is writing psalms in praise of his Maker. His delight in the "feathered" creatures and in "insects" is contagious. His awe as he contemplates man is reverent acknowledgment of God's creative genius.

The lesson of *The Christian Philosopher* is that Man, endowed with soul and intellect, may contemplate, as far as his mind will take him, the infinite wisdom of God "by whom all things were created." Finally in rhapsodic apostrophe, he appeals to the Christian: "O CHRISTIAN, *lift up now thine Eyes, and look from the place where thou art* to all Points of the Compass, and concerning *whatever thou seest,* allow that all these things were formed *for the Sake* of that Glorious-One, who is now *God manifest in the Flesh* of our JESUS; 'tis on *His* Account that the eternal Godhead has the *Delight* in all these things, which preserves them in their Being, and grants them the *Help,* in the *obtaining* whereof they *continue to this day.*"

JOSEPHINE K. PIERCY

Indiana University
March 2, 1968

THE
Christian Philosopher :
A
COLLECTION
OF THE
Best Discoveries in Nature,
WITH
Religious Improvements.

By COTTON MATHER *D. D.*
And Fellow of the ROYAL SOCIETY.

LONDON;
Printed for EMAN. MATTHEWS, *at the* Bible *in*
Pater-Noster-Row. M. DCC. XXI.

T O

Mr. *THOMAS HOLLIS*,
Merchant in *London*.

S I R,

 H E Learned Author of the enfuing Treatife, has already diffus'd his Name and Reputation in a great Variety of Ufeful Works; by which the better Part of Mankind do fufficiently know him to be *in Labours more abundant.* The Reader will find in this Treatife, a Collection

A 2   from

from Writers of the firſt and beſt Character, both in our own and other Nations; and every Obſervation improv'd to the Ends of Devotion and Practice. The Remarks that the Author gives, are ſo mingled with the Diſcoveries that he has brought together, that as it ſhows us with what Spirit He has purſued His Enquiries into the Wonders of the Univerſe, ſo it is both an Inſtruction and a Pattern to a ſerious Mind. He has generally drawn into his Application, all that the Bible ſaith upon the ſeveral Subjects: And thus he lays open the two great Books of God, Nature and Scripture. In this way, our Curioſity is not only entertain'd, but ſanctified; *the Inviſible Things of God from the Creation of the World are ſeen,* and improv'd to the Glory of Him whoſe they are.

Your ſurprizing Generoſity to the Academy in *New-England,* has made this Dedication more proper to you than any other Perſon. Such a Beneficence

ficence is an Argument how thorowly you defire that the Doctrines of the Gofpel, and the Purity of Difcipline, may be tranfmitted to future Generations. And certainly, it is the nobleft, and the moft divine Application of your Charity, when by it you are *a Fellow-helper to the Truth.* This is given to thofe from whom you can have no Expectation of Recompence; but as it's all done to the Lord, and not unto Men, fo by him it will be remember'd at *the Refurrection of the Juft.* You know how much it is againft my Temper to give *flattering Words*, and I'm convinc'd that it is againft yours to receive 'em. But I have reafon to think, that the Reverend Author, and the whole Country where God has placed him, will believe this Dedication well directed, to the BEST of all their Benefactors. *This Adminiftration of Service is abundant, by many Thankfgivings to God, (whilft by this Miniftration, they glorify God for your profefs'd Subjection to the Gofpel*

of Chriſt, and for your liberal Diſtri-
bution to them and to all Men) and by
their Prayer for you.

I have no more to add, but the
Apoſtle's Wiſh, that *your Faith may*
grow exceedingly, and *your Charity*
daily *abound;* that whatever you do,
may be done *faithfully to the Bre-*
thren, and to Strangers.

I am,

SIR,

London,
Sept. 22.
1720.

Your Sincere Friend,

and Obedient Servant,

Tho. Bradbury.

[vii]

An INDEX.

THE

THE
INTRODUCTION.

T HE Essays now before us will demonſtrate, that *Philoſophy* is no *Enemy*, but a
mighty and wondrous *Incentive* to *Religion*; and they will exhibit that PHILOSO-
PHICAL RELIGION, which will carry with
it a moſt ſenſible *Character*, and victorious *Evidence* of a
*reaſonable Service. GLORY TO GOD IN THE HIGH-
EST*, and *GOOD-WILL TOWARDS MEN*, animated
and exerciſed; and a Spirit of *Devotion* and of *Charity*
inflamed, in ſuch Methods as are offered in theſe *Eſſays*, cannot but be attended with more Benefits, than
any *Pen* of ours can declare, or any *Mind* conceive.

In the *Diſpoſitions* and *Reſolutions* of PIETY thus enkindled, a *Man* moſt effectually *ſhews himſelf a* MAN,
and with unutterable Satisfaction anſwers the grand
END of his Being, which is, *To glorify GOD*. He
diſcharges alſo the Office of a *Prieſt* for the *Creation*,
under the Influences of an admirable Saviour, and
therein aſſerts and aſſures his Title unto that *Prieſt-
hood,*

B

hood, which the Blessedness of the *future State* will very much consist in being advanced to. The whole *World* is indeed a *Temple* of GOD, *built* and *fitted* by that Almighty *Architect*; and in this *Temple,* every such one, affecting himself with the Occasions for it, will *speak of His Glory.* He will also rise into that *Superiour Way* of *Thinking* and of *Living,* which the *Wisest* of Men will chuse to take; which the more *Polite Part* of Mankind, and the *Honourable of the Earth,* will esteem it no Dishonour for them to be acquainted with. Upon that Passage occurring in the best of Books, *Ye Sons of the Mighty, ascribe unto the Lord Glory and Strength*; it is a Gloss and an Hint of *Munster,* which carries with it a Cogency: *Nihil est tam sublime, tamque magnificum, quod non teneatur laudare & magnificare Deum Creatorem suum.* Behold, a *Religion,* which will be found *without Controversy*; a *Religion,* which will challenge all possible Regards from the *High,* as well as the *Low,* among the People; I will resume the Term, a PHILOSOPHICAL RELIGION: And yet how *Evangelical!*

In prosecuting this *Intention,* and in introducing almost every *Article* of it, the Reader will continually find some *Author* or other *quoted.* This constant Method of *Quoting,* 'tis to be hoped, will not be censured, as proceeding from an *Ambition to intimate and boast a Learning,* which the *Messieurs du Port-Royal* have rebuked; and that the Humour for which *Austin* reproached *Julian,* will not be found in it: *Quis hæc audiat, & non ipso nominum strepitu terreatur, si est ineruditus, qualis est hominum multitudo, & existimet te aliquem magnum qui hæc scire potueris?* Nor will there be discernible any Spice of the impertinent Vanity, which *La Bruyere* hath so well satirized: ' *Herillus* will always ' *cite,* whether he speaks or writes. He makes the ' *Prince of Philosophers* to say, *That Wine inebriates*; and ' the *Roman Orator, That Water temperates it.* If he ' talks of *Morality,* it is not he, but the Divine *Plato,*
' who

' who affirms, *That Virtue is amiable, and Vice odious.*
' The moſt common and trivial things, which he him-
' ſelf is able to think of, are aſcribed by him to *Latin*
' and *Greek* Authors.' But in theſe *Quotations,* there
has been propoſed, firſt, a due *Gratitude* unto thoſe,
who have been my *Inſtructors;* and indeed, *ſomething
within me* would have led me to it, if *Pliny,* who is
one of them, had not given me a Rule; *Ingenuum eſt
profiteri per quos profeceris.* It appears alſo but a piece
of *Juſtice,* that the *Names* of thoſe whom the Great
GOD has diſtinguiſhed, by employing them to make
thoſe *Diſcoveries,* which are here collected, ſhould live
and ſhine in every ſuch Collection. Among theſe, let
it be known, that there are eſpecially Two, unto
whom I have been more indebted, than unto many
others; the Induſtrious Mr. RAY, and the Inquiſitive
Mr. DERHAM; *Fratrum dulce par:* upon whom, in divers Paragraphs of this *Rhapſody,* I have had very much
of my Subſiſtence; (I hope without doing the part of
a *Fidentinus* upon them) and I give thanks to Heaven
for them.

'Tis true, ſome Scores of other *Philoſophers* have
been conſulted on this Occaſion; but an *Induſtry* ſo
applied, has in it very little to beſpeak any *Praiſes* for
him that has uſed it: He earneſtly renounces them,
and ſollicits, that not only *he,* but the *Greater Men,*
who have been his *Teachers,* may diſappear before the
Glorious GOD, whom theſe *Eſſays* are all written to
repreſent as *worthy to be praiſed,* and by whoſe *Grace we
are what we are;* nor have we *any thing but what we
have received* from Him.

A conſiderable Body of Men (if the *Janſeniſts* may
now be thought ſo) in *France,* have learnt of Monſieur
Paſcal, to denote themſelves by the *French* Imperſonal
Particle *On;* and it was his opinion, that an honeſt
Man ſhould not be fond of *naming himſelf,* or uſing
the word I, and ME; that *Chriſtian Piety* will annihi-

late our I, and Me, and *Human Civility* will suppress
it, and conceal it.

Most certainly there can be very little Pretence to
an I, or Me, for what is done in these *Essays.* '*Tis
done,* and entirely, *by the Help of God:* This is all that
can be pretended to.

There is very little, that may be said, really to be
performed by the Hand that is now writing; but only the *Devotionary Part* of these *Essays,* tho they are
not altogether destitute of *American* Communications:
And if the *Virtuoso's,* and all the *Genuine Philosophers* of
our Age, have approved the Design of the devout
Ray and Derham, and others, in their *Treatises*; it
cannot be distasteful unto them, to see what was more
generally hinted at by those Excellent Persons, here more
particularly carried on, and the more *special Flights* of
the true Philosophical Religion exemplified. Nor
will they that value the Essays of the memorable Antients, *Theodoret,* and *Nazianzen,* and *Ambrose,* upon
the Works of the six Days, count it a Fault, if among
lesser Men in our Days, there be found those who say,
Let me run after them. I remember, when we read,
Praise is comely for the Upright, it is urged by *Kimchi,*
that the Word which we render *comely,* signifies *desirable,* and *acceptable*; and the Sense of that Sentence is,
that *Qui recti sunt, aliud nihil desiderant quam Laudem &*
Gloriam Dei. Sure I am, such *Essays* as these, to observe, and proclaim, and publish the *Praises* of the
Glorious GOD, will be *desirable* and *acceptable* to all
that have a *right Spirit* in them; *the rest,* who are *blind-
ed,* are Fools, and unregardable: As little to be regarded as a *Monster* flourishing a *Broomstick! Vix illis*
optari quidquam pejus potest, quam ut fatuitate sua fruan-
tur. For such *Centaurs* to be found in the Tents of
professed *Christianity!——Good God, unto what Times hast*
thou reserved us! If the *self-taught Philosopher* will not,
yet *Abubeker,* a *Mahometan* Writer, by whom such an
one was exhibited more than five hundred Years ago,
will

will *rife up in the Judgment with this Generation, and condemn it.* Reader, even a *Mahometan* will fhew thee one, without any *Teacher*, but *Reafon* in a ferious View of *Nature*, led on to the Acknowledgment of a Glorious GOD. Of a Man, fuppofed as but ufing his *Rational Faculties* in viewing the Works of GOD, even the *Mahometan* will tell thee; ' There appeared
' unto him thofe Footfteps of Wifdom and Wonders
' in the *Works of Creation*, which affected his Mind
' with an exceffive Admiration; and he became hereby affured, that all thefe things muft proceed from
' fuch a *Voluntary Agent* as was *infinitely perfect*, yea,
' above all Perfection: fuch an one to whom the
' Weight of the leaft Atom was not unknown, whether in Heaven or Earth. Upon his viewing of the
' *Creatures*, whatever *Excellency* he found of any kind,
' he concluded, it muft needs proceed from the Influence of that *Voluntary Agent*, fo illuftrioufly glorious, the *Fountain* of *Being*, and of *Working*. He
' knew therefore, that whatfoever Excellencies were
' by Nature in *Him*, were by fo much the greater, the
' more perfect, and the more lafting; and that there
' was no proportion between thofe Excellencies which
' were in *Him*, and thofe which were found in the
' *Creatures*. He difcerned alfo, by the virtue of that
' more Noble Part of his, whereby he knew the *neceffarily exiftent Being*, that there was in him a certain Refemblance thereof: And he faw, that it was
' his Duty to labour by all manner of Means, how
' he might obtain the Properties of that *Being*, put on
' *His Qualities*, and imitate *His Actions*; to be diligent
' and careful alfo in promoting *His Will*; to commit
' all his Affairs unto *Him*, and heartily to acquiefce
' in all thofe *Decrees* of *His* which concerned him, either from within, or from without: fo that he pleafed himfelf in *Him*, tho he fhould *afflict* him, and
' even *deftroy* him.' I was going to fay, *O Mentis aureae Verba bracteata!* But the Great *Alfted* inftructs me,

that we *Chriftians*, in our valuable Citations from them that are Strangers to *Chriftianity*, fhould feize upon the Sentences as containing *our Truths*, detained in the hands of *Unjuft Poffeffors*; and he allows me to fay, *Audite Ciceronem, quem Natura docuit.* However, this I may fay, *God has thus far taught a* Mahometan! And this I will fay, *Chriftian*, beware left a *Mahometan* be called in for thy *Condemnation!*

Let us conclude with a Remark of *Minutius Fælix:* ' If fo much Wifdom and Penetration be requifite to ' *obferve* the wonderful Order and Defign in the Struc- ' ture of the World, how much more were neceffary ' to *form* it!' If Men fo much admire Philofophers, becaufe they *difcover* a fmall Part of the *Wifdom* that made all things; they muft be ftark blind, who do not admire that *Wifdom* itfelf!

Religio Philosophica;

OR, THE

Chriſtian Philoſopher :

BEING

A Commentary, of the more Modern
and Certain Philosophy, upon
that Inſtruction,

JOB xxxvi. 24.

*Remember that thou magnify His Work which
Men behold.*

HE Works of the Glorious GOD in the
Creation of the World, are what I now
propoſe to exhibit; in brief *Eſſays* to enu-
merate *ſome of them*, that He may be glorified in them : And indeed my *Eſſays* may
pretend unto no more than *ſome of them*; for, *Theophilus*
writing, *of the Creation*, to his Friend *Antolycus*, might
very juſtly ſay, That if he ſhould have a *Thouſand
Tongues*, and live a *Thouſand Years*, yet he were not
able

able to defcribe the admirable Order of the Creation, διὰ τὸ ὑπερβάλλον μεγεϑὸς ϗ ᾋ ϖλῦτον σοφίας τῦ Θεῦ. *Such a Tranfcendent Greatnefs of God, and the Riches of his Wifdom appearing in it !*

Chryfoftom, I remember, mentions a *Twofold Book* of GOD; the Book of the *Creatures*, and the Book of the *Scriptures :* GOD having taught firft of all us διὰ ϖεϱ͗σμάτων, by his *Works*, did it afterwards διὰ γϱαμμάϭων, by his *Words*. We will now for a while read the *Former* of thefe *Books*, 'twill help us in reading the *Latter :* They will admirably affift one another. The Philofopher being asked, What his *Books* were; anfwered, *Totius Entis Naturalis Univerfitas.* All Men are accommodated with that *Publick Library. Reader*, walk with me into it, and fee what we fhall find fo legible there, *that he that runs may read it.* Behold, a Book, whereof we may agreeably enough ufe the words of honeft *Ægardus ; Lectu hic omnibus facilis, etfi nunquam legere didicerint, & communis eft omnibus, omniumque oculis expofitus.*

ESSAY I. *Of the* LIGHT.

WOULD it not be proper, in the firft place, to lay down thofe *Laws of Nature*, by which the *Material World* is governed, and which, when we come to confider, we have in the Rank of *Second Caufes*, no further to go? All *Mechanical Accounts* are at an end ; we ftep into the Glorious GOD *Immediately :* The very *next Thing* we have to do, is to Acknowledge Him, who is the *Firft Caufe* of all : and the CHRISTIAN PHILOSOPHER will on all Invitations make the *Acknowledgments.* The acute Pen of **Dr.** *Cheyne* has thus delivered them.

I. All *Bodies* perfevere in the fame State of *Reft*, or of *Moving* forwards in a *ftrait Line*, unlefs forced out of that State, by fome *Violence* outwardly impreffed upon them.

II. The

II. The *Changes* made in the *Motions* of *Bodies*, are always proportional to the *Impreſſed Force* that moves them; and are produced in the ſame *Direction* with that of the Moving Force.

III. The *ſame Force* with which one *Body* ſtrikes another, is *returned* upon the firſt by that other; but theſe Forces are impreſſed by *contrary Directions.*

IV. *Every Part* of every Body *attracts* or *gravitates* towards *every Part* of every other Body : But the *Force* by which one Part attracts another, in different Diſtances from it, is reciprocally as the *Squares* of thoſe Diſtances; and at the ſame Diſtance, the *Force* of the Attraction or Gravitation of one Part towards divers others, is as the Quantity of Matter they contain.

Theſe are *Laws* of the Great **GOD**, *who formed all things.* **GOD** is ever to be ſeen in theſe *Everlaſting Ordinances.* But now, in proceeding to *magnify that Work of God which Men behold,* it ſeems proper to begin with *that* by which it is that we *Behold* the reſt.

The Light calls firſt for our Contemplation. **A** moſt marvellous Creature, whereof the Great **GOD** is the *Father :*

Illic incipit DEUM *noſſe.*

The *Verus Chriſtianiſmus* of the pious *John Arndt* very well does inſiſt upon that Strain of Piety; **GOD** and His **LOVE** exhibited in the *Light.*

It was demanded, *In what Place is the Light contained? By what Way is the Light divided?*

Ariſtotle's Definition of *Light*; Φῶς εςιν ἡ ἐνέρϳεια τῦ διαϕανῦς, *Light is in the Inworking of a Diaphanous Body*; is worth an attentive Conſideration.

Light is undoubtedly produced, as Dr. *Hook* judges, by a *Motion,* quick and vibrative.

It is proved by Mr. *Molyneux,* That *Light* is a *Body.* Its *Refraction,* in paſſing thro a *Diaphanous Body,* ſhews that it finds a *different Reſiſtance*; *Reſiſtance* muſt proceed from a Contact of *two Bodies.* Moreover, it requires

quires *Time* to pass from one place to another, tho it has indeed the quickest of all Motions. Finally, it cannot by any means be *increased* or *diminished.* If you *increase* it, it is by robbing it of some other part of the Medium which it would have occupied, or by bringing the *Light,* that should naturally have been diffused thro some other Place, into that which is now more enlightened.

Sir *Isaac Newton* judges, 'Tis probable, that *Bodies* and *Light* act mutually on one another. *Bodies* upon *Light,* in emitting it, and reflecting it, and refracting it, and inflecting it : *Light* upon *Bodies,* by *heating* them, and putting their Parts into a *Vibrating Motion.*

All *Hypotheses* of *Light* are too *dark,* which try to explain the *Phænomena* by *New Modifications* of *Rays;* they depend not on any such *Modifications,* but on some *Congenite* and Unchangeable Properties, essentially inherent in the Rays.

The *Rays of Light* are certainly little Particles, actually emitted from the *Lucent Body,* and refracted by some *Attraction,* by which *Light,* and the *Bodies* on which it falls, do mutually act upon one another. It is evident, That as Rays pass by the Edges of Bodies, they are *incurvated* by the Action of these *Bodies,* as they pass by them.

And it is now perceived, That *Bodies* draw *Light,* and this *Light* puts Bodies into *Heat :* And that the Motion of *Light* is therefore swifter in *Bodies,* than *in vacuo,* because of this Attraction; and slower after its being *reflected,* than in its Incidence.

Irradiated by the Discoveries of the Great Sir *Isaac Newton,* we now understand, That every *Ray of Light* is endowed with its *own Colour,* and its different Degree of *Refrangibility* and *Reflexibility.* One Ray is *Violet,* another *Indigo,* a third *Blue,* a fourth *Green,* a fifth *Yellow,* a sixth *Orange,* and the last *Red.* All these are *Original Colours,* and from the Mixture of these, all the intermediate ones proceed; and *White* from an equa-

ble

ble Mixture of the whole : *Black*, on the contrary, from the ſmall Quantity of any of them reflected, or all of them in a great meaſure ſuffocated. It is not *Bodies* that are *coloured*, but the *Light* that falls upon them ; and their *Colours* ariſe from the *Aptitude* in them, to *reflect* Rays of one Colour, and to *tranſmit* all thoſe of another. 'Tis now decided, *No Colour in the dark!*

Tho *Light* be certainly a *Body*, it is almoſt impoſſible to conceive how *ſmall* the Corpuſcles of it are. Dr. *Cheyne* illuſtrates it with an Experiment, That it may be propagated from innumerable different Luminous Bodies, without any conſiderable Oppoſition to one another. Their ſeveral *Streams of Light* will be together tranſmitted into a dark Place, thro the leaſt Orifice in the World. Suppoſe a Plate of Metal, having at the top the ſmalleſt Hole that can be made, were erected *perpendicularly* upon an *Horizontal Plane*, and about it were ſet numberleſs luminous Objects of about the ſame Height with the Plate, at an ordinary Diſtance from it; the *Light* proceeding from every one of theſe Objects, will be propagated thro this Hole, without interfering.

Mr. *Romer*, from his accurate Obſervations of the *Eclipſes* on the *Satellits* of *Jupiter*, their Immerſions and Emerſions, thinks he has demonſtrated, That *Light* requires one Second of Time to move 9000 Miles. He ſhews, that the Rays of *Light* require ten Minutes of Time to paſs from the *Sun* to us. And yet Mr. *Hugens* hath ſhewn, That a Bullet from a Cannon, without abating its firſt Velocity, would be 25 Years paſſing from us to the *Sun*. So that the Motion of *Light* is above a million times ſwifter than that of a Cannon-Ball ; yea, we may carry the Matter further than ſo.

We ſuppoſe the Diſtance of the *Sun* from the Earth to be 12000 Diameters of the *Earth*, or ſuppoſe 10000, the *Light* then runs 1000 Diameters in a Minute; which is at leaſt 130,000 Miles in a Second. Dr. *Cheyne* ſhews,

shews, That *Light* is about six hundred thousand times
more swift than *Sound.*   Amazing Velocity!

To chequer the Surprize at so *swift* a Motion, I
may propound one that shall be as very surprizingly
slow.   *Dee* affirms, that he and *Cardan* together saw
an Instrument, in which there was one Wheel constantly moving with the rest, and yet would not finish
its Revolution under the space of seven thousand Years.
'Tis easy to conceive with *Stevinus*, an Engine with
twelve Wheels, and the Handle of such an Engine to
be turned about 4000 times in an Hour, (which is as
often as a Man's Pulse does beat) yet in ten Years
time the Weight at the Bottom would not move near
so much as an Hair's Breadth : And as *Mersennus* notes,
it would not pass an Inch in 1,000,000 Years ; altho it
be all this while in Motion, and have not stood still
one Moment : for 'tis a Mistake of *Cardan, Motus valde tardi, necessario quietes habent intermedias.*

' Behold the *Light* emitted from the *Sun ;*
' What more familiar, and what more unknown ?
' While by its spreading Radiance it reveals
' All Nature's Face, it still itself conceals.
' See how each Morn it does its Beams display,
' And on its golden Wings brings back the Day !
' How soon th' effulgent Emanations fly
' Thro the blue Gulph of interposing Sky !
' How soon their Lustre all the Region fills,
' Smiles on the Valleys, and adorns the Hills !
' Millions of Miles, so rapid is their Race,
' To chear the Earth, they in few Moments pass.
' Amazing Progress ! At its utmost Stretch,
' What human Mind can this swift Motion reach ?
' But if, to save so quick a Flight, you say,
' The ever-rolling Orb's impulsive Ray
' On the next Threads and Filaments does bear,
' Which form the springy Texture of the Air,

' That

‘ That thofe ftill ftrike the next, till to the Sight
‘ The quick Vibration propagates the Light :
‘ Still ’tis as hard, if we this Scheme believe,
‘ The Caufe of Light’s fwift Progrefs to conceive.

Sir *Richard Blackmore’s Creation*, Book 2.

The *Jews* have a good Saying, *Opera Creationis exter-næ habent in fe Imaginem Creationis internæ.* It will well enough become a *Chriftian Philofopher*, to allow for that *Image* in his Contemplations, and with devout Thoughts now and then refleĉt upon it.

Before I go any further, I confefs myfelf unable to *refift* the Invitation, which, I think, that I have, to infert an Obfervation of *Hugo de Sanĉto-Viĉtore*; That every Creature does addrefs a *Treble Voice* unto us : *ACCIPE, REDDE, FUGE;* indeed, *there is no Speech nor Language where their Voice is not heard.* It is an Exercife highly becoming the *Chriftian Philofopher*, to fetch *Leffons of Piety* from the whole Creation of GOD, and hear what *Maxims of Piety* all the Creatures would, in the way of *Refleĉtion* and *Similitude*, mind us of. In the Profecution of thefe *Meleteticks*, what better can be confidered, than this *Treble Voice*, from all thefe Thoufands of *Powerful Preachers*, whom we have continually furrounding of us ? Firft, *Accipe Beneficium :* Confider, *What is the Benefit which a Good GOD has, in this Creature, beftowed upon me ?* Secondly, *Redde Servitium :* Confider, *What is the Service which I owe to a Gracious GOD, in the Enjoyment of fuch a Creature ?* Laftly, *Fuge Supplicium :* Confider, *What is the Sorrow which a Righteous GOD may inflĭĉt upon me by fuch a Creature, if I perfift in Difobedience to Him ?* Even a Pagan *Plutarch* will put the Chriftian *Philofopher* in mind of this, That the World is no other than the *Temple* of GOD; and all the *Creatures* are the *Glaffes*, in which we may fee the *Skill* of Him that is the Maker of all. And his Brother *Cicero* has minded us, *Deum ex Operibus cognifcimus.* ’Tis no wonder then
that

that a *Bernard* ſhould *ſee* this; *Verus Dei Amator, quocunque ſe vertit, familiarem Admonitionem ſui Creatoris habet.* The famous *Hermite's* Book, of thoſe three Leaves, the *Heaven*, the *Water*, and the *Earth*, well ſtudied, how nobly would it fill the *Chambers* of the Soul with the moſt *precious and pleaſant Riches?* *Clemens* of *Alexandria* calls the World, *A Scripture of thoſe three Leaves*; and the Creatures therein ſpeaking to us, have been juſtly called *Concionatores Reales*, by thoſe who have beſt underſtood them:

Obvia dum picti luſtro Miracula Mundi,
  Naturæ intueor dum parientis Opus:
Emicat ex ipſis Divina Potentia Rebus;
  Et levis eſt Ceſpes qui probat eſſe Deum.

But the *Light* now calls for me.

¶. How *Glorious* a Body! ' But how infinitely,
' and beyond all Comprehenſion *Glorious* then, the In-
' finite GOD, who has challenged it as His Glory!
' *Iſa.* xlv. 7. *I form the Light.* The GOD of whom
' we have that *Sublime Stroke*, in the Hiſtory of the
' Creation; he ſaid, *Let there be Light, and there was*
' *Light!* The GOD whoſe Majeſty is within that
' *Holy of Holies*, where He *dwells in the Light, that no*
' *Man can approach unto!* *Lord*, thou haſt in a won-
' drous Diſplay of thy Benignity, afforded the Benefit
' of the *Light* unto thy Creatures: *Whatſoever does*
' *make manifeſt, is Light.* How miſerable ſhould we
' be, and in what inexpreſſible Confuſion, if the *Light*
' were withheld from us! What could be *manifeſt*
' unto us; what enjoyed or performed by us! O let
' all that *walk in the Light of the Living*, unite in Prai-
' ſes to the Creator of the *Light!* O! *give thanks to the*
' *Lord, for He is good, and his Mercy endureth for ever.*
' But, *Lord*, wilt thou leave my *Soul* in *Darkneſs!* The
' *Light* granted unto the *Soul*, in the Knowledge of
' thoſe things, *which to know is Life eternal*, is more
' precious and needful, than that in which our *Body*
                                                    ' finds

' finds itfelf fo much befriended. *O Father of Glory,*
' *let me have the Eyes of my Underftanding enlightened.*
' I have a moft Glorious Redeemer, of whom I am
' affured, That he is *the true* LIGHT, and *the* LIGHT *of*
' *the World.* A *Light* which, like other *Light,* carries
' its own *Evidence* with it : there needs no more to
' prove, that our Bleffed JESUS is the *Son* of GOD,
' and the *Saviour* of the World, than attentively to
' *Behold* Him. He can be no other, than what he af-
' ferts Himfelf to be, *The Light of Men. Lord, in thy*
' *Light I fhall fee Light.* When I fee the *Truth as it is*
' *in JESUS,* in fuch a Revelation and fuch an Exhi-
' bition, as my JESUS gives of it, then I fee every
' thing *in a true Light. My Saviour,* thou art more
' precious, and more needful, and more ufeful to me
' than the *Light.* I will walk in thee, and under thy
' Conduct ; fo fhall *I walk in the Light continually.*
' But what fignifies the *Light,* unto him that has no
' *Eyes* to perceive it. *O my Redeemer!* Beftow thou an
' *Eye* upon me : A *Faculty* to difcern the Things that
' are *fpiritually to be difcerned.*
' For the *Light* of *Reafon,* which *enlightens every Man*
' *that comes into the World;* every Man has all poffible
' *Reafon* to glorify GOD, and never do any thing,
' whereof any Man may juftly fay, *It feems to me un-*
' *reafonable.*
' But, *O my GOD,* thou haft favoured us with a
' rich Conglobation of *Light,* in the *Book* of thy lively
' Oracles, wherein we have a *Light fhining in a dark*
' *Place.* I would confider every thing in the *Light*
' wherein this lovely *Book* fets it before me : But, let
' me not *rebel againft the Light!*
' *The Light is truly fweet.* But, what fhall I find
' *the Inheritance of the Saints in Light!* They that are
' fhut out of that *Light,* and caft into *outer Darknefs,*
' and where they fhall *never fee Light;* Oh! the *Weep-*
' *ing,* and *Wailing,* and *Gnafhing of Teeth,* which they
' muft be expofed unto! *My Saviour,* I am under thy
' Conduct,

' Conduct, paffing through a gloomy Valley into thy
' *Light;* and when *I fit in Darkness, the Lord will be a*
' *Light unto me.*

‘ How *fwift* the Motion of the *Light !* But, *O my*
' *Saviour,* why no more *fwift* in thy coming to vifit
' and relieve a World lying in the perpetual Night of
' *Wickedness? Why thy Chariot fo long in coming?*

‘ And, *O my Soul,* why art thou *flow* in thy Con-
' templations of GOD, and CHRIST, and HEA-
' VEN; fly thou thither, with a Swiftnefs beyond
' that of the *Light,* [for fo thou canft] upon all Oc-
' cafions.’

ESSAY II. *Of the* STARS.

LET us proceed, and, conforming to the End of
our *Erect Stature, behold the Heavens, and lift up
our Eyes unto the Stars.*

The learned *Hugens* has a Sufpicion, that every
Star may be a *Sun* to other Worlds in their feveral
Vortices. Confider then the vaft Extent of our *Solar
Vortex,* and into what Aftonifhments muft we find the
Grandeur and Glory of the Creator to grow upon us !
Efpecially if it fhould be fo, (as he thinks) that all
thefe Worlds have their *Inhabitants,* whofe Praifes are
ofter'd up unto our GOD!

*Quantula de Cœli fpectanti Vertice celfo
Terra videretur, fi Cœli è Vertice Terra
Ulla videretur !*   So *Buchanan.*

His Improvement of the Thought is, How *little* of
this *little* has vain Man to ftrive for, and to boaft of!

O Pudor ! O ftolidi præceps vefania voti !

Mr. *Childrey* mentions two Curiofities, which ought
to be a little further enquired into. The one is, That
between the two Conftellations of *Cygnus* and *Cepheus,*
there lies crofs the *Milky-Way,* a black, long, little
                                                     Cloud,

Cloud, neither increaſing, nor abating, nor changing the Place in which it makes its Appearance.

The other is, That in *February*, and a little before and after that Month, in the Evening, when the Twilight has near deſerted the Horizon, there is a very diſtinguiſhing Way of the *Twilight*; a *Bright Path* ſtriking up towards the *Pleiades*, and almoſt reaching them, which is not obſerved any other time of the Year.

The *Jews* have a Fancy among them, That when the Almighty firſt beſpangled the Heavens with *Stars*, he left a Spot near the *North Pole* unfiniſhed and unfurniſhed, that ſo if any other ſhould ſet up for a GOD, there might be this trial made of his Pretenſions; *Go, fill up, if you can, that part of the Heavens, which is yet left imperfect.* But without any ſuch Suppoſitions, we may ſee enough in the Heavens to proclaim this unto us; *Lift up your Eyes on high, and behold: Who has created theſe things? None but an Infinitely Glorious GOD could be the Creator of them!*

The TELESCOPE, invented the Beginning of the laſt Century, and improved now to the Dimenſions even of *Eighty Feet*, whereby Objects of a mighty Diſtance are brought much nearer to us; is an Inſtrument wherewith our Good GOD has in a ſingular manner favoured and enriched us: A *Meſſenger* that has brought unto us, from very diſtant Regions, moſt wonderful Diſcoveries.

My GOD, I cannot look upon our Glaſſes without uttering thy Praiſes: By them I ſee thy Goodneſs to the Children of Men!

By this *Enlightener of our World*, it is particularly diſcovered,

That all the *Planets* at leaſt, excepting the *Sun*, are *denſe* and *dark* Bodies; and that what *Light* theſe *opake* Bodies have, is borrowed from the *Sun*.

That every one of the *Planets*, excepting the *Sun*, do change their Faces like the *Moon. Venus* and *Mercury*

C

cury appear fometimes like an *Half-Moon*, and fometimes quite *round*, according as they are more or lefs oppofite to the *Sun*. *Mars* has his Times of appearing in a Curvi-lined Figure. *Jupiter* has four little Stars, that continually move about him, and in doing fo, caft a *Shadow* upon him. *Saturn* has a *Ring* encompaffing of him.

That each of thefe *Planets* have *Spots* in their Superficies, like thofe of the *Moon*.

That not only each of thefe *Planets*, but the *Sun* alfo, befides whatever other Motion they may have, do move themfelves upon their own Centers; fome of them with a Motion of *Revolution*, others by that of *Libration*.

It was a good Remark made by one of the Antients, *Quid eft Cœlum, & totius Naturæ Decor, aliud, quam quoddam fpeculum, in quo fummi Opificis relucet Magifterium?*

The Pagan *Tully*, contemplating, *Cœleftium admirabilem Ordinem, incredibilemque Conftantiam*, the admirable Order, and the incredible Conftancy of the Heavenly Bodies and their Motions, adds upon it, *Qui vacare Mente putat, ne ipfe Mentis expers habendus eft:* Whofoever thinks this is not governed by *Mind* and *Underftanding*, is himfelf to be accounted void of all *Mind* and *Underftanding*.

According to Mr. *Hugens*, the Diftance of the *Sun* from us is 12,000 Diameters of the Earth. A Diameter of the Earth is 7,846 Miles. The Diftance of the nearest *Fixed Stars* from us, compared with that of the *Sun*, is as 27,664 to 1: So then the Diftance of the nearest *Fixed Stars* is at leaft 2,404,520,928,000 Miles; which is fo great, that if a Cannon-Ball (going all the way with the fame Velocity it has when it parts from the Mouth of the Gun) would fcarce arrive there in 700,000 Years. *Great GOD, what is thy Immenfity!*

The Number of the *Stars!* The learned *Arndt* has a good Thought upon it: *Si Deus tantam Stellarum Multi-*

*Multitudinem condidit, quis dubitet, illum multo majorem
Copiam habere Spirituum Cœleſtium, ſine intermiſſione illum
laudantium?* If the *Morning-Stars* are ſo many, how
many are the *Sons of GOD!*

¶. ' *Glorious GOD,* I give Thanks unto thee, for
' the Benefits and Improvements of the *Sciences,* gran-
' ted by thee unto theſe our latter Ages. The *Glaſ-*
' *ſes,* which our GOD has given us the *Diſcretion* to
' invent, and apply for the moſt noble Purpoſes, are
' Favours of Heaven moſt thankfully to be acknow-
' ledged.

' The World has much longer enjoyed the *Scrip-*
' *tures,* which are *Glaſſes,* that bring the *beſt of Hea-*
' *vens* much nearer to us. But, tho the *Objeἀ-Glaſſes*
' are here, the *Eye-Glaſſes* are wanting. *My GOD,*
' beſtow thou that *Faith* upon me, which, uſing the
' *Proſpeἀive* of thy Word, may diſcover the *Heavenly*
' *World,* and acquaint me with what is in that World,
' which, I hope, I am going to.

' I hear a *Great Voice* from the *Starry* Heavens, A-
' *ſcribe ye Greatneſs to our GOD. Great GOD,* what a
' Variety of *Worlds* haſt thou created! How aſto-
' niſhing are the Dimenſions of them! How ſtupen-
' dous are the Diſplays of thy *Greatneſs,* and of thy
' *Glory,* in the Creatures, with which thou haſt reple-
' niſhed thoſe Worlds! Who can tell what *Angelical*
' *Inhabitants* may there ſee and ſing the *Praiſes* of the
' Lord! Who can tell what *Uſes* thoſe *marvellous*
' *Globes* may be deſigned for! Of theſe *unknown*
' *Worlds* I know thus much, *'Tis our Great GOD that*
' *has made them all.*'

ESSAY III. *Of the* FIXED STARS.

OUR Great Proſpeἀive having made Enquiry,
finds a far greater Number of *Stars,* than what
we can diſcern with the naked Eye. The Antients
reckon'd only *One Thouſand and Twenty Two* Stars in

their

their *Fifty* Conſtellations. *Kepler* augments the Number to *One Thouſand Three Hundred and Ninety Two.* *Bayer* carries it on to *One Thouſand Seven Hundred and Nine.* Travellers to the Southward increaſed the Number of their Conſtellations to Sixty Two. The Number of the *Stars,* brought down into our *lateſt Globes,* is about *Nineteen Hundred;* but thoſe in the Heavens are inconceivably more. Among the *Pleiades,* in a Circle of but one Degree diameter, where our naked Eye ſees but *Six,* thus aſſiſted we ſee *Forty Six.*

The *Milky-Way* is nothing but an infinite Number of *Stars,* which are ſo ſmall, and lie ſo thick, as to give but a confuſed Glare unto us: And ſo the *Nebuloſæ,* in the Head of *Orion.*

The *Præſepe* is a Cluſter of more than Forty Stars. Thoſe adjacent unto the Sword and Girdle of *Orion* about Fourſcore. Mr. *Derham* ſuſpects, that the *Whiteneſs* of the *Milky-Way* is not cauſed by the great Number of the *Fixed Stars* in that Place, but partly by their *Light,* and partly by the Reflections of their *Planets,* which blend their *Light,* and mix it.

It is a little ſurprizing, that all the *Planets* appear *greater* in the Glaſs than to the naked Eye; but the *Fixed Stars* appear *ſmaller* there.

The Words of the ingenious **Dr.** *Cheyne* are worth conſidering: ' Since our Fixed Stars are exactly of ' the ſame Nature with our *Sun,* it is very likely that ' they have their *Planets;* and theſe *Planets* have *Satel-* ' *lits;* and theſe *Planets* and *Satellits* have Inhabitants, ' rational and irrational; Plants and Vegetables, Wa- ' ter and Fire; analogous to thoſe of our Syſtem.' *Aſcribe ye Greatneſs to our God!*

That which renders it probable, that the *Fixed Stars* are Bodies like our *Sun,* is this: 'Tis plain they ſhine by their *own Light.* It is impoſſible they ſhould appear ſo lucid as we ſee them, from the Light of our *Sun* tranſmitted unto them. 'Tis their aſtoniſhing Diſtance from us that cauſes the beſt of our *Teleſcopes*

to

to leſſen them. Tho we in this Globe approach nearer to them, ſome 24,000 Diameters of the Earth, or 188,304,000 Miles, one time of the Year than another; yet their *Parallax* is hardly ſenſible, or any at all: which could not be, if the Diſtance were not wonderful.

Hence alſo, it is impoſſible they ſhould be all in the Surface of the ſame Sphere, ſince our *Sun*, which is one of them, cannot be reduced unto this Rule. They are doubtleſs at as immenſe Diſtances frome one another, as the neareſt of them is from us. Were we at ſuch a Diſtance from the *Sun*, we ſhould not have the leaſt Glimpſe of the *Planets* that now attend it. Their Light would be too weak to affect us, and all their Orbs would be united in that one lucid Point of the *Sun*.

There are diſcovered *New Stars* in the Firmament, which having appeared a certain Time, do again diſappear.

A *New Star* appeared about 125 Years before the Birth of our Saviour.

Claudian mentions one which appeared, *A. C.* 388. *Albumazer Haly* mentions one, which appeared in the fifteenth Degree of *Scorpio*, and continued four Months.

In the Year 1571, and the Month of *November*, there appeared in that Conſtellation, which we call the Chair of *Caſſiopeia*, a moſt notable and wonderful Star of the firſt Magnitude, which held a Place among the other Stars, not having any Parallax, and kept a Courſe like theirs: It continued ſixteen Months; then decreaſed; anon grew quite inviſible. A Noble Perſon affirms, there was a *black Spot* remaining in the Place where that *Star* appeared.

In the Year 1601, there appeared a *New Star* of the third Magnitude, in the *Swan*'s Breaſt, which continued viſible twenty five Years, and then diſappeared. Thirty three Years after, it appeared again in its former Magnitude; but went away again in a Year or two. It re-appeared five Years after, and was extant for ſeveral Years, but of no more than the ſixth or ſeventh Magnitude.

In the Year 1671, another *Star*, which arrived unto the third Magnitude, appeared in the *Swan*'s Bill; it increaſes, and then decreaſes, and is about a Month making its Revolution.

There is an admirable Star in the *Whale*'s Neck: This firſt appears as one of the ſixth Magnitude, and then increaſes by little and little, for one hundred and twenty Days together, till it arrives to its full Bigneſs and Brightneſs, which is that of the third Magnitude; wherein it continues fifteen Days together: after which, it then decreaſes until it becomes inviſible. It appears every Year in its greateſt Luſtre, thirty two or thirty three Days earlier than in the foregoing Year; ſo that its Revolution is compleated in about three hundred and thirty three Days.

In the Years 1612, and 1613, there appeared a *Cloudy Star* in the Girdle of *Andromeda*; which diſappeared until the Year 1664, and then appeared again.

There is another Star, between *Eridanus* and the *Hare*, which alſo ſhows itſelf, and then withdraws, like the former.

There is one Star of the fourth Magnitude, with two of the fifth, in *Caſſiopeia*, which in all probability are new ones.

Mr. *Caſſini* has obſerved four towards the *Artick* Pole, which are probably new ones too.

Some Stars formerly appearing, do now diſappear. One ſuch there was in *Urſa Minor*. Another or two in *Andromeda* One which *Tycho Brahe* inſerts in his Catalogue, for the twentieth of *Piſces*. For time out of mind, there were *Seven Stars* obſerved in the *Pleiades*. The Writer of *Aſtronomy's Advancement* enquires, whether the *Seven Stars* in the Firſt of the *Revelation* have no Alluſion to them. However, at preſent there are but *Six* to be ſeen, probably one of them is retired.

Mr.

Mr. *Derham* thinks thefe *New Stars* may be Planets, belonging to fome of the Syftems of the Fixed Stars, and thofe Planets become vifible, when they are in that part of their Orbits which is neareft the Earth, and again gradually difappear, as they move in their Orbits farther from us.

It is a furprizing Obfervation of Dr. *Cheyne:* ' Sup-
' pofing that every *Fixed Star* is a *Sun,* and governs
' in a *Mundane Space,* equal to our Syftem, then there
' muft be only as many *Fixed Stars* of the *Firft Magni-*
' *tude,* as there are Syftems that can ftand round ours.
' But there are but about twelve or thirteen *Spheres*
' that can ftand round a middle one, equal to them :
' And fo many are the Stars of the firft Magnitude.
' Again, if we examine how many *Spheres* can ftand
' round this firft Range of *Spheres,* we fhall find their
' Number between Forty-Eight and Fifty-Two. And
' fo we find the Number of the *Stars* of the *fecond*
' *Magnitude.* As for the feveral other Magnitudes, it
' is not altogether poffible to determine their Number,
' becaufe they are not fo diftinguifhable from thofe of
' the other Magnitudes, as the firft and fecond are.'
He adds moft reafonably and religioufly : *It is impof-*
fible for any body ferioufly to confider in his Mind, what is
certain about thefe Heavenly Bodies, and to hinder himfelf
from being ravifhed with the Power and Wifdom of the
Great GOD of Heaven and Earth !

Mr. *Derham* fuppofes the particular Star *Syrius* to be above two Millions of Millions of Miles diftant from us.

Dr. *Grew,* from a very probable Computation, makes the Diftance of the *Pole-Star* from the Earth to be Four Hundred and Seventy Millions, and Eight Hundred and Forty Thoufand Miles.

Confidering the mean and vile Fables of the *Pagan Poetry,* yea, and the fcandalous Actions of fome *Greater Devils* among the *Pagans,* which are commemorated and celebrated in the Names which our *Globes* give

C 4 unto

unto the *Conftellations*, I cannot but move you, *O Chriftian Aftronomers*, to attempt a Reformation of fo fhame-
ful an Abufe. For fhame, let thofe Glorious Bodies
no longer fuffer the Affronts of our *Bafe Denominations*.
To put *Chriftian Names* on the *Conftellations*, and allowing the prefent Figures upon our *Globes* to remain ftill
as they are, neverthelefs to transfer them into *Scriptural
Stories*, was a thing endeavoured by *Schillerus*, and by
Novidius.

The Caution ufed in the antient *Hebraick* and *Ara-
bick* Aftronomy, about the Names of the Conftellations,
is well known to all that are verfed in *Antiquities*. Dif-
miffing that Reflection, what remains is this : A learned
Frenchman pretends to tell us, That the *Stars* in the
Heavens do ftand ranged in the Form of *Hebrew Letters*, and that it is poffible to *Read there, whatever is to
happen of Importance throughout the Univerfe.* Amazing!
That fo much Learning fhould be *Confiftent* with, and
much more, that it fhould be *Subfervient* to fuch *Futi-
lities !* The true *Reading of the Stars* is to look up,
and fpell out, the glorious Perfections of that GOD,
who is the *Father of thofe Lights,* and who *made* and
moves them all.

¶. ' I would by no means look up unto the *Stars,*
' with the foolifh *Aftrology* of the *Star-gazers,* who try
' to *read,* what the Great GOD that made them has
' not *written* there. But there is very plainly to be
' read there, the Power and the Grandeur of the Glo-
' rious GOD. This, this I will obferve, proftrate
' in the Duft before Him. *The Heavens declare the
' Glory of GOD ;* and fhall not I *obferve* it ? *When I
' confider thy Heavens, O Lord, and the Stars which thou
' haft ordained,* I cannot but cry out, *What is Man, that
' thou art mindful of him, and the Son of Man, that thou
' vifiteft him !*

' Unto the Father of the Faithful, my GOD faid,
' *Look now toward Heaven, and tell the Stars, if thou be
' able to number them ; fo fhall thy Offspring be. Glorious*
' *Lord,*

' *Lord*, make me one of them. A *Worm* of the Duſt,
' filled with the Love of GOD and of his Neigh-
' bour, becomes a *Star* in the Eye of the Glorious
' GOD: And if he be one of much Grace, and one
' of much *Uſe*, he is then a *Star* of the *greater Magni-*
' *tude.*

 ' GOD, *my Maker* and theirs, gives me that *Song*
' *for the Night*, wherein I view them; *He tells the*
' *Number of the Stars; He calls them all by their Names.*
' 'Tis true of the *Juſt*, who are to *ſhine as the Stars for*
' *ever and ever.* May I be known by the Lord as one
' of that *Number*, and have a *Name* in *His Book of*
' *Life !*

 ' Are the very *Stars* themſelves liable to *Viciſſitudes?*
' And ſhall not I look for them in this our miſerable
' World ?

 ' How little can I comprehend the Condition and
' Intention of the *Stars ?* O *Incomprehenſible GOD*, I
' will not cavil, but adore, when I find *Myſteries* in
' thy *Providence*, altogether beyond my *Penetration !*'

ESSAY IV. *Of the* SUN.

A Moſt Glorious and moſt Uſeful *Creature !* But
ſtill a *Creature !*
By Old Aſtronomers call'd, *Cor Planetarum.*
There will be no *Athenians* now to araign me for
it, if I call it, *The Carbuncle of the Heavens.* Kircher
ſuppoſes the *Sun* to be a Body of wondrous *Fire*, unequal in Surface, compoſed of Parts which are of a
different Nature, ſome fluid, ſome ſolid : The Diſque
of it, a *Sea of Fire*, wherein Waves of aſtoniſhing
Flame have a perpetual Agitation.
 Sir *Iſaac Newton*, as well as Dr. *Hook*, takes the *Sun*
to be a ſolid and opake Body. Dr. *Hook* thinks this
Body to be encompaſſed with a vaſt Atmoſphere, the
Shell whereof is all that ſhines. The *Light* of the Sun
he takes to be from the Burning of the more ſuper-
ficial

ficial Parts, which are set on fire, which may be without hazard of being burnt out in a vast Number of Ages. And Sir *Isaac Newton* thinks the *Sun* to be a sort of a mighty Earth, most vehemently hot; the Heat whereof is conserved by the marvellous Bigness of the Body, and the mutual Action and Re-action between *That*, and the *Light* emitted from it. Its Parts are kept from fuming away, not only by its *Fixity*, but also by the *Density* of the Atmosphere incumbent on it, and the vast Weight thereof. The *Light* seems to be emitted much after the manner as *Iron*, when heated unto such a Degree, as to be just going into Fusion, by the vibrating Motion of its Parts emits with Violence plentiful Streams of liquid Fire. So great a Body will continue its Heat a great while, perhaps in proportion to its Diameter.

Upon the Convexity of the Body of the *Sun*, there are observed *black Spots*, which are moveable, and changeable. These move regularly towards the West, and finish their Revolution in about five and twenty Days; and so testify unto us, that the *Sun* turns upon its own Center; the *Axis* of the Motion inclining to the *Ecliptick*.

These *Macula Solares* are probably Evaporations, which arise from the Body of the *Sun*, somewhat as Vapours do from the Earth; and they form themselves into *Clouds*. That which adds to this Probability, is, that the *Spots* are always changeable in their Bulk, and Form, and Configuration. Sometimes their *Number* is greater, and sometimes lesser, and sometimes there are none at all. Some of them shine, and others that shone, become dark. Diligent Astronomers, who have waited on them for nine or ten Years together, have never found them in all this time to return unto the *same Configuration*. In *Charlemain's* time, every one saw a *Spot* in this great Luminary. And there have been divers Days together, [as in the Year 1547,] wherein the *Sun* has appeared little brighter than the

Moon

Moon in her total Eclipse, and the *Stars* have been vifible at Noon-Day. *Virgil* and *Ovid* intimate fuch a
Darknefs upon the *Sun* once for a whole Year together, that the Fruits of the Earth could not be ri-
pened.

The apparent Diameter of the *Sun* being fenfibly
fhorter in *December* than in *June*, it is plain, and Obfervation confirms it, that the *Sun* is proportionably
nearer to the Earth in *Winter* than in *Summer*. It is
alfo confirmed, by the Earth's moving fwifter in *December* than in *June*; which it does about five Fif-
teenths. And for this reafon there are about eight
Days more from the *Sun*'s vernal *Equinox* to the autumnal, than from the autumnal to the vernal.

Mr. *Tompion*'s Obfervations, from the *Equation of
natural Days*, render it evident, That the Motion of
the *Sun* (if we muft fpeak in thofe Terms) muft be
fwifter at fome times, than at others. *Great GOD,
the Motion is always under thy Glorious Guidance!*

According to *Caffini*, the Sun's mean Diftance from
the Earth is 22,000 Semidiameters of the Earth. And
the Sun's Diameter is equal to 100 Diameters of the
Earth : And therefore the Body of the Sun muft be
1,000,000 times greater than the Earth.

Caffini more directly expreffes himfelf; That the
Sun's Diftance from the Earth is 172,800,000 *English*
Miles.

Take Mr. *Derham*'s Computation; *Saturn* is computed at 93,451 Miles in Diameter, and confequently
427,318,300,000,000 Miles in Bulk : *Jupiter* at
120,653 Miles in Diameter, and by confequence
920,011,200,000,000 Miles in Bulk. But yet, as a-
mazing Maffes as thefe all are, they are all far out-
done by that Globe of Fire, the *Sun*: which, as it is
the *Fountain* of *Light* and *Heat* unto all the Planets a-
bout it, by its kind Influences affording them the great
Comforts of Life; fo does it in *Bulk* furpafs them all.
Its Diameter is computed at 822,148 Miles; and fo
there

there muſt be 290,971,000,000,000,000 Miles in the ſolid Content of it.

Dr. *Grew* is of opinion, that for ought we know, the *Sun* may afford us his *Light*, without ſuch an intenſe *Heat*, as has been imagined. The Beams of the *Sun*, he thinks, may firſt conceive their *Heat*, when they come to be mixed with our *Atmoſphere*. There are things intenſely *hot*, which give no *Light* at all; but *Rotten Wood*, or *Fiſh*, and the *Gloworm*, and ſome other Bodies, give a brisk *Light*, without any *Heat*. *Light* and *Heat*, he thinks, have no neceſſary Conjunction, at leaſt not in any ſenſible Proportion. It is known alſo, how neceſſary the *Air* is to produce *Fire*, and even *Light* itſelf, in ſome of thoſe Bodies that ſhine in the dark. If the Sun were a *burning Body*, and the *Heat* of it ſo much greater than that we feel of it, as to be in proportion to its *Diſtance*; how comes the Subſtance of it ſo little to be altered by ſo intenſe an *Heat*, and to hold this *Heat* with ſo great an *Equality* for near ſix Thouſand Years? One way or t'other; either ſo *luminous* a Body without *Fire*, or ſo *burning* a Body, not *conſumed* or *altered*; it is wonderful!

But Sir *Iſaac Newton* ſuppoſes, That a very large, denſe, and fixed Body, when *heated* beyond ſuch a degree, may emit *Light* ſo copiouſly, that by ſuch Emiſſion, and by the Re-action of its *Light*, and by the Reflection and Refraction of the Rays within its hidden *Meatus*, it may come to grow ſtill hotter and hotter, as deriving more *Degrees of Heat* by thoſe Ways, than it can of *Cold* by any other. Thus, he ſuppoſes the *Sun* a vaſt Globe that is vehemently heated, and the Heat thereof preſerved by its great Magnitude, and the mutual Action and Re-action which there is between it, and the *Light* emitted by it. And its Parts are preſerved from evaporating in *Flame* and *Fume*, not only by the Great *Fixity* of its Nature, but alſo by the mighty Weight and Thickneſs of the Atmoſphere,

sphere, which environs it, and condenses its Vapours, whenever they are emitted.

However, behold the *Sun* seated by the Glorious GOD, like a powerful *Monarch*, on his Throne, (as Dr. *Cheyne* expresses it) from thence distributing Light, and Life, and Warmth, in a plentiful Effusion, to all the Attendants that surround him; and that so equally, that the nearest have not too much, nor the farthest too little: His Bulk and Situation so contrived, in respect of the *Planets*, as to have Quantity of Matter just enough to draw round him these Massy Bodies, and their *Satellits*, who are so various in their Quantities, and their Distances, and that in regular and uniform Orbits. The Doctor says well, *These are things that clearly speak the Omnipotence and Omniscience of their Author.*

What a Fancy is that of Dr. *Wittie!* That the Sun is probably the *Seat of the Blessed*; the *Sun*, which is the Center of the *Heavens*, and the Seat of *inherent Light*. It is true, of the Blessed we read, *They shall shine as the Sun*; and their Blessedness is called, *The Inheritance of the Saints in Light.* But this is very short of Demonstration, that the Saints must be lodged there. Tho the Church Militant were once represented as *clothed with the Sun*, it follows not, that the Church Triumphant must be *Dwelling in the Sun.*

And Mr. *Arndt* propounds a Thought, which cannot be too much dwelt upon: *Sicut Sol Ornamentum est Cœli, ita CHRISTUS est Ornamentum suæ Ecclesiæ.*

Dr. *Cheyne* with good reason apprehends, That the Quantity of *Light* and *Heat* in the *Sun* is daily decreasing. It is perpetually emitting Millions of *Rays*, which do not return into it. *Bodies* attract them, and suffocate them, and imprison them; and they go no more back into their Fountain.

Mr. *Bernoulli*, from the Flashes of the *Light*, in the Vacuity of a Tube accommodated with *Mercury*, whereby a dark Room is enlightned, renders it likely
that

that our Atmosphere, and all the Bodies on our Globe, are saturated at all times with Rays of *Light*, which never do return unto their Fountain.

'Tis true, this Decrease of the *Sun* is very inconsiderable. It shews that the Particles of *Light* are extremely small, since the *Sun* for so many Ages has been constantly emitting Oceans of *Rays*, without any very sensible Diminution. However, 'tis from hence evident, that the Sun had a Beginning; it could not have been from *Eternity*; *Eternity* must have wasted it: It had long e'er now been reduced unto less than the *Light* of a *Candle*.

Glorious GOD, thou art the Father of Lights, the Maker of the Sun!

In a late *Act of the Faith*, as they call their inhuman Butcheries, performed by that execrable *Hell upon Earth*, the *Inquisition* in *Portugal*; a Confessor being brought forth to die a grievous Death, as soon as he came into the *Light* of the *Sun*, which he had not seen in some Years before, he broke forth into this Expression, *Who that has Reason in him, could worship any but the Maker of that Glorious Creature!* They *gagg'd* him immediately!

My Pen shall not be served so. Enjoying the Benefits of the *Sun*, I will glorify him that made it: *Thou alone art for ever to be adored, O thou Maker of that Glorious Creature!*

An eminent Writer of *Natural Theology* has this Remark, 'That the *Sun* is *Imago illorum qui aliis præsunt*. And that all *Superiours* in every Station, looking towards the *Sun*, should have shot into their Minds the Rays of such Thoughts as these; *What good Influences ought I to dispense unto those that have Dependance on me!*

The Apocryphal Book of *Wisdom* does wisely, to call the *Light* of the SUN, *An Image of the Divine Goodness.*

The *Diameter* of the *Earth* is near Eight Thousand Miles; and the Diameter of the *Orbis Magnus* Ten Thousand

Thousand Diameters of the Earth. This *Orbis Magnus*, or the Orbit of the Earth, in its annual Revolution about the *Sun*; Dr. *Gregory* makes the Semidiameter of it 94,696,969 *English* Miles: which is the Distance of the *Earth* from the *Sun*. But the Semidiameter of *Saturn's* Orbit is no less than ten times as great. All Astronomers before *Kepler* supposed this Orbit a *perfect Circle*; but he has proved it an *Ellipsis.* If our *Solar System* have such large Dimensions, and if every *Fixed Star* be a *Sun*, that has a *System*, of the like Dimensions perhaps, belonging to it :——

Great is our GOD, and greatly to be praised: His Greatness is unsearchable!

How is it possible to consider the *Grandeur* of our GOD, without *Annihilating* ourselves before Him, or without Horrour at the View of the *matchless Evil*, in sinning against so Glorious a Majesty!

It is a Passage in a little Treatise, entitled, *The Book of Nature*; not unworthy to be transcribed here:
' If thou never observe the Sky with thine Eyes, but
' to guess at Rain and Fair Weather; or if thy look-
' ing up to Heaven be bounded with the *Starry Firma-*
' *ment*; and, if thou removest from thee the Love and
' Honour of GOD, and the Contemplation of Him
' who dwelleth in the Heavens, thou hast no cause to
' raise thyself above the *Brutes*, thy Fellow-Inhabi-
' tants of this Lower World.'

And now, let *Hugo de S. Victore* conclude for us: *Quis Solem per hyberna descendere Signa præcipit? Quis rursum per æstiva Signa ascendere facit? Quis eum ab Oriente in Occidentem ducit? Quis iterum ab Occidente in Orientem revehit? Hæc cuncta sunt mirabilia, sed soli Deo possibilia.*

How Glorious will the Righteous be in that World, when they shall *shine as the Sun?*

ESSAY

ESSAY V. *Of* SATURN.

ALL the *Maſter Planets*, as they may be called, move about the *Sun*, as their *Common Center.* They move with different Velocities: but there is this Common Law obſerved in all of them; *That the Squares of the Times of their Revolutions, are proportional to the Cubes of their Diſtances.* And the *Lunar Planets* obſerve the ſame Law in their Motions about their *Maſter Planets.* And another Common Law with them, is, That Lines drawn from the *Foci* of the Curves they move in, to their Bodies, will ſweep over equal *Area's* in equal Times on the Planes of other Orbits. Who but the Great GOD could make and fix theſe Laws? *Lord, they continue this day according to thine Ordinances, for all are thy Servants.*

It is now found, that *Saturn*, beſides his round *Body*, has alſo a luminous *Ring*, which encompaſſes him, as the Horizons of our Artificial Globes do uſually encompaſs them; and is flat upon the Verge, as they uſe to be. The *Ring* ſhews itſelf in an *Oval*, and at certain times it wholly diſappears.

It appears not, however, that *Saturn* revolves upon his own *Center.*

When this *Planet* appears at 20 degr. 30 min. of *Piſces*, and of *Libra*, then 'tis that he appears round; or without his *Anſæ*, as they are called, which is once in fifteen Years; or half his Courſe, which every one knows to be compleated in thirty Years, or 10,950 Days.

The *Ring* ſeems to be *Opake* and *Solid*, encompaſſing the *Planet*, but no where touching it. The Diameter of it is two and a quarter of *Saturn's* Diameters; and the Diſtance of the *Ring* from the *Planet* is about the Breadth of the *Ring* itſelf. Mr. *Hugens* takes the Breadth of the *Ring* to be about Six Hundred *German* Miles.

The

The Proportion of the Body of *Saturn* to the Earth, is that of 30 to 1.

The Diſtance of *Saturn* from the *Sun* is about ten times as great as the Diſtance of our Earth from him; and by conſequence, that Planet will not have above an hundredth Part of that Influence from the *Sun*, which this Earth enjoys.

The Ring of *Saturn*, being diſtant from him no more than two and a quarter of his Semidiameters, it cannot be ſeen at the Diſtance of 64 Degrees from *Saturn*'s Equator, in whoſe Plane the Ring is placed. So that there is a *Zone* of almoſt 53 Degrees broad, towards either Pole, to which this famous *Ring* does never appear.

Saturn is attended with five *Satellits*.

The Firſt *Satellit* makes a Revolution about *Saturn* in 1 Day, 21 Hours, and 19 Minutes; and makes two Conjunctions with *Saturn* in leſs than two Days. It is diſtant from the Center of *Saturn* $4\frac{3}{8}$ of his *Semidiameters*.

The Second makes his Revolution in 2 Days, 17 Hours, and 43 Minutes. It is diſtant from *Saturn* $5\frac{3}{7}$ *Semidiameters* of the Planet.

The Third is diſtant from *Saturn* eight of his *Semidiameters*, and makes his Revolution in almoſt $4\frac{3}{7}$ Days.

The Fourth revolves in 15 Days, 22 Hours, 41 Minutes. 'Tis diſtant from the Center of *Saturn* about 18 of his *Semidiameters*.

The Fifth is diſtant from the Center of *Saturn* 54 of his *Semidiameters*, and revolves about him in $79\frac{1}{7}$ Days.

Mr. *Huygens*, who firſt of all diſcovered the Fourth, (for which cauſe 'tis called the *Huygenian Satellit*, tho Dr. *Halley* afterwards corrected the Theory of its Motion) thinks, the mighty Diſtance between the Fourth and Fifth *Satellits* to be a ground for Suſpicion, that

D there

there may be a *Sixth* between them, or that the *Fifth* may be attended with some of his own.

On the Revolutions of the *Planets*, the incomparable Sir *Richard Blackmore*, in his Noble Poem of *Creation*, thus drives us to consider the *First Cause* of all :

' *Saturn* in Thirty Years his Ring compleats,
' Which swifter *Jupiter* in Twelve repeats.
' *Mars* Three and Twenty Months revolving spends,
' The Earth in Twelve her Annual Journey ends.
' *Venus*, thy Race in twice Four Months is run ;
' For his *Mercurius* Three demands ; the *Moon*
' Her Revolution finishes in One.
' If all at once are mov'd, and by One Spring,
' Why so *unequal* is their *Annual Ring* ?

The Motions of the Heavenly Bodies can be produced and governed by none but an Infinite GOD. It is well argued by *Lactantius* ; *There is indeed a Power in the Stars, of performing their Motions ; but that is the Power of God who made and governs all things, not of the Stars themselves that are moved.* And by *Plato* before him ; *Let us think, how it is possible for so prodigious a Mass to be carried round for so long a time by any natural Cause ? For which reason I assert God to be the Cause, and that 'tis impossible it should be otherwise.*

ESSAY VI. *Of* JUPITER.

JUPITER's Globe, according to *Cassini*'s Measures, must be greater than that of the Earth, by 2460 Times. The Periodical Time of his Revolution about the *Sun*, is Twelve Years, or 4380 Days.

In the Body of *Jupiter*, and overthwart his luminous Part, there are observed three darkish *Belts*, like the *Spots* which appear in the *Moon*. These *Belts* or *Girdles* are near strait and parallel, and extending from East to West, after the manner of the Ecliptick. They make a kind of *Equinoctial* with Tropicks. The

Southern

Southern is larger a little than the *Northern*, and a little nearer to the South than the other is to the North.

Dr. *Hook* has obferved alfo a fmall and a dark Filament, and the *Zones* growing a little darker, as they draw nearer to the Poles. And fome have obferved in them fomething of *Curvity*, tho their Borders are perfectly round,

Jupiter has *Four Satellits*, or little Moons, waiting on him.

The neareft is diftant from him, according to Mr. *Flamftead*'s moft accurate Obfervations, a little more than Five of his Semidiameters; and finifhes his Courfe in 1 Day, 18 Hours, 28 Minutes, and a few Seconds.

The Second is diftant from him about 8 of his Semidiameters, and finifhes his Courfe in 3 Days, 13 Hours, 17 Minutes, and a few Seconds.

The Third is diftant from him about 14 of his Semidiameters, and finifhes his Courfe in 7 Days, 3 Hours, and 59 Minutes, and fome Seconds.

The Fourth is diftant from him about 24 of his Semidiameters, and finifhes his Courfe in 16 Days, 18 Hours, 5 Minutes, and fome Seconds.

Thefe *Guards* of *Jupiter* caft a Shadow upon him, when they are found interpofed between the Sun and him.

The Fourth would appear to an Eye in *Jupiter*, as big as the Moon does to us. A Spectator there would have alfo four kinds of Months. In one of *Jupiter's* Years, which is Twelve of ours, there would be 2407 of the leaft Months; Half that Number for the next *Satellit*: The Months of the Third would be near fubduple of the Second, or fubquadruple of the Firft: The Months of the greateft would be about Two Hundred Fifty-four. A Year of *Jupiter* has a great Number of Days; but of the four Sorts of Months,

D 2   the

the leaft contains only *four Days* and a Quarter; the greateft fomething more than *Forty*.

Mr. *Caffini* has obferved a Couple of *Spots* in the Body of *Jupiter*, which make a Revolution on the Center of this Planet, from Eaft to Weft, in about 9 Hours, 56 Minutes. Others have lately confirmed it by better Obfervations. This proves, that the Planet moves about upon its own Center. Behold the *fhorteft Period* that is made in the Firmament! The Days and the Nights, each of them *Five Hours* a-piece.

Campani obferved, with a more than ordinary *Telefcope*, certain Protuberances and Inequalities in the Surface of this Planet.

We may here infert a Remark upon the Periodical Motions of the *Planets*; both the *Primary* and their *Secondaries*.

One thing very confiderable in the Periodical Motion of the *Secondary Planets*, is, That it is mixed with a kind of *Cochleous Direction* towards one or other Pole of its *Primary Planet*; by which means every *Satellit*, by gentle Degrees, changes its Latitude, and makes its Vifits towards each Pole of its *Primary*.

We will here break off with the Words of Mr. *Molyneux*. 'From hence may we juftly fall into the
' deepeft Admiration, that one and the fame *Law of*
' *Motion* fhould be obferved in Bodies fo vaftly diftant
' from each other, and which feem to have no De-
' pendance or Correfpondence with each other. This
' doth moft evidently demonftrate, that they were all
' at firft put into Motion by one and the fame uner-
' ring *Hand*, even the infinite Power and Wifdom of
' GOD, who hath fixed this Order among them all,
' and hath eftablifhed a *Law* which they cannot tranf-
' grefs.
' *Chance*, or dull *Matter*, could never produce fuch
' an harmonious *Regularity* in the Motion of Bodies fo
' vaftly diftant: This fhews a Defign and Intention
' in the *Firft Mover*.'

ESSAY

ESSAY VII. *Of* MARS.

MARS borrows his Light from the *Sun*, as well as the rest of his *Planetary Brethren.* He has his Increase and his Decrease of *Light* ; like the *Moon* ; may be seen almost *bisected*, when in his Quadrature with the *Sun*, or in his *Perigæon* ; tho never corniculated or forked, like his Inferiours.

Dr. *Hook* discovered several *Spots* in *Mars*, and particularly a triangular one, which has a Motion. Mr. *Cassini* afterwards discovered *four Spots*, the two first on one Face of *Mars*, afterwards two more that were larger, on the other Face. Upon further Observation it was found, that the *Spots* of these two Faces turned by little and little from East to West, and returned at the Space of twenty-four Hours and forty Minutes. In such a Term therefore, there is a Revolution of *Mars* upon his own *Axis.*

The Year of *Mars* is near twice as long as ours ; his *Natural Day* a little greater than ours : his *Artificial Day* is almost every where equal to his Night, besides what belongs to Twilight. *Mars* as well as *Jupiter* has a perpetual *Æquinox.* Hence there can be but little *Variety of Seasons* in any one particular Place of these Planets.

Whence the *Fasciæ*, or Fillets observed in *Mars* ? There appear certain *Swathes*, as we may call them, which are posited parallel to his Æquator. Are they owing to the Heat and Cold there, like our *Clouds* and *Snows* ?

It is thought that *Mars* has an *Atmosphere*, because *Fixed Stars* are obscured, and as it were extinct, when they are seen just by his Body.

ESSAY

ESSAY VIII. *Of* VENUS.

VENUS has various Appearances; *round* sometimes; anon *half-round*; by and by like a *Crescent.*

Mr. *Cassini* discovered certain *Spots* on this *Planet*,
by the Motion whereof it appeared that it moved upon its own Center, and upon an *Axis*, which carries
it from North to South; a Motion wholly unknown
any where else in the Heavens. *Two Spots* it has,
which are very thin, long, uncertainly terminated;
and a shining Part belongs to one of them.

He discover'd also, as he judges, a *Satellit* attending this Planet; which Dr. *Gregory* assents to, as more
than probable. This is not usually seen, perhaps
because it may not have a fit Surface to reflect the
Light of the *Sun*; which is the Case of the *Spots* in
the Moon.

Herigone, and *Keplerus*, and *Rhætensis*, conclude, that
Venus moves about its Axis in about fourteen Hours.
Dr. *Cheyne* says in twenty-three.

ESSAY IX. *Of* MERCURY.

THE Great *Hevelius* hath observed, That *Mercury*
changes his Face, like *Venus*, and like our Moon;
appearing sometimes *round*, sometimes *half-round*, sometimes like a *Crescent.*

This Planet has his Abode so near the *Sun*, that as
yet there has been little discovered of him.

It appears not yet, whether he revolves upon his
own *Axis*, and so what may be the Length of his Days.
But it is probable, he may have such a Motion, as
well as the other Planets. However, his Year is hardly equal to a Quarter of ours.

Sir *Isaac Newton* has terrible Apprehensions of the
Heat in this Planet, as being seven times as much as
the

the Heat of the Summer-Sun in *England*; which according to his Experiments made by the *Thermoſcope*, would be enough to make Water boil. If the Bodies in this Planet be not enkindled by this Heat, they muſt be of a peculiar Denſity. But Mr. *Azout* pretends to prove, That tho this Planet be ſo near the Sun, yet the Light there is not capable of burning any Objects.

¶. But let us now entertain ourſelves with a *Synopſis*, of certain Matters relating to the Planets, as they are determined by the lateſt and moſt accurate Aſtronomers.

The Diſtance from the Sun, in Engliſh *Miles.*

Of *Mercury*	Miles	32,000,000
Venus		59,000,000
The *Earth*		81,000,000
Mars		123,000,000
Jupiter		424,000,000
Saturn		777,000,000

The Diameter in Engliſh *Miles.*

Of *Mercury*	Miles	4,240
Venus		7,906
The *Earth*		7,935
Mars		4,444
Jupiter		81,155
Saturn		67,870
The *Sun*		763,460

The Time of the Periodick Revolution.

	Days		Hours
Of *Mercury*	87		23
Venus	224		17
The *Earth*	365		6
Mars	686		23
Jupiter	4,332		12
Saturn	10,759		7

D 4

To this we will add Mr. *Derham*'s Account of their Magnitude.

Saturn has an Orb of 1,641,526,386 *English* Miles Diameter.

Jupiter an Orb of 895,134,000 Miles.

Mars an Orb of 262,282,910 Miles.

Venus an Orb of 124,487,114 Miles.

Mercury an Orb of 66,621,000 Miles.

¶. ' *Great GOD, thou haft lifted me up to Heaven:*
' *Oh! let me not be caft after all down to Hell.*
' The Philofopher, who gazing on the *Stars* with
' his attentive Obfervation, tumbled into a Pit that
' he obferved not, was not fo unhappy as he that has
' vifited *Heaven* on the noble Intentions of *Aftrono-*
' *my*, but by an ungodly Life, procures to himfelf a
' Condemnation to that *Hell*, which is a State and
' Place of *Utter Darknefs*. Wretched Aftronomers!
' *Who are among the wandring Stars, to whom is referved*
' *the Blacknefs of Darknefs for ever.*'

We will conclude what we collect about the *Stars*,
with tranfcribing a Paffage out of the *Mifcellanea Cu-*
riofa. ' The Honourable Mr. *Roberts* computes the
' Diftances of the *Fixed Stars* ;—— which he fuppofes
' to be fo many *Suns* of a different Magnitude. He
' thinks, that it feems hardly within the reach of any
' of our Methods to determine it. The Diameter of
' the *Earth's Orb*, which is at leaft One Hundred and
' Sixty Millions of Miles, is but a Point in compari-
' fon of it. At leaft Nine Parts in Ten, of the Space
' between us and the *Fixed Stars*, can receive no grea-
' ter Light from the *Sun*, or any of the *Stars*, than
' what we have from the *Sun* in a clear Night. *Light*
' takes up more time in travelling from the *Stars* to
' us, than we in making a *Weft-India* Voyage, which
' is ordinarily performed in fix Weeks. A *Sound*
' would not arrive to us from thence in *Fifty Thoufand*
' *Years*

' *Years,* nor a Cannon-Bullet in a much longer Time.
' This is eafily computed, by allowing ten Minutes
' for the Journey of *Light* from the *Sun* hither; and
' that *Sound* moves about *Thirteen Hundred* Foot in a
' Second.'

ESSAY X. *Of* COMETS.

TIS an admirable Work of our GOD, that the
many *Globes* in the Univerfe are placed at fuch
Diftances, as to avoid all violent Shocks upon one
another, and every thing wherein they might prove a
prejudice to one another.

Even *Comets* too, move fo as to ferve the Holy Ends
of their Creator! COMETS, which are commonly called *Blazing Stars,* appear unto later Obfervations to
be a fort of *Excentrical Planets,* that move periodically
about the *Sun.*

Sir *Ifaac Newton,* from whom 'tis a difficult thing
to diffent in any thing that belongs to *Philofophy,* concludes, That the Bodies of *Comets* are folid, compaƈt,
fixed, and durable, even like thofe of the other *Planets.*

He has a very critical Thought upon the *Heat,*
which thefe *Bodies* may fuffer in their Tranfits near
the *Sun.* A famous one, in the Year 1680, paffed fo
near the *Sun,* that the *Heat* of the *Sun* in it muft be
twenty-eight thoufand times as intenfe as it is in
England at Midfummer; whereas the Heat of boiling
Water, as he tried, is but little more than the dry
Earth of that Ifland, expofed unto the Midfummer-
Sun: and the *Heat* of *red-hot Iron* he takes to be three
or four times as great as that of *boiling Water.* Wherefore the *Heat* of that *Comet* in its *Perihelion* was near
two thoufand times as great as that of *red-hot Iron.*
If it had been an Aggregate of nothing but Exhala-
tions, the *Sun* would have render'd it invifible. A
Globe of *red-hot Iron,* of the Dimenfions of our Earth,
would fcarce be cool, by his Computation, in 50,000
Years.

Years. If then this *Comet* cooled an hundred times as faft as *red-hot Iron*, yet, fince his Heat was 2,000 times greater than that of *red-hot Iron*, if you fuppofe his Body no greater than that of this Earth, he will not be cool in a Million of Years.

The *Tails* of *Comets*, which are longeft and largeft juft after their *Perihelions*, he takes to be a long and very thin Smoke, or a mighty Train of Vapours, which the ignited *Nucleus*, or the Head of the *Comet*, emits from it And he eafily and thoroughly confounds the filly Notion of their being only the *Beams of the Sun*, fhining thro the Head of the *Star*.

The Phænomena of the *Tails* of *Comets* depend upon the Motion of their *Heads*, and have their Matter fupplied from thence.

There may arife from the Atmofphere of *Comets*, Vapours enough to take up fuch immenfe Spaces, as we fee they do. Computations made of and from the Rarity of our *Air*, which by and by iffue in Aftonifhments, will render this Matter evident.

That the Tails of *Comets* are extremely rare, is apparent from this; the *Fixed Stars* appearing fo plainly thro them.

The Atmofphere of *Comets*, as they defcend towards the *Sun*, is very fenfibly diminifhed by their vaft running out, that they may afford Matter to produce the *Blaze*. *Hevelius* has obferved, that their Atmofphere is enlarged, when they do not fo much run out into *Tail*.

This *Lucid Train* fometimes, as Dr. *Cheyne* obferves, extends to four hundred thoufand Miles above the Body of the *Star*.

Sir *Ifaac Newton* has an Apprehenfion, which is a little furprizing, That thofe Vapours which are dilated, and go off in the *Blazes* of *Comets*, and are diffufed thro all the Celeftial Regions, may by little and little, by their own proper *Gravity*, be attracted into the *Planets*, and become intermingled with their Atmofpheres.

mospheres. As to the Constitution of such an *Earth* as ours, it is necessary there should be *Seas*; thus, for the Conservation of the *Seas*, and Moisture of the Planets, there may be a necessity of *Comets*; from whose condensed Vapours, all that *Moisture*, which is consumed in Vegetations and Putrefactions, and so turned into dry Earth, may by degrees be continually supplied, repaired, and recruited. Yea, he has a suspicion, that the Spirit, which is the finest, the most subtile, and the very best part of our *Air*, and which is necessarily requisite unto the Life and Being of all things, comes chiefly from *Comets*. If this be so, the Appearance of *Comets* is not so dreadful a thing, as the *Cometomantia*, generally prevailing, has represented it.

Mr. *Cassini* will thus far allow bad Presages to *Comets*, That if the Tail of a *Comet* should be too much intermingled with our *Atmosphere*, or if the Matter of it should, by its *Gravity*, fall down upon our Earth; it may induce those Changes in our *Air*, whereof we should be very sensible.

Bernoulli, in his *Systema Cometarum*, supposes, That there is a *Primary Planet*, revolving round the *Sun* in the space of four Years and 157 Days; and at the distance of 2,583 Semidiameters of the *Orbis Magnus*. This *Primary Planet*, he supposes, either from his mighty *Distance*, or his minute *Smallness*, to be not visible unto us; but however to have several *Satellits* moving round him, tho none descending so low as the Orbit of *Saturn*; and that these becoming visible to us, when in their *Perigæon*, are what we call *Comets*.

Seneca's Prediction, That a Time should come, when our Mysteries of *Comets* should be unfolded, seems almost accomplished. However *Seneca* has not obliged us with the *Phænomena* observed by him, which encouraged this Prediction.

No Histories of *Comets* were of service to the Theory of them, until *Nicephorus Gregoras*, a *Constantinopolitan*

litan Aſtronomer, deſcribed the Path of a Comet in
1337.

All that conſider'd *Comets* until *Tycho Brahe*, conſider'd them as no other than Vapours below the *Moon.*

Anon, the ſagacious *Kepler* improving on *Tycho's*
Diſcoveries, came at a true Syſtem of *Comets*, and
found, that they moved freely through the Planetary
Orbs, with a Motion that is not much different from
a *Rectilinear* one.

The incomparable *Hevelius* went on, and though he
embraced the *Keplerian* Hypotheſis, of the *Rectilinear
Motion of Comets*, yet he was aware, *That the Path of
a Comet was bent into a curve Line towards the Sun.*

At laſt the illuſtrious Sir *Iſaac Newton* arrives with
Demonſtrations, That all the Phænomena of *Comets*
would naturally follow from the *Keplerian* Principles.
He ſhewed a Method of delineating the *Orbits* of *Comets* geometrically; which cauſed Admiration in all
that conſidered it, and comprehended it.

The moſt ingenious Dr. *Halley* has made Calculations, upon which he ventures to foretell the *Return* of
Comets; but he obſerves, that ſome of them have their
Nodes pretty near the annual Orb of the Earth. I
will tranſcribe the Words he concludes with : ' What
' may be the *Conſequences* of ſo near an *Appulſe*, or of
' a *Contact*, or laſtly, of a *Shock* of the Celeſtial Bodies,
' (which is by no means impoſſible to come to paſs)
' I leave to be diſcuſſed by the Studious of Phyſical
' Matters.'

The Sentiments of ſo acute a Philoſopher as Dr.
Cheyne upon *Comets*, deſerve to be tranſcribed.

' I think it moſt probable, that theſe frightful Bo-
' dies are the Miniſters of *Divine Juſtice*, and in their
' Viſits lend us *benign* or *noxious* Vapours, according
' to the Deſigns of Providence; That they may have
' brought, and may ſtill bring about the great Cata-
' ſtrophe of our Syſtem; and, That they may be the
' Habitation of *Animals* in a State of *Puniſhment*, which

' if

' if it did not look too notional, there are many Ar-
' guments to render not improbable.'

And elsewhere: ' 'Tis most likely, they are the
' Ministers of Divine Justice, sending baneful Steams,
' from their long Trains, upon the *Planets* they come
' nigh. However, from them we may learn, that the
' Divine Vengeance may find a *Seat* for the *Punishment*
' of his disobedient Creatures, without being put to
' the expence of a New Creation.'

¶ When I see a vast Comet, blazing and rolling
about the unmeasurable *Æther*, I will think;

' Who can tell, but I now see a wicked World
' *made a fiery Oven in the Time of the Anger of GOD!*
' *The Lord swallowing them up in his Wrath, and the Fire*
' *devouring them!*

' What prodigious Mischief and Ruin might such
' a *Ball of Confusion* bring upon our sinful *Globe*, if the
' Great GOD order its Approach to us!

' How happy they, that are in the Favour and
' Friendship of that Glorious Lord, who *knows how*
' *to deliver the Pious* out of Distresses, and *reserve the*
' *Unjust for a Punishment of a Day of Judgment!*

> ——*Si fractus illabatur Orbis,*
> *Impavidum ferient Ruinæ.*

APPENDIX. *Of* HEAT.

WE should be forgetful, if we take our leave of
the *Heavenly Bodies*, and say nothing of *Heat*,
whereof they have so much among them.

To the *Heat* of Bodies it is requisite, that the small
Parts of it be agitated with much Vehemence and
Rapidity; and that the Determinations of the insensible Corpuscles thus agitated be also very *various*; and
that likewise the variously agitated Particles be so
small, as generally speaking to be singly insensible: for
unless they be exceeding fine, they cannot penetrate

readily

readily into the Pores of contiguous Bodies, and so warm or burn them.

The Operation of *Heat* upon our Senses, the Result of which we commonly call *Heat*, is usually estimated by its Relation to the Organs of our *Feeling.* If the Motion of the small Parts be more languid in the *Object* than it is in the *Sentient*, we pronounce the Body to be *cold*; but if it be more violent in the *Object* than in the *Sentient*, we say the Body is *hot.*

The *Intenseness* of *Heat* (as of *Light*) always is as the *Density* of the Rays, or Particles of *Fire*, that occasion it; and this *Density* is as the *Distance* from the radiating Point reciprocally.

Dr. *Slare* has published surprizing Experiments, of producing *Fire* and *Flame*, from the bare Mixture of two Liquors *actually cold*; a vegetable Oil, and a compound Spirit of *Nitre.*

The incredible Force of *Burning-Glasses!*

A burning Concave, made at *Lusace* in *Germany*, near three *Leipsick* Ells in Diameter, made of a Copper-Plate, scarce twice as thick as the Back of a common Knife; makes Wood in the *Focus* (which is two Ells off) to flame in a moment; and Water in an earthen Pot boil immediately: *Tin* three Inches thick, to be melted quite through in three Minutes; a Plate of *Iron* to be presently red-hot, and very quickly perforated: it will run in five or six Minutes; Tiles, and Slates, and earthen Potsheards, melt in a little time, and run into Glass; a Clod of Earth turns into a *greenish Glass.*

Mr. *Tschirnhaus* makes Convex Burning-Glasses of three or four Foot Diameter, the *Focus* at the Distance of twelve Foot Diameter; which in a moment vitrify Tiles, and Slates, and Pumice-Stones, and earthen Vessels; melt all resinous Things under Water; melt all Metals in a moment, and *Gold* itself is turned into Glass of a purple Colour: Of such efficacy are the Rays, when strip'd of an *unctious Matter*, which we may suppose them generally clothed with.

¶. ' The

¶. ' The antient *Persians* were the Worshippers of
' the *Fire*: But I will abhor their *Fire-Places*. The
' *Indians* of my Country, while unchristianized, con-
' cluded from the strange Effects of the *Fire*, *It must*
' *be a God*. I will adore the Glorious G O D that
' made the *Fire*. *Great G O D*, I bless thee for the Be-
' nefits, which thy Creatures, and I among them, re-
' ceive by the *Fire*, which is fetch'd *from Heaven* unto
' us., May my *Zeal* for thy Service be always kept
' *boiling* in the *Heat* proper for it.

' Since *Fire* is thus irresistible, and *Heat* so insup-
' portable, surely I should beware of that Impiety,
' which will expose me to the Revenges of G O D.
' *Who can dwell with such a devouring Fire, such ever-*
' *lasting Burnings?* My G O D, be not thou unto me
' a *Confuming Fire*. My G O D, who can abide the *Heat*
' of *thine Anger!*'

I have seen a Book of Devotion, entitled, *Christia-*
nus per Ignem; or, *A Difciple warming himself, and*
owning his Lord. It is there actually evident, and
performed, That this one Object, the *Fire on the*
Hearth, will afford a whole *Book-full* of profitable Contemplations.

ESSAY XI. *Of the* MOON.

WE are now coming down unto our *Terraqueous*
Globe. The M O O N, a sort of *Satellit* unto this
Globe, salutes us in our Way. Paying an Homage to
none but her Glorious Maker, we will now *behold her*
walking in her Brightness.

What shall we think of the *Protuberant Parts* observed on that Celestial Body? What of the *Round*
Hollows, like Pits or Wells of several Magnitudes,
which have been formerly mistaken for *Mountains?*

The Periodical Revolution of the *Moon*, in reference to the *Fixed Stars*, according to Mr. *Flamstead*,
is 27 Days, 7 Hours, 43 Minutes, 7 Seconds.

In

In the fame Space, with a ftrange Correfpondence of the two Motions, it revolves the fame way about its own *Axis*; by which the *fame Side* is always expofed unto our fight. But becaufe in the Space of a Periodical Month, the Earth is alfo with this her *Satellit*, moved on almoft an entire Sign, the *Moon* can't yet come to a new Conjunction with the *Sun*, but wants 2 Days, 5 Hours of it; which muft be paffed before the entire *Lunation* will be over, and before the Moon has exhibited all her *Phafes.* Thefe 2 Days 5 Hours, added unto the Periodical Month, make the *Synodical One*; which is 29 Days, 12 Hours, and ¾ of an Hour.

Thofe *Librations* of the Moon's Body, which occafion that the *Hemifphere* expofed unto our Sight is not always exactly and precifely the fame, arife from the Excentricity of the Moon's Orbit, and from the Perturbations it fuffers by the Sun's Attraction, and from the Obliquity of the Axis of the Diurnal Rotation of the Moon's own Orbit. Without the Knowledge of thefe Things, the *Phænomena* of the *Moon* would be inexplicable : but upon the Confideration of thefe, they are very demonftrable.

'Tis very fure, that although it be almoft the fame Face which the *Moon* turns to the Earth, yet it is not entirely fo. There is a *Libratory Motion*, whence it comes to pafs, that fometimes the more Eaftern and Weftern Parts of it, fometimes the more Northern and Southern appear alternately.

According to Sir *Ifaac Newton*, the mean Diftance of the *Moon* from the Earth, is about 60 Semidiameters of the Earth ; or about 24,000 *Englifh* Miles. The mean Diameter of the *Moon* is 32 Minutes, 12 Seconds ; as the *Sun's* is 31 Minutes, 27 Seconds. The *Denfity* of the *Moon*, to that of the Earth, he concludes to be nearly as 9 to 5. And the Mafs of Matter in the *Moon*, to that of the *Earth*, to be nearly as 1 to 26.

The

The *Moon* hath properly no *Atmoſphere*, ſuch as belongs to our Earth, of Clouds, Winds, Thunders; her Face is always clear, and by our Teleſcopes we can ſee the *Sun*'s Light paſs regularly and uniformly, from one mountainous Place to another.

The *Light* of the *Moon* reflected on us, is of ſuch a Weakneſs, that even in the *Full-Moon*, it will be brought by no Burning-Glaſs to afford the leaſt Degree of *Heat*. The Rays have their Force decreaſed, at leaſt as the Square of their Diſtance. The Force of the *Sun*'s Rays reflected unto us from the Moon, to thoſe that come to us directly, is decreaſed, at leaſt in proportion of the Square of the *Moon*'s Diſtance from the Earth, to the Square of the *Moon*'s Semidiameter. And by Calculation it will be found, That the *Light* of the *Moon* brought hither, will be in force but the *Fifty Thouſandth* Part of what comes hither directly from the *Sun*.

Dr. *Hook* finds, That the Quantity of *Light* which falls on the Hemiſphere of the *Full-Moon*, is rarefied into a Sphere about 288 greater in Diameter than the *Moon*, before it arrive to us. Conſequently, the *Moon*'s *Light* is 104,368 times weaker than the *Sun*'s; and it would require 104,368 *Full-Moons* to give a *Light* equal unto that of the *Sun* at Noon.

There is a *Secondary Light* of the *Moon*; that is to ſay, the obſcure Part of the Moon appears like to kindled Aſhes, juſt before and after the Change. This is the *Sun*'s Rays reflected from the bright Hemiſphere of the Earth, to the dark Parts of the *Moon*; and thence again reflected unto the Earth, deſtitute of the Light of the *Sun*. This is by *Tacquet* and *Zucchius* more largely diſcourſed on. When the *Moon* is at *Change* to us, the *Earth* is at *Full* to the *Moon*; and the Light of the *Earth* is about fifteen times greater than that of the *Moon*. The *Moon* alſo being ſo little, as not to obſcure above a twentieth Part of the *Earth*, it may be ſuppoſed that the Light from the *Earth*

E   may

may render her a little vifible to us even in *Solar Eclipfes.*

The *Moon* is almoft one Semidiameter of the Earth nearer to us, when fhe is in the *Meridian*, than when fhe is nigh the *Horizon*. But why doth fhe then appear bigger to our fight when fhe is nigh the *Horizon*, than when fhe is in the *Meridian?* Dr. *Wallis* agrees with *Des Cartes* in the Solution : the Horizontal *Moon* is capable of being compared with many intervening Objects, Hills, Trees, and the like ; but the Meridian *Moon* hath nothing to be compared with.

Tho the *Moon*, as well as the *Earth*, and probably all the Planets, be of a Figure *oblately fpheriodical*, that is to fay, having its Diameter at the *Æquator*, longer than its Axis ; yet the Excefs of the Æquatorial Diameter in her is fo inconfiderable, that fhe may well enough pafs for a Globe. And perhaps this almoft fpherical Figure of the *Moon* may be the Refult of her flow Motion round her Axis ; for *Jupiter*, which moves the fwifteft of any round its Axis, is of a Figure more *oblate* than any other Planet.

Dr. *Cheyne* obferves, If our *Moon* were bigger, or nearer the Earth, or if we had more than one, we fhould be every now and then in hazard of being drowned. And if our prefent *Moon* were lefs, or at a greater diftance, or if there were none at all, we fhould be in hazard of being ftifled with the baneful Steams of a ftagnating Ocean. It is evident our *Satellit* is moft wifely contrived for our Purpofes,--by thee, O our Gracious GOD!

The incomparable Sir *Ifaac Newton* has at length obliged the World with a *Theory of the Moon*, which has performed that which all former Aftronomers thought almoft impoffible.

Hugenius had Glaffes in perfection, and wrote fince the accurate Maps of the *Moon*, taken by *Hevelius* and *Ricciclus*; but he could obferve no *Seas* and *Rivers* there. It is alfo argued, That if any fuch were there, they

they could not but raife a mighty *Atmofphere*, and fuch *Clouds* as muft needs darken the Body of the *Moon*, fometimes in one part, fometimes in another. They carry on their Inferences; if no *Waters* in the *Moon*, then there are no *Plants*, nor *Animals*, nor *Men*. About the Conftitution of this *Queen of the Night*, there feems a neceffity for us to *remain in the dark!*

For Mr *Derham* has confuted *Hugenius* with his own *Glaffes*, and has demonftrated, that there are great Collections of *Waters* in the *Moon*, and by confequence Rivers, and Vapours, and Air; and in a word, a confiderable *Apparatus* for *Habitation*.

But by what Creatures inhabited? A Difficulty this, that cannot be folved without *Revelation*.

¶. ' *My GOD*, I blefs thee for that *Luminary*, by
' which we have the uncomfortable Darknefs of our
' *Night* fo much abated! That *Luminary*, the Influ-
' ences whereof have fuch a part in the *Flux* and *Re-*
' *flux* of our *Seas*; without which we fhould be very
' miferable! That *Luminary*, whofe Influences are fo
' fenfibly felt in the Growth of our *Vegetables*, and our
' *Animals!*'

Thefe are fome of the *Songs*, which *GOD*, *the Maker of* us both, has *given me in the Night*.

The Influences of the *Moon* upon *Sublunary* Bodies, are very wonderful. An *Hiftory* of them is yet among the *Defiderata* of our Philofophy. With my confent, he fhall merit more than the Title of a *Rabbi Solomon Jarchi*, who gives it unto us. Dr. *Grew*, in his *Cofmologia*, has enumerated more than a dozen remarkable *Heads* of *Effects*, and *Motions*, and *Changes* in the World, over which the *Moon* has a fenfible Dominion. Our *Lunaticks* are not the only Inftances. Our *Husbandmen* will multiply the Inftances upon us, till they make a Volume, which neither a *Columella*, nor a *Tom Tuffer* have reached unto. The *Georges* of my Neighbourhood juft now furnifh me with two Inftances, which have in them fomething that is notable. If our *Chef-*

E 2   *nut-*

nut-Wood, whereof we fometimes make our Fuel, be fell'd while the *Moon* is *waxing,* it will fo fparkle in the Fire, that there fhall be no fitting by it in fafety. If it be cut while the *Moon* is *waning,* there will be no fuch Inconvenience. Moreover, we find, whatever *Timber* we cut, in two *Wanes* of the *Moon* in a Year, the *Wane* in *Auguft,* and the *Wane* in *February,* will be for ever free from *Worms*; no *Worms* will ever breed in it. What Monfieur *Andry* relates, confirming the Obfervation of *Borellus,* about the Succefs of Medicines for *Worms* in *Human Bodies,* taken in the *Wane* of the *Moon,* is wonderful.

' I am fure, to be under fuch Influences of the
' *Moon,* as to fee the Great G O D managing many of
' his Gracious Intentions by fuch an *Inftrument*; and
' to be awakened to his Praifes in the *Night,* when we
' fee the *Moon walking in her Brightnefs*; would not be
' a *Lunacy,* that the moft *Rational* of Men could be
' afhamed of.'

ESSAY XII. *Of the* RAIN.

WE are now coming down into our *Atmofphere.* Here we are quickly furrounded with *Clouds.* And here we quickly find ourfelves in the midft of that *Rain,* whereof the Great G O D, in his Book, fo often claims the *Glory* of being the *Maker* and *Giver.*

'The *Rain* is Water by the *Heat* of the *Sun* divided into very fmall and invifible Parts; which afcending in the *Air,* till it encounters with the *Cold* there, is by degrees condenfed into *Clouds,* and thence defcends in *Drops.* A *Mift* is a multitude of little, but *folid* Globules; which therefore defcend. A *Cloud* is a Congeries of little, but *concave* Globules; which therefore afcend unto that height, wherein they are of equal weight with the *Air,* where they remain fufpended, till by a Motion in the Air they are *broken*: and fo they come down in *Drops*; either fmaller, as in a *Mift*;

or

or bigger, when many of them run together, as in a *Rain*.

'Tho the *Rain* be much of it exhaled from the *Salt-Sea*, yet by this *Natural Diſtillation*, 'tis rendred freſh and drinkable to a degree, which hardly any *Artificial Diſtillation* of ours has yet effected.

The *Clouds* are ſo carried about by the Winds, as to be ſo *equally diſperſed*, that no part of the Earth wants convenient Showers, unleſs when it pleaſes GOD, for the Puniſhment of a ſinful People, to withhold *Rain*, by a ſpecial Interpoſition of his Providence: Or, if any Land wants *Rain*, they have a Supply ſome other way; as in the Land of *Egypt;* wherein little *Rain* falls, there is an abundant recompence made for that want, by the annual Overflowing of the River. Mr. *Ray* well obſerves, 'That this Diſtribution proclaims the *Providence* of GOD, and is from a *Divine Diſpoſition*. Without this, there would be either de-ſolating *Floods*, or ſuch *Droughts* as that of *Cyprus*, in which no *Rain* fell for thirty Years together, and the Iſland was deſerted, in the Reign of *Conſtantine*. The *gradual Falling* of the *Rain* by *Drops*, is an admirable Accommodation of it to the Intention of watering the Earth. 'Tis the beſt way imaginable. If it ſhould fall in a *continual Stream*, like a River, every thing would be vaſtly incommoded with it.

¶. When GOD *gives Rain from Heaven,* he will give alſo *fruitful Seaſons* in our Minds, if they be thereby led to due Acknowledgments of him. 'Twill be-ſpeak, 'twill procure, the richeſt *Showers of Bleſſings* upon us. ' How ſeaſonable will it be for us now
' humbly to acknowledge the *Witneſs*, which our
' GOD gives us of his *Power* and *Goodneſs!* To ſee
' the *Paths of GOD* in the Clouds which *drop Fatneſs*
' upon us! To wiſh for thoſe Influences of Heaven,
' which may come upon ourſelves *like Rain upon the*
' *Graſs, as the Showers that water the Earth,* and *rain*
' *down Righteouſueſs* upon the World! To reſolve up-

E 3 ' on

' on an Imitation of our merciful GOD, who *fends*
' *Rain upon the Juft, and the Unjuft!* To fend up our
' Defires, that we may not be like the Earth, *which*
' *drinks in the Rain that comes often upon it, but bears*
' *Thorns and Briars, rejected, and nigh unto curfing!* In
' fine, To glorify our GOD with Confeffions of this
' importance ; *Can the Heavens give Showers? Art not*
' *thou he, O Lord our God? Therefore we will wait upon*
' *thee ; for thou haft made all of thefe things.*'

The Archbifhop of *Cambray* fhall exprefs our Sentiments. ' If I lift up my Eyes, I perceive in the
' Clouds that fly above us, a fort of hanging Seas,
' that ferve to temper the Air, break the fiery Rays
' of the Sun, and water the Earth when it is too dry.
' What Hand was able to hang over our Heads thofe
' great Refervatories of Waters! What Hand takes
' care never to let them fall, but in moderate
' Showers!'

ESSAY XIII. *Of the* RAINBOW.

AFTER we have given the common Definition
of it, *Arcus Cœleftis, qui fit ex Solis Luce, in Nu-
bem variè compofitam & temperatam, fed ex Diametro Soli
ipfi, incurrente ac incidente, pluviofo tempore* ; and fhould
add more than there be *Colours in the Rainbow,* and
with the modern Corrections of antient Errors, proceed to the Differences between the *Solar Iris* and the
Lunar, and between the *Iris* and the *Halo:* we have
yet made fo little Progrefs in real and certain *Knowledge,* that we fhould be left after all, with the Subject of our Difcourfe, *ftill in the Clouds.*

But we are called upon, *To confider the wondrous
Works of God;* and particularly that, wherein *he
caufes the Light of his Cloud to fhine,* that is to fay, his
Rainbow.

A famous Clergyman of *Spalato,* in a Book *De Ra-
diis Vifus & Lucis,* written before the former Century,
began

began mathematically to defcribe how the *interiour Bow* of the *Iris* is formed in round Drops of *Rain*, by a Refraction of the Sun's Light, and one Reflection between them; and the *Exteriour* by two Refractions, and two forts of Reflections between them, in each Drop of Water.

Des Cartes (who don't ufe to betray his Tutors) took the Hints from *Antonius de Dominis*, and went on *mathematically*, and with much demonftration, to give us a Theory of the *Iris*, from the Laws of *Refraction*, which lucid Rays do fuffer in paffing through diaphanous Bodies. He clearly demonftrated the *Primary Iris* to be only the *Sun's Image*, reflected from the concave Surfaces of an innumerable Quantity of fmall fpherical Drops of falling Rain; with this neceffary Circumftance, That thofe Rays which fell on the Objects, parallel to each other, fhould not after one Reflection, and two Refractions, (to wit, at going into the Drop, and coming out again) be difperfed, or made to diverge, but come back again alfo to the Eye, parallel to each other. The *Secondary Iris*, he fuppofes produced by thofe Rays of the Sun, which fall more obliquely, but after the fame manner as before: only in thefe there are two Reflections, before the Sun's Rays, refracted a fecond time, and tending towards the Eye in a parallel Pofition, can get out from the aqueous Globules.

The acute and accurate Mr. *Halley* comes after the *French* Philofopher, and fhows how the *Cartefian* Problems were more eafily folved, than the Author himfelf imagin'd. He fhows how to determine the Angle, by which the *Iris* is diftant from the oppofite Point of the Sun; and the *Ratio* of the Refraction being given *geometrically*, or *vice verfa*, the *Iris* being given, to determine the refractive Power of the Liquor. And he goes on to cultivate the Subject with the Ingenuity proper to fo accomplifh'd a Gentleman.

But

But then comes the admirable Sir *Iſaac Newton,* whom we now venture to call the *Perpetual Dictator* of the learned World, in the *Principles of Natural Philoſophy;* and than whom, there has not yet ſhone among Mankind a more ſagacious Reaſoner upon the *Laws of Nature.* This rare Perſon, in his incomparable Treatiſe of *Opticks,* has yet further explained the *Phænomena* of the *Rainbow;* and has not only ſhown how the *Bow* is made, but how the Colours (whereof Antiquity made but *Three*) are formed; how the Rays do ſtrike our Senſe with the *Colours,* in the Order which is required by their Degrees of *Refrangibility,* in the Progreſs from the Inſide of the *Bow* to the Outſide: the *Violet,* the *Indigo,* the *Blue,* the *Green,* the *Yellow,* the *Orange,* and the *Red.*

In a Book lately publiſhed at *Norimberg,* intitled, *Thaumantiadis Thaumaſia,* which has not yet reached *America;* the skilful Author lays together whatever is to be found upon this Argument, among the modern, as well as the antient Writers.

It is good Advice given by the Son of *Sirach; Look upon the Rainbow, and praiſe Him that made it.*

The Goſpel of the Rainbow, offered by *Frytſchius.*

Sic ubi Cœleſtem ſuboriri adſpexeris Arcum,
 Quo Cœlum melius non Meteoron habet :
Ille quidem varios ducens è Nube Colores,
 Humano generi conſpiciundus adeſt.
Hunc ita conſpicias, ſeu veri Pignus amoris,
 Ac olim facti fœderis eſto Memor.
Quod Deus omnipotens Noah ſancto contulit ipſi,
 Se ſervaturum totius Orbis Opus.
Nec perpeſſurum ſubmerſum Fluminis Unda
 Iri Hominem ſicut fecerat ante quidem.

Engliſhed :

‘ When you diſcern the *Bow of Heaven* to riſe,
‘ The *brighteſt Meteor* there ſalutes your Eyes:
　　　　　　　　　　　　　　‘ Producing

' Producing various Colours on the *Cloud,*
' *Mankind* beholds it, and ſurvives the *Flood.*
' Behold it, Sirs, a Sign of Heavenly Love,
' And of a Covenant made by GOD above:
' Almighty GOD did by that *Sign* engage
' To keep his *Noah's* World from Age to Age.
' 'Tis thus engag'd, GOD will no more employ
' Deep *Waters,* as of old, Men to deſtroy.

The *Halo* is of ſo near kindred unto the *Rainbow,* that it claims a mention with it : A Circle that ſurrounds the *Sun,* or the *Moon,* (or a *Star* ;) ſometimes 'tis coloured like a *Rainbow.* According to Sir *Iſaac Newton,* it ariſes from the Sun's or Moon's ſhining through a thin Cloud, conſiſting of Globules of Hail or Water, all of the ſame Size. Mr. *Huygens* conceives it formed by ſmall round Grains of a kind of *Hail,* made up of two Parts ; one of which is opake, and incloſed in the other, which is tranſparent. The ſame way he accounts for the *Parhelia.* Only there he apprehends, that the icy Grains are of an oblong Figure, and rounding at the Ends like Cylinders, with round convex Tops.

¶. May we *look upon the Rainbow, and praiſe Him that made it !* My Readers, will you give me leave to *teach you the Uſe of the Bow ?* *Mercer* tells us, the religious *Jews* in many places, upon the appearance of a *Rainbow,* go forth and fall down, and confeſs their Sins, and own themſelves worthy to be drowned with a *Flood* for them. To us *Chriſtians,* our Lord ſays, *What do you more than they ?* ' As the ſight of the ' *Rainbow* ſhould bring to remembrance, *What a woful,* ' *what a fearful Deſolation, once came upon a wicked World,* ' *whoſe Foundation was overflown with a Flood !* So ' the *Sacramental Importance,* now inſtamped by the ' Will of GOD upon the *Rainbow,* ſhould be acknow- ' ledged with us. It ſhould be conſidered as a *Sign* ' and a *Seal* of a *Covenant,* which the Great GOD

' has

' has made, That He will not have *this World*, though
' a finful one, to be *drowned any more*; nor his *Church*
' in the World. Upon the View of the admirable
' *Meteor*, how proper this Doxology? *Bleſſed be our*
' *Gracious, and Merciful, and Long-ſuffering Lord*; *who*
' *hath ſworn, that the Waters of Noah ſhall go over the*
' *Earth no more!* But then, how can we forget the
' Glorious CHRIST, who is our *Head* in the *Cove-*
' *nant*; and about whoſe *Head* there has been the ap-
' pearance of a *Rainbow*, in the Viſions of his Pro-
' phets, betokening our Dependance upon Him for all
' our Preſervations! But then we are not excuſed
' from, but rather excited to theſe further Thoughts
' on this occaſion: *That though a watery Flood, which*
' *may drown the World, is no more to be feared; yet there*
' *is a fiery Flood, for the Depredations whereof, a miſera-*
' *ble World is growing horribly combuſtible.* We are to
' expect,

   ' ―――――――――――― *Affore Tempus*
   ' *Quo Mare, quo Tellus, correptaque Regia Cæli*
   ' *Ardeat, & Mundi Moles operoſa laboret.*'

ESSAY XIV. *Of the* SNOW.

OF the *Snow*, there are many Curioſities obſerved
by the excellent Dr. *Grew.*

It is obſerved by him, as well as by *Des Cartes*, and
Dr. *Hook*, That very many Parts of the *Snow* are of a
moſt regular Figure; they are generally ſo many Row-
els, or Stars of *ſix Points*, being as real, as perfect, as
tranſparent Ice, as any one may ſee upon a Veſſel of
Water: On each of which *ſix Points*, there are ſet
other *collateral Points*, and thoſe always at the ſame
Angles as are the main Points themſelves.

Theſe are of divers Magnitudes; many are large
and fair, but ſome are very minute.

                                 Among

Among thefe, there are found fome irregular ones, which are but *Fragments* of the regular. But fome feem to have loft their original Regularity, not by being broken, but by various Winds, firft gently thaw'd, and then froze into fuch irregular Clumpers again.

A *fnowy Cloud* feems then to be an infinite Mafs of *Icicles* regularly figured, not fo much as one of the many Millions being irregular. A Cloud of Vapours is gathered into *Drops;* the *Drops* forthwith defcend. On the Defcent they pafs through a *foft Wind* that freezes them, or a cold Region of the Air, by which each Drop is immediately froze into an *Icicle,* that fhoots forth into feveral *Stiriæ* from the Center. But ftill continuing their Defcent, and meeting with fome fprinkling little Gales of a warmer Air, or in their continual Motion or Waftage to and fro, touching upon each other; fome are a little thaw'd, blunted, frofted, clumper'd; others broken: but the moft hank'd and clung in feveral Parcels together, which we call *Flakes of Snow.*

It fhould feem, that every *Drop of Rain* contains in it fome fpirituous Particles. Thefe meeting in the Defcent, with others of an acido-falinous Nature, the fpirituous Parts are apprehended by them, and with thofe the watery; and fo the whole Drop is fixed, but ftill according to the Energy of the fpirituous, as the *Pencil,* and the determinate Poffibility of the faline Parts, as a *Ruler,* into a *little Star.*

Though the *Snow* feem *foft,* yet it is truly *hard;* it is *Ice:* but the *Softnefs* of it is from this; Upon the firft touch of the Finger on the fharp Edges, it thaws immediately; the Points would elfe pierce the Fingers like fo many Lancets.

Again, though the *Snow* be true *Ice,* and fo hard, and fo denfe a Body, yet it is very *light:* This is be-caufe of the extreme *Thinnefs* of each *Icicle,* in compa-rifon of the *Breadth.* As *Gold,* though the moft ponderous

derous of all Bodies, beaten into Leaves, rides on the leaſt Breath of Air.

We read of Heaven *giving Snow like Wool.* I have known it *give a Snow of Wool.* In a Town of *New-England*, called *Fairfield*, in a bitter ſnowy Night, there fell a Quantity of *Snow*, which covered a large frozen Pond, but of ſuch a *woollen* Conſiſtence, that it can be called nothing but *Wool.* I have a Quantity of it, that has been theſe many Years lying by me.

Res admiranda Nix, & optimarum Rerum in ſacro Sermone Symbolum : 'Tis the Expreſſion of the pious and learned Mr. *Gale.*

¶. ' When we ſee *the Snow, that comes down from* ' *Heaven, and returns not thither, but waters the Earth,* ' *and makes it bring forth and bud* ; we cannot but hope, ' that the Word of our G O D, which comes like it, ' will continue with us, and *accompliſh* the Intentions ' of it.

' Whereof one, upon the Soul of thy Servant, *O* ' *my G O D !* is, to produce my Deſires, That my *Sins,* ' which have been like *Scarlet,* may become *white like* ' *Snow,* in thy free and full Pardon of them. *O waſh* ' *me in the Blood of my Saviour, and I ſhall be whiter than* ' *the Snow !* But, *Lord,* let a Work of real *Sanctifica-* ' *tion,* at the ſame time upon me, render me *purer than* ' *the Snow !* '

ESSAY XV. *Of the* H A I L.

'TIS *Gutta Pluviæ acerrimo frigore congelata.*

Hail is very often a Concomitant of *Thunder* and *Lightning.* 'Tis well known, as Dr. *Wallis* obſerves, That in our *Artificial Congelatious*, a Mixture of *Snow* and *Nitre*, or even common *Salt*, will cauſe a very ſudden Congelation of Water. Now the ſame in the Clouds may cauſe *Hail-Stones* ; and the rather, becauſe not only in ſome that are prodigiouſly great, but alſo in common *Hail-Stones*, there ſeems to be ſomething
like

like *Snow*, rather than *Ice*, in the midſt of them. The large *Hail-Stones*, that weigh half or three quarters of a Pound, by the Violence of their Fall manifeſt that they have deſcended from a conſiderable height. And though perhaps in their firſt Concretion, their Bulk might not exceed the moderate Size of the common *Hail*; yet in their long deſcent, if the *Medium* through which they fell, were alike inclined unto Congelation, they might receive a great Acceſſion to their Bulk, by perhaps many of them coaleſcing and incorporating into one.

¶. ' Worſe than *Egyptians* they, whom an *Hail-Storm*
' will not cauſe to *fear the Word of the Lord.* The *ir-*
' *reſiſtible* Judgments of GOD are ſometimes compar'd
' unto *Hail-Storms*, and *great Hail-Stones.* Theſe things
' come down upon the World with that Voice, *Trem-*
' *ble to be in ill Terms with a GOD, who with a Tempeſt*
' *of Hail, and a deſtroying Storm, can immediately cruſh all*
' *that is oppoſed unto him.*'

Of all the *Meteors*, both the *fiery* and the *watery*, the Poet has well acknowledged ;

Qui Meteora videt liquido radiantia Cœlo,
  Hic videt Æterni ſaĉta ſtupenda Dei.

Who ſees bright *Meteors* in the liquid Skies,
Has the great Works of GOD before his Eyes.

Chriſtian, take the Advice ; ['tis honeſt *Frytſchius's.*]

—— *Rumpe Moras, Meteoraque ſuſpice Cœli.*
Illa aliquid ſemper quo movearis habent.

ESSAY XVI. *Of the* THUNDER *and* LIGHTNING.

HIS *powerful Thunder, who can underſtand ?* Yet our Philoſophy will a little try to ſee and ſay ſomething of it.

The

The Account of *Thunder*, given by **Dr.** *Hook*, is this. The Atmoſphere of the Earth abounds with *nitrous Particles* of a ſpirituous nature, which are every where carried along with it. Beſides which ſort of Particles, there are alſo others raiſed up into the *Air*, which may be ſomewhat of the Nature of *ſulphureous*, and *unctious*, and other combuſtible Bodies. We ſee Spirit of *Wine*, of *Turpentine*, of *Camphire*, and almoſt all other combuſtible Bodies, will by *Heat* be rarefied into the Form of *Air*, or *Smoke*, and be raiſed up into the Air. All theſe, if they have a ſufficient Degree of *Heat*, will catch *Fire*, and be turned into *Flame*, from the *nitrous* Parts of the Air mixing with them; as it has been proved by Thouſands of Experiments. There are alſo other ſorts of ſuch Steams, that ariſe from *ſubterraneons* and *mineral* Bodies; which only by their coming to mix with the *Nitre* of the Air, though they have no ſenſible *Heat* in them, will ſo ferment and act upon one another, as to produce an actual *Flame*. Of this, the *Mines* are too frequent Witneſſes and Sufferers. The *Lightning* ſeems to be very much of ſuch an Original.

Dr. *Wallis* obſerves, That *Thunder* and *Lightning* have ſo much reſemblance to *fired Gunpowder* in their *Effects*, that we may very well ſuppoſe much of the ſame *Cauſes*. The principal Ingredients in *Gunpowder*, are *Nitre* and *Sulphur*. Suppoſe in the Air, a convenient Mixture of *nitrous* and *ſulphureous* Vapours, and thoſe to take *fire* by accident, ſuch an *Exploſion*, and with ſuch *Noiſe* and *Light* as that in the firing of *Gunpowder*, may well follow upon it; and being once kindled, it will run from place to place, as the Vapour leads it, like as in a Train of *Gunpowder*. This Exploſion, high in the Air, and far from us, will do no conſiderable miſchief. But, if it be very near us, it has terrible Conſequences. The Diſtance of its *Place* may be eſtimated by the Diſtance of the *Time*, which there is between ſeeing the *Flaſh*, and hearing the *Clap:* For

For though in their Generation they be fimultaneous, yet *Light* moving fafter than *Sound*, they come fuccefively to us. That there is a *nitrous* Vapour in it, we may reafonably judge, becaufe we know of no other Body fo liable to fo fudden and furious Explofion. That there is a *fulphureous* one, is manifeft from the Smell that attends it, and the fultry Heat, that is commonly a Forerunner of it.

¶. ' The *natural Caufes* of the *Thunder* do not at all
' releafe me from confidering the *Intereft* and *Providence*
' of the Glorious G O D, concerned in it. It is a
' Note prepared for the Songs of the Faithful, *The*
' G O D *of Glory thundereth.* It is He, who

' *Fulmina mol tur dextra, quo maxima motu*
' *Terra tremit, fugere Feræ, & mortalia Corda*
' *Per Gentes humilis ftravit Pavor.*

' And indeed, as the *Thunder* has in it *the Voice of*
' *God,* [*Paganifm* itfelf owned it, as being Φωνὴ Διὸς]
' thus there are feveral Points of *Piety,* wherein I am,
' as with a *Bath Kol,* inftructed from it.
' There is this *Voice* moft fenfibly to be heard in
' the *Thunder, Power belongeth unto God.* There is no-
' thing able to ftand before thofe *Lightnings,* which are
' ftiled the *Arrows of God.* We fee Caftles fall, Me-
' tals melt, Bricks themfelves vitrify; all flies, when
' *hot Thunderbolts* are fcattered upon them. The very
' *Mountains* are torn to pieces, when ——*Feriunt fum-*
' *mos fua Fulmina Montes.* It becomes me now to fay,
' *The Thunder of his Power who can underftand?* An
' haughty Emperor fhrinks, and fhakes, and hides
' his guilty Head, before the powerful *Thunder* of
' God.
' How can I hear the *Voice* of the *Almighty Thun-*
' *derer,* without fuch Thoughts as thefe? *Glorious God,*
' let me, through the Blood of a facrificed Saviour, be in
' good Terms with One fo able to deftroy me in a moment !
' And,

' And, let me be afraid of offending Him, who is
' poſſeſſed of ſuch an *irreſiſtible Artillery* !

' At the ſame time, do I not ſee the *Mercy* and *Pa-*
' *tience* of a Good God to a ſinful World ? The De-
' ſolations of the World, how wonderfully would
' they be,

> ' *Si quoties peccant Homines ſua Fulmina mittat* !

' It is no rare thing for the Children of Men to die
' by a *Thunderbolt* : A *King* has been ſo ſlain in the
' midſt of his Army. There was a Puniſhment of
' old uſed upon Criminals, by pouring hot Lead into
' their Mouths, which was called *Combuſtio Animæ,*
' and uſed in imitation of God's deſtroying Men with
' *Lightning* ; whereby the *inward* Parts are burnt with-
' out any viſible Touch upon the *outward.* This *Com-*
' *buſtio Animæ,* a Death by *Lightning,* has been fre-
' quently inflicted. Their being *aſleep* at the time
' has not preſerved them, though there be a Fancy in
' *Plutarch* that it would ; nor would a Tent of *Seal-*
' *Skin* have done it, though ſome great ones have re-
' paired unto ſuch an *Amulet* for their Protection. *My*
' *God, I adore thy Sovereign Grace, that ſuch a Sinner as*
' *I have not yet been by Lightning turned into Duſt and*
' *Aſhes before thee* !

' I take notice of one thing, That as Guilt lying
' on the Minds of Men, makes them ſtartle at a
' *Thunder-Clap* ;

> ' *Hi ſunt qui trepidant, & ad omnia Fulgura pallent,*
> ' *Cum tonat, exanimes primo quoque Murmure Cœli :*

' So the Miſcarriages about which our Hearts do firſt
' and moſt of all miſgive us in a *Thunder-Storm,* are
' thoſe which moſt of all call for a *thorough Repentance*
' with us. There are ſome Writings which I cannot
' read, except I hold them againſt the Fire ; by hav-
' ing my Heart held up againſt the *Lightning,* I may
' quickly read *my own Iniquity.*

' Impious

' Impious People are *deaf to Thunder!* '

Herlicius, in his *Tractatus de Fulmine*, reckons up a conſiderable number of thoſe, which might be called *Fœlicia Fulmina.* Such will they be that make theſe Impreſſions upon us.

ESSAY XVII. *Of the* AIR.

THE *Air* of our Atmoſphere, in which we breathe, is a diaphanous, compreſſible, dilatable *Fluid*; a Body covering the Earth and the Sea, to a great height above the higheſt Mountains: in this, among other things, differing from the *Æther*, that it refracts the Rays of the Moon, and other Luminaries.

There ſeem to be three different ſorts of *Corpuſcles*, whereof the *Air* is compoſed. There are ſuch as are carried up into the *Air* from other Bodies, as *Vapours* exhaled by the *Sun's Heat*, or by ſubterraneous. There may be alſo a more ſubtile kind, mixed with our *Air*, emitted from the *Heavenly Bodies*, and from the *Magnetick Steams* of the Globe on which we ſojourn. But there may be a third ſort of Particles, which may moſt properly merit the Name of *Aerial*; as being the diſtinguiſhing Parts of the Air, taken in the ſtricter ſenſe of the 'Term. Theſe Particles have an *Elaſticity* in them; are ſpringy; reſemble the *Spring* of a *Watch*. *Elaſticity* is an eſſential Property of the *Air*, and it is thought no other *Fluid* has any thing of it, but only ſo far as it participates of *Air*, or has *Air* contain'd in the Pores of it. Our *Air* abounds with Particles of ſuch a nature, that in caſe they be bent, or preſs'd by the Weight of the incumbent part of the *Atmoſphere*, or of any other Body, they endeavour to free themſelves from that Preſſure, by bearing againſt the Bodies that keep them under it; and as ſoon as the Removal of theſe Bodies gives them way, they expand the whole parcel of *Air* which they compoſed.

F

Dr.

Dr. *Hook* thinks the Air to be little elfe than a Tincture or Solution of terreftrial and aqueous Particles, diffolved in, and agitated by the *Æther*, and to have fomething *faline* in their Nature.

Mr. *Boyle* found, that one and the fame Portion of Air may take up 52,000 times the Space it doth at another time. He found, that the fame Quantity of Air, by only having the Preffure of the Atmofphere taken off in the *Pneumatick Engine*, and without increafing the Spring with any adventitious Heat, would poffefs above 13,000 times its natural Dimenfions. Dr. *Gregory* proceeds, That accordingly a Globe of *Air*, of one Inch diameter, would at the Diftance of the Semidiameter of the Earth from the Earth, fill all the Planetary Regions as far as, and much beyond the Sphere of *Saturn*. Admirable Rarefaction!

The *Weight of Air* was difcover'd firft by *Galilæus*, who finding that *Water* could not by pumping be raifed any higher than 34 or 35 Foot, concluded that the old Notion of an infinite *Fuga Vacui* would never do; and fo fell to thinking on the Counterbalance of *the Weight of the Air*. *Torricellius* afterwards purfued and improved the Thought, and as a further Proof of *the Weight of the Air*, invented that which we call *the Torricellian Experiment*.

Mr. *Boyle* found by repeated Experiments, that the Weight of *Air* to *Water* is as 1 to 1000.

Dr. *Halley* rather determines the *Specifick Gravity* of Air to Water, to be about 1 to 800. *Mercury* is to Air as 10,800 to 1. And fo, a Cylinder of *Air*, of 900 Feet, is equal to an Inch of *Mercury*.

We will, with Dr. *Wainwright*, fuppofe a cubical Foot of *Water* to weigh 76 Pounds *Troy* Weight. The Compafs of a Foot fquare upon the Superficies of our Bodies, muft fuftain a Quantity of *Air*, equal to 2660 Pounds Weight. If the Superficies of a Man's Body contains fifteen fquare Feet, which is pretty near the Truth, he would fuftain a Weight equal to 39,900 Pounds

Pounds *Troy*, which is above thirteen *Tun*. The difference between the greateſt and the leaſt Preſſure of the *Air* upon our Bodies, is equal to 3982 Pounds *Troy*. On which the Doctor ſays, ' No wonder then ' we ſuffer in our Health by Change of Weather ; 'tis ' ſurprizing that every ſuch Change does not entirely ' break the Frame of our Bodies to pieces, and be the ' conſtant Harbinger of ſudden **Death**.'

My God, it is becauſe I have obtained Help from thee, that I continue to this Day !

Sir *Iſaac Newton* thinks *true and permanent Air* to be made by Fermentation and Rarefaction of Bodies, that are of a very fixed Nature. And it is plain, thoſe Particles *fly* and *avoid* one another with the greateſt Force *at a diſtance,* which when they are *very near,* do *attract* and *adhere* to one another with the greateſt Violence.

The Particles of *true and permanent Air,* being extracted from the denſeſt and moſt fixed Bodies, will be more denſe and craſs than thoſe of *Vapour,* and from hence, it's likely, may be heavier than thoſe ; and the Parts of an *humid Atmoſphere* may be lighter than thoſe of a *dry* one, as in fact they appear to be. He thinks therefore, that the Rarefaction and Condenſation of the Air cannot be accounted for from the *Spring,* or Elaſtick Forms of the Particles, without a Suppoſition, that they are endued with ſome *Centri-fugal* Force or Power, by which they *fly* and *avoid* one another, and the denſe Bodies, from whence they are extracted.

This may be the cauſe for *Filtration,* and the Aſcent of Water in ſmall capillary Tubes, to a much greater height, than the Surface of the Water in the open Veſſel, in which they are placed. The Air within the Tubes is much rarer than in more open Spaces, and by that means not preſſing ſo much on the Surface of the Water within the Tubes, as without.

It

It is admirable to confider the Neceffity of *Air* to the whole *animal* World; how foon the *vital Flame* does languifh and expire, if *Air* be withheld from it! Even the Inhabitants of the Water cannot live without the Ufe of it.   It is evident that the *Air*, at the leaft that part of it which is the Aliment of *Fire*, and the Fuel of the *vital Flame* in Animals, eafily penetrates the Body of Water expofed to it, and with a wondrous Infinuation diffufes itfelf thro every part of it.   Put Fifhes into a Veffel of a narrow mouth, full of Water, they will continue to live and fwim there whole Months and Years.   But if with any Covering you ftop the Veffel, fo as to exclude the *Air*, or interrupt the Communication of it with the Water, they will fuddenly be fuffocated; which was an Experiment often made by *Rondeletius*.   The *Infeθs* rather need more *Air* than other Creatures, having more *Air-Veffels* for their Bulk, and many Orifices on each fide of their Bodies for the Admiffion of *Air*, which if you ftop with Oil or Honey, they prefently die, and revive no more.   *Pliny* knew not the reafon of his own Obfervation; *Oleo illito Infeθa omnia exanimantur.* Yea, *Malpighius* has difcovered and demonftrated, that the *Plants* themfelves have a kind of Refpiration, being furnifhed with a Plenty of Veffels for the Derivation of *Air* to all their Parts.   Dr. *Hulfe*, and Mr. *Ray*, and others, have now alfo render'd it very evident, That the *Fœtus* in the Womb does receive a meafure of *Air* from the maternal Blood, by the *Placenta Uterina*, or the *Cotyledons*.   When this Communication is broken off, what is it that now, to preferve the Life of the Animal, fpeedily raifes the *Lungs*, and fetches into them an abundance of *Air*, which caufes a fudden and mighty Accenfion in the Blood, for the Maintenance whereof a far greater Quantity of Air is requifite?   Certainly fome intelligent Being muft now interpofe, to put the Diaphragm, and all the Mufcles that ferve to Refpiration, into their Motion!

My

My God, I know thee! And now, as our ingenious *Waller* ſings;

    ' Thus wing'd with Praiſe, we penetrate the Sky,
    ' Teach Clouds and Stars to praiſe Him as we fly.
    ' For that He reigns, all Creatures ſhould rejoice,
    ' And we with Songs ſupply their want of Voice.
    ' Angels and we, aſſiſted by this Art,
    ' May ſing together, tho we dwell apart.

¶. ' The *Syrians* worſhipped the *Air* as a *God.* I
' will worſhip Him that created it.

' I will give Thanks to the Glorious God, for the
' Benefits with which the *Air* is repleniſhed by his
' Bounty. It was long ſince called the *Paranymph,* by
' which the Eſpouſal and Communion between *Hea-*
' *ven* and *Earth* is carried on.

' I *breathe* in the *Favours* of God continually. An
' ungrateful Wretch, if I do not *breathe out* his
' *Praiſes!*

' How juſtly might the Great God fill the Air with
' inviſible *Arrows* of Death, and ſuch deleterious
' *Miaſms,* and peſtilential *Poiſons,* as might ſuffer the
' *Unholy* and *Unthankful* to *breathe* no longer in it!'

ESSAY XVIII. *Of the* WIND.

WHAT better Definition of the *Wind,* than *the
Stream of the Air?* *Plato* long ſince defin'd it,
The Motion of the Air about the Earth.

Other Hypotheſes for this Current of the Air not
well anſwering all *Phænomena,* the learned Mr. *Halley* recommends this to Conſideration, as the Cauſe of
it; The Action of the *Sun-beams* on the *Air* and *Water,* as the Sun paſſes every day over the Oceans, conſider'd with the Nature of the Soil, and the Situation
of the Continents adjoining.

According to the Laws of *Staticks,* the *Air,* which
is leſs rarefied and expanded by *Heat,* and conſe-

          quently

quently more ponderous, muſt have a Motion round thoſe Parts thereof, which are more rarefied and leſs ponderous, to bring it into an Æquilibrium. The Preſence of the *Sun* alſo continually ſhifting to the Weſtward, that Part unto which the *Air* tends, by reaſon of the Rarefaction made by his greateſt Meridian Heat, is with him carried Weſtward, and conſequently the Tendency of the whole Body of the *lower Air* is that way. Thus a general *Eaſterly Wind* is formed. From this Principle, the *Eaſterly Wind* on the *North* Side of the Æquator, ſhould be to the *Northwards* of the *Eaſt* ; and in *South* Latitudes, it ſhould be to the *Southwards* thereof: inaſmuch as near the Line, the *Air* is much more rarefied than at a greater diſtance from it. Here all the *Phænomena* of the general *Trade-Winds* are anſwer'd for; which if the whole Surface of the Globe were Sea, would undoubtedly blow all round the World, as they are found to do in the *Atlantick* and *Ethiopick* Oceans. But ſince great Continents interpoſe, and break the Continuity of the *Oceans*, regard muſt be had to the Nature of the Soil, and the Poſition of the high Mountains, which cauſe the Variation of the Winds, from the general Rule that has been propoſed. If a Country, which lies near the *Sun*, prove to be low, flat, and ſandy, the *Heat* occaſion'd by the Reflection and Retention of the Sun-beams there, will ſo rarefy the Air, that the denſer and cooler Air will run thither, to reſtore the Æquilibrium. Hence may be the *conſtant Calms* in that part of the Ocean, called *The Rains.* This Tract being placed in the middle, between the Weſterly Winds blowing on the hot Coaſt, and the Eaſterly Winds that blow to the Weſtwards, the Tendency of the Air there is indifferent to either, and ſo ſtands *in æquilibrio*, between both; and the Weight of the incumbent *Atmoſphere* being diminiſhed by the continual contrary Winds blowing from hence, the *Air* here holds not the copious Vapour it receives, but lets it fall into frequent *Rains*.   It

It is very hard to conceive, why the Limits of the *Trade-Wind* should be fixed about the thirtieth Degree of Latitude all round the Globe, and that they should so seldom transgress those Bounds, or fall short of them.

Behold the *Wings of the Wind!*

The inquisitive and ingenious Mr. *Derham* found by many Trials, That the *Wind* in a great Storm does move about *fifty or sixty Miles* in an Hour; That a common brisk *Wind* moves about *fifteen Miles* an Hour. But so gentle is the Course of many Winds, that they do not exceed *one Mile* an Hour.

Dr. *Grew* observes, That there are Winds (besides the *Trade-Winds*) especially from the West, which blow sometimes two or three Days upon one Point, and will in this time drive before them a Ship an hundred and fifty Leagues, or four hundred and fifty *English* Miles.

The *Wind* is of great Use to ventilate the Air, and to dissipate contagious Vapours; which if they should stagnate, would produce grievous Diseases on the animal World. ——*Si non ventosa, venenosa,* It also transfers the *Clouds* from one place to another, for the more commodious watering of the Earth. It likewise tempers the *Heats* of many Countries, which else would be excessive. It carries *Vessels* on their Voyages to remote Countries. *Windmills* are driven by it, whereof there are many Benefits. But as the excellent Mr. *Ray* observes, That it is rarely so violent, as to destroy all before it, and overwhelm the World; this proclaims a superiour Power moderating of it, the *Wisdom* and *Goodness* of Him, *who brings the Wind out of his Treasures.*

What amazing things the *Winds,* called the *Tuffoons* (or *Typhons!*) and how irresistibly furious! But our merciful God *stays the rough Winds.*

The *Hurricanes* in the *West-Indies,* and their Brethren the *Monsoons* in the *East*; what shocking Stories

do

do the Travellers give us of them! How direful Effects are ſometimes cauſed by them! They blow down mighty *Trees* by the Roots. They chaſe mighty *Ships* up into the Woods. They make every thing to tremble, and give way, that is in their way. *Great God, who rideſt on the Wind, and makeſt it move which way thou ſhalt pleaſe; who can ſtand in thy ſight, if thou art angry!*

¶. Whatever Point of the Compaſs the *Wind* blows upon, it may blow ſome Good Thoughts into our Minds; and then it will be no *Ill Wind* unto us.

‘ We ought certainly to conſider *the ſtormy Wind,*
‘ *as fulfilling the Word of God.* And there are *Tempeſts,*
‘ and *Whirlwinds* of the Divine Wrath to be depre-
‘ cated. But then there are Influences of Heaven to
‘ be deſired, which are, *As the Wind bloweth where it*
‘ *liſteth, and we hear the Sound thereof, but cannot tell*
‘ *whence it cometh, nor whither it goeth.*’

ESSAY XIX.   *Of the* COLD.

THERE is much Diſpute about the *Primum Fri-gidum.* None, I hope, about the *Firſt Cauſe* of the *Cold,* which ſometimes mortifies us.

It is queſtioned by ſome, whether the *Cold* be any thing that is *poſitive,* and not a mere *Privation.* The *Coldneſs* of any thing, they ſay, ſignifies no more, than its not having its inſenſible Parts agitated ſo much as thoſe of our *Senſories,* by which we judge of *Tactile Qualities.* To make a thing become *cold,* there needs no more, than that the *Sun,* or *Fire,* or ſome other Agent, that more vehemently agitated its Parts before, do now ceaſe to do it.

But then, on the other ſide, there are Inſtances of *Cold* produced by vehement Agitations.

To ſome there ſeems to be a mighty ſtore of *Cor-puſcles,* a little a-kin to *Nitre,* exhaled from the terre-ſtrial Globe, (of the Figure which *Philoponus* tells us,

Democritus assigned to *Frigorifick Atoms*) which may more than a little contribute to our *Cold.*

That *Cold* (and so *Freezing*) may arise from some saline Substance floating in the Air, seems probable from this; That all *Salts*, but some above others, when mixed with *Snow* or *Ice*, do prodigiously increase the Force of *Cold.* And all *saline* Bodies produce a *Stiffness* in the Parts of those Bodies, into which they enter.

The Force of the *Cold* is truly wonderful. *Olearius* tells us, in *Muscovy* their Spittle will freeze e'er it reach the Ground. So violent the *Cold* there, that no *Furs* can hinder it, but sometimes the *Noses*, the *Ears*, the *Hands*, and the *Feet* of Men will be frozen, and all fall off. 'Tis reported by *Fletcher* and *Herberstein*, That not only they who travel abroad, but many in the very Markets of their Towns are so mortally pinched, as to fall down dead with the *Cold.* Captain *James* and *Gerat de Veer* tell us frightful things of the *Cold* they found in their Northern Coasting. *Beauplan* adds, That without good Precautions, the *Cold* produces those *Cancers*, which in a few Hours destroy the Parts they seize upon. What mighty Rands of *Ice* (the *magnum Duramen Aquarum*, as *Lucretius* calls it) have been encounter'd by such Navigators as *Munchius* and *Baffin*, who found some *Icy Islands* near three hundred Foot high above the Water! In the River of *Canada* sometimes are seen *Icy Islands*, computed fourscore Leagues in length.

The irresistible Force of *Congelation!*

Congelation seems to be from the Introduction of the *Frigorifick Particles*, into the Interstices between the Particles of the Water; and thereby getting so near to them, as to be just within the Sphere of one another's attracting Force, on which they cohere into one solid Body.

Was it not then a Mistake in *Pliny*, when *Ice* was defined by him, *Aqua Copia in Angusto?* The Dimenſions of Water are increaſed by *Freezing*; and with ſuch a Force in the Expanſion, that the *Weights* raiſed by it, the *Stones* broke in it, the *Metals* obliged to give way to it, were hardly credible, if theſe Eyes had not ſeen them!

¶. ' When we conſider the *Cold*, eſpecially if we
' have it under our more *ſenſible* Conſideration, we
' cannot but ſubſcribe to that Word, *Who can ſtand*
' *before his Cold!* How naturally are we now led to
' a Dread, and a Deprecation of lying under the *Diſ-*
' *pleaſure* of the *Glorious God*, who by that one Part
' of his *Artillery*, the *Cold* alone, can ſoon deſtroy his
' Enemies!'

'The *Mitigations* of our *Cold*, and our *Comforts* and *Supports* againſt the Aſſaults of it, beſpeak our thankful Praiſes to our Glorious *Benefactor*: That we are not, as *Livy* ſays of the *Alps*, *Æternis damnati Nivibus!*

It is obſervable, That the Degrees of *Cold* in ſeveral Climates are not according to their Degrees of *Latitude*. Some have met with very tolerable Weather under the *Arctick Pole*. But *Martinius*, in his *Atlas Chinenſis*, reports of *China, Majus in hac Provincia Frigus eſt, quam illius poſcat Poli Altitudo*. The Country lies in little more than *forty Degrees* of Latitude, and yet for four Months together in the Year, the Rivers there are ſo frozen, that the *Ice* will bear the Paſſage not only of Men, but of *Horſes* and of *Coaches* too upon it. The like Report could I give of my own Country, which lies in the ſame Latitude. In my warm Study, from the Billets of Wood lying on a great Fire, the *Sap* forced out at the ends of the ſhort Billets by the Fire, has frozen there, and been turned into *Ice*, while the Wood has been conſuming. However, our *Cold* is much moderated ſince the opening and clearing of our *Woods*, and the Winds do not blow ſuch Razours, as in the Days of our Fathers, when *Water*, caſt up into the *Air*, would commonly

be

be turned into *Ice* e'er it came to the Ground. I have ſometimes wiſhed, that Wiſe-Men would make the Reflection of *Petronius* upon this Matter : *Incultis aſperiſque Regionibus, diutius Nives hærent ; aſt ubi Aratro domefacta Tellus nitet, dum loqueris levis Pruina dilabitur. Similiter in Pectoribus Ira conſidit ; Feras quidem Mentes obſidet, Eruditas præterlabitur.*

ESSAY XX. *Of the Terraqueous* GLOBE.

THE Diſtance at which our *Globe* is placed from the *Sun,* and the Contemperation of our Bodies and other Things to this Diſtance, are evident Works of our Glorious GOD!

According to the accurate Obſervations of the *Engliſh Norwood,* and the *French Picart,* the Ambit of our Globe will be twenty-four thouſand nine hundred and thirty Miles. Wherefore ſuppoſing it ſpherical, the whole Surface will be 197,831,392 Miles ; which in the ſolid Content will be found no leſs than 261,631,995,920 Miles. The cubick Feet will be 30,000,000,000,000,000,000,000,000. The *Earth,* with her Satellit the *Moon,* moving about the *Sun,* this *Orbis Magnus,* as 'tis uſually called, according to our *Derham,* is a Space of more than 540 Millions of Miles in Circumference, or 172 Millions of Miles in Breadth.

The *Copernican* Hypotheſis is now generally preferred, which allows a *Diurnal* and an *Annual* Motion to our *Globe,* rather than to the *Sun.* According to this, the *Diurnal* Motion of our *Globe* is near 1,039 Miles in an Hour.

The Arguments that prove the Stability of the *Sun,* and the Motion of the *Earth,* have now render'd it indiſputable. It is impoſſible to account for the Appearances of the *Planets,* and their *Satellits,* and the *Fixed Stars,* in any tolerable manner, without admitting the Motion of the *Earth ;* or to account for *Comets ;*

mets; or for that Analogy of the *Periodical Times,* to the *middle Distances,* which is the necessary Consequence of the establish'd Law of *Gravitation.* Unless we would subvert the whole System of *Astronomy,* and (as Dr. *Cheyne* observes) disprove the Causes of all the *Celestial Motions,* we shall never be able to assert, that the *Earth stands unmoved.* Nor is there any Objection against the Motion of the *Earth,* but what has had a full Solution.

These Motions, performed so regularly for near six thousand Years, how much do they oblige us to cry out, *Great GOD, thou that art the Creator, art also the Governour of the World!*

Even a *Pagan Cleanthes,* as his Brother *Cicero* will tell us, would assign this as a sufficient Cause for a Belief of a Deity; *Æquabilitatem Motus, Conversionem Cœli, Solis, Lunæ, Syderumque omnium Distinctionem, Varietatem, Pulchritudinem, Ordinem; quarum rerum Aspectus ipse satis indicaret, non esse fortuita.* And *Plutarch* says, This Observation was the first that led Men to the Acknowledgment of a GOD.

The Prophet *Habakkuk* mentions the Stop to this Course in the Days of *Joshua,* as a real Matter of Fact. The same *Infinite Power* that gave the *Motion,* gave the *Check.*

The Circumvolutions of the *Globe* are of admirable *Conveniency,* yea, of absolute *Necessity,* to the Inhabitants. As *Tully* notes, *Conservat Animantes.*

The *Spherical Figure* of our Globe has numerous and marvellous Conveniencies, whereof no Man that seriously considers it can be insensible. How incommodious must an *Angular Figure* have been; or such an one as many of the Antients, and particularly the *Epicureans,* with Stupidity enough imagin'd?

It is admirably well order'd, (as Dr. *More* observes) That the *Axis* of the Globe should be steddy, and perpetually parallel to itself; not carelesly tumbling this way and that way, as it might happen: and that

the

the Poſture of the *Axis* be inclining as it is, and not perpendicular to a Plane going thro the Center of the *Sun*, or coincident. Hence comes the *Globe* to be ſo habitable in all Parts ; and even under the *Line* itſelf, as 'tis noted by Sir *Walter Raleigh,* the Parts are as pleaſant, and as fruitful, and as fit for a *Paradiſe,* as any in the World. And the *Longevity* of the Natives there does rather exceed the reſt of Mankind, as we learn from the Relations of *Piſo,* and *Rochefort,* and *Pirard,* and *Le Blanc,* and other Teſtimonies. Yea, Mr. *Keill* demonſtrates, that from the preſent Poſition of the Globe, and the Inclination of its *Axis* to the Plane of the *Ecliptick,* we reap this Advantage ; They who live beyond forty-five Degrees of Latitude, and have moſt need of it, have more of the Heat of the *Sun* throughout the Year, than if he had ſhined always in the *Æquator :* Whereas in the *Torrid Zone,* and even in the *Temperate,* almoſt as far as forty-five, the Sum of the *Sun's* Heat, in Summer and Winter, is leſs than it would be, if the Axis of the Globe were perpendicular to the Plane of the *Ecliptick.* He very well adds, This Conſideration cannot but lead us into a tranſcendent Admiration of the *Divine Wiſdom !* Yea, were the whole Creation ſurveyed, it would be every where found, as Mr. *Ray* obſerves, *That God has choſen better for us, than we could have done for ourſelves.*

And then, the Collection of the *Waters* on the *Globe* into ſuch vaſt *Conceptacula,* wherein the innumerable *Fiſhes* are nouriſhed, and whereon *Voyages* are performed ; and the Diſtinction of the *Dry Land,* furniſhed with ſo many *Vegetables* and *Animals :* What can it be any other than the Reſult of Counſel, of Deſign, of *Infinite Wiſdom !* How blind art thou, O *Man,* and under what a brutal and fatal Darkneſs, if thou ſee it not !——*The Brutiſh among the People will not be wiſe.*

The

The *Figure* of our Globe is most probably that of an *Oblate Spheroid.* It swells towards the *Æquatorial* Parts, and flats towards the *Polar;* according to Sir *Isaac Newton,* the *Diameter* of the Globe is about thirty-four Miles longer than the *Axis.*

Dr. *Gregory* shews, that this is the reason why the *Axis* of our Globe does twice every Year change its Inclination to the *Ecliptick,* and as often return back again to its former Position.

That most accurate Astronomer, Mr. *Flamstead,* found the Distance of the *Pole-Star* from the Pole, to be greater about the *Summer* Solstice than about the *Winter,* by about forty or forty-five Seconds. He found also, by repeated Observations, a sensible annual Parallax in others of the Fixed Stars. This proves our Globe to move annually about the *Sun.*

Mr. *Halley* shows the annual Motion of the Earth to be so swift, as far to exceed that of a Bullet shot out of a Cannon, and to be after the rate of 210 Miles in a Minute, and 12,600 Miles in an Hour.

Our Globe is nearer to the *Sun* in *December* than in *June.* Its *Perihelion* is in *December.* The *Sun's* apparent Diameter is greater then; and our Globe then has a *swifter Motion* by a twenty-fifth Part. Hence there are about eight Days more in the Summer Half-Year, than in the Winter Half-Year. The colder and more Northern Places of our Globe are indeed brought some hundreds of thousands of Miles nearer the *Sun* in *Winter* than in *Summer.*

Upon the Occurrences of the whole GLOBE.

'OMAN! we are now come down into thy *Territories.* How many SERVANTS may MAN here see himself attended and surrounded with! The most *reasonable Thing* in the World is for MAN hereupon to contrive and resolve in this manner; *O that my Service to the Glorious GOD may be as obedient,*

' dient, as willing, as ready, as what his Creatures yield
' to me!

' It has been excellently well proposed; *Cum cæteræ
' Creaturæ universæ omnibus Viribus, in Hominis Utilitatem
' connituntur, discat hinc Homo, similiter ex totis Viribus
' DEO servire, ad illumque se convertere, qui omnes Cre-
' aturas usui, servitioque suo destinavit.*

' But then, to this we will annex a further Dispo-
' sition of *Piety: Can a Man be profitable to GOD?*
' My *Service* to Him does not advantage Him. When
' I have done all, I am an *unprofitable Servant.* Where-
' fore let me study to transfer to my *Neighbour,* the
' *Service* which by the Creatures of GOD is done to
' me. Yea, let me so far as my Tenuity can attain
' to it, labour to do to my *Neighbour* such Things as
' the Great GOD pleases to do to me. In this *Cha-
' rity,* there will be that *Image* of the Glorious GOD,
' which is the *Glory* of the MAN that arrives to it.

' One says well, *Quocunque vertamus Oculos, ecce
' Testimonia, Oratores, & Laudatores Dei, qui totum Li-
' brum Mundi Laudum suarum Historiam, & Panegyricum
' esse voluit.*

' MAN, let the Glorious GOD have *Praises* from
' thee, and have thy *Homage* and *Service.* Hereby the
' Creatures will be returned and united to GOD
' their Maker, and it will be brought about, that
' they shall not be made in vain. It was a wise
' Thought ; *Per Hominem, & illius Religionem, omnes
' Creaturæ cum Deo connectuntur, ne frustra à Deo sint
' creatæ.*

' There is another pathetick Remark, made more
' than an hundred Years ago, but worthy to be for
' ever thought upon ; *Omnes Creaturæ naturaliter Deum
' plus amant, quam seipsas, dum illius Mandata exequendo,
' seipsas consumunt ; solus autem Peccator seipsum impensius
' quam Deum amat.* Every *Creature,* but only the
' wicked Sinner, *loves GOD* more than it *loves itself.*

' Two

' Two Inftru&ions of the pious *Ægardus* will be
' worth remembring here.

' The one ; *Dulces tibi fint Creaturæ, propter Deum,*
' *a quo funt ; fed dulcior ipfe Creator, qui omnibus major*
' *& melior.*

' The other ; *In quibus plus Dei, in iis plus fanEta*
' *fit Voluptatis, & cum iis te conjungi cupias.*

' GOD muft be the *Sweet* of all Creatures to me ;
' and the more of GOD in any Creatures, the more
' muft be my Regard, the more my Relifh for them.'

¶. As we go along, we cannot well avoid a Touch
upon *Cohefion.* We fee two very plain, fmooth, well-
polifh'd Bodies, will firmly *cohere,* even in an *exhaufted
Receiver.* This renders it evident, that *Cohefion* is not
owing to the *Gravity,* nor to any other Property of
of the *Air.* What appears in the Surfaces of cohering
Bodies upon their breaking, fhows us, That a neceffary Condition of *Cohefion* is a Congruity of *Surfaces* ;
and fuch as excludes any *Fluid* from lying between
them. We may fuppofe, with Dr. *Cheyne,* that fome
of the *Primary Atoms,* whereof Bodies are conftituted,
are terminated with *plain* and *fmooth* Surfaces on all
fides ; which will produce Bodies of the *ftrongeft Cohefion :* Others are partly terminated with *plain* and
fmooth, and partly with *curve* Surfaces, which will
produce Bodies of a *meaner Cohefion.* Others are entirely terminated with *curve* Surfaces, which will produce *Fluids* ; and between thefe entirely *plain* and
fmooth, and entirely *curve,* there are infinite *Combina-
tions of Surfaces, plain,* and *fmooth,* and *curve,* which
will account for all the various Degrees of *Cohefion* in
Bodies, in refpe& of their Figures. But now the *Cement,*
which hinders the Separation of Bodies, when the
Points of their Surfaces are brought into Conta& ;
[this] can be nothing but the *univerfal Law of Attraction,* whereby all the Parts of *Matter* endeavour to
embrace one another, and cannot be feparated but
by

by a *Force*, that ſhall be ſuperiour to that by which they *attract*.

' Being arrived here, we are gotten within a little
' of the Glorious G O D.   The very *next Step* we
' take muſt be into Him, who is the *immediate Cauſe*
' of *Weight* in *Matter*.   None but He producing, im-
' printing, preſerving that *Property* in *Matter*, is to be
' now conſidered.   We will go on to take notice of
' that Property.'

ESSAY XXI.   *Of* GRAVITY.

TO our Globe there is one Property ſo exceedingly and ſo generally ſubſervient, that a very great
Notice is due to it ; that is, GRAVITY, or the Tendency of Bodies to the *Center*.

A moſt noble Contrivance (as Mr. *Derham* obſerves)
to keep the ſeveral Globes of the Univerſe from ſhat-
tering to pieces, as they would elſe evidently do in a
little Time, thro their ſwift Rotation round their
own *Axes*.   Our *Globe* in particular, which revolves
at the rate of above a thouſand Miles an Hour, would,
by the centrifugal Force of that Motion, be ſoon diſſi-
pated, and ſpirtled into the circumambient Space,
were it not kept well together by this wondrous Contrivance of the Creator, *Gravity*, or the *Power of Attraction*.   By this Power alſo all the Parts of the *Globe*
are kept in their proper Place and Order ; all Bodies
gravitating thereto do unite themſelves with, and pre-
ſerve the Bulk of them entire ; and the fleeting Waters are kept in their conſtant Æquipoiſe, remaining
in the *Place which God has founded for them, a Bound
which He hath ſet, that they may not paſs, that they turn
not again to cover the Earth*.   It is by the virtue of this
glorious Contrivance of the *great God, who formed all
Things*, that the Obſervation of the Pſalmiſt is perpetually fulfilled : *Thou ruleſt the raging of the Sea ; when
the Waves thereof ariſe, thou ſtilleſt them.*

G   Very

Very various have been the Sentiments of the Curious, what *Cause* there should be assign'd for this great and catholick Affection of Matter, the *Vis Centripeta*: I shall wave them all, and *bury* them in the *Place of Silence*, with the *Materia Striata* of *Descartes*, which our *Keil* has very sufficiently brought to *nothing*; and perhaps the *Fluid* of Dr. *Hook* must go the same way. 'Tis enough to me what that incomparable Mathematician, Dr. *Halley*, has declar'd upon it: That, after all, *Gravity* is an Effect insolvable by any *philosophical Hypothesis*; it must be religiously resolv'd into the *immediate Will* of our most wise CREATOR, who, by appointing this *Law*, throughout the material World, keeps all Bodies in their proper Places and Stations, which without it would soon fall to pieces, and be utterly destroy'd.

All Bodies descend still towards a Point, which either is, or lies near to, the *Center* of the *Globe*. Should our Almighty G O D change that *Center* but the two thousandth part of the *Radius* of our Globe, the Tops of our highest Mountains would be soon laid under Water.

In all Places equi-distant from the *Center* of our Globe, the Force of Gravity is nearly equal.

Indeed, as it has been proved by Sir *Isaac Newton*, the *Equatorial* Parts are something higher than the *Polar* Parts; the difference between the Earth's *Diameter* and *Axis* being about thirty-four *English* Miles.

Gravity does equally affect all *Bodies*. The *absolute Gravity* of all is the same. Abstracting from the resistance of the Medium, the most *compact* and the most *diffuse*, the *greatest* and the *smallest*, would descend an equal Space in an equal Time. In an exhausted Receiver a *Feather* will descend as fast as a *Pound of Lead*. But this resistance of the *Medium* has produc'd a *comparative Gravity*. And upon the difference of *specifick Gravity* in many Bodies, the Observations of our Philosophers have been very curious.

According

According to the exquifite *Halley* and *Huygens,* the *Defcent of heavy Bodies* is after the rate of about *fixteen Foot* in *one Second* of Time.

Neverthelefs this Power *increafes* as you defcend to, *decreafes* as you afcend from the *Center* of the Globe, and that in proportion to the Squares of the Diftances therefrom reciprocally; fo as, for inftance, at a double diftance to have but a quarter of the Force. A *Ton* Weight on the Surface of the Earth, raifed Heaven-wards unto the height of one Semidiameter of the Earth from hence, would weigh but one quarter of a *Ton.* At three Semidiameters from the Surface of the Earth, it would be as eafy for a Man to carry a *Ton,* as here to carry little more than an hundred Pounds. At the diftance of the *Moon,* which fuppofe to be fixty Semidiameters of the Earth, 3600 Pounds weigh but *one Pound;* and the Fall of Bodies is but fixteen Foot in a whole Minute.

I remember I have fomewhere met with fuch a devout Improvement of this Obfervation : ' The further ' you fly towards *Heaven,* the more (if I may ufe the ' *Falconers* Word) you muft *leffen.* There is great ' reafon why it fhould be fo. *Defamations* particular-' ly will be Things by which you muft be *leffen'd:* ' you muft meet with *heavy* Things; *Defamations* are ' in a fingular manner fuch ; they are not eafy to *car-* ' *ry*; 'tis not eafy to carry it well under them; fome ' of them are a *Ton* Weight. But, *my Friend,* if you ' were as near *Heaven* as you ought to be, you would ' make *light* of them ; you would bear them wonder-' fully !'

The *acute Borelli* has demonftrated that there is no fuch thing as *pofitive Levity,* and that *Levity* is only a leffer degree of *Gravity.* But how ufeful is this, not only to divers Tribes of *Animals,* but alfo to the raifing up of the many *Vapours,* which are to be convey'd about the World ? The Evaporations, which, according to Mr. *Sedileau*'s Obfervations, and others, are the

feweft

feweſt in the Winter, and greateſt in the Summer, the moſt of all in windy Weather, and conſiderably exceed what falls in *Rain*, many being tumbled about and ſpent by the Winds, and many falling down in Dews.

The ingenious *Halley* has yet a ſuſpicion that there may be ſome certain Matter, which may have a *Conatus* directly contrary to that of *Gravity*; as in *Vegetation* the Sprouts directly tend againſt the *Perpendicular.*

Dr. *Gregory* demonſtrates, that the antient Aſtronomers were not ignorant of the heavenly Bodies *gravitating* towards one another, and being preſerv'd in their Orbits by the Force of Gravity.

Mr. *Keil* ſhews, that the Force of *Gravity* to the *centrifugal Force*, in a Body placed at the Equator of our Globe, is as 289 to 1; ſo that by the *centrifugal Force* ariſing from the Earth's Rotation, any Body placed in the Equator loſes a 289th part of the Weight it would have if the Globe were at reſt. And ſince there is no *centrifugal Force* at the *Poles*, a Body there weighs 289 Pounds, which at the Equator would weigh but 288. On our Globe the decreaſe of *Gravity*, in going from the Poles towards the *Equator*, is always *as the Square of the Coſine of the Latitude.* — *Quod facit Natura* (to uſe *Tully*'s Words) *per omnem Mundum, omnia Mente & Ratione conficiens.*

Mr. *Samuel Clark* obſerves, 'Tis now evident that the moſt univerſal Principle of *Gravitation*, the Spring of almoſt all the great and regular inanimate Motions in the World, anſwering not at all to the *Surfaces* of Bodies, by which alone they can act one upon another, but entirely to their *ſolid Content;* cannot poſſibly be the reſult of any *Motion* originally impreſſed on *Matter*, but muſt of neceſſity be cauſed by ſomething which penetrates the very Subſtance of all Bodies, and continually *puts forth in them* a *Force* or *Power* entirely different from that by which *Matter* acts on *Matter.* This (he adds) is *an evident Demonſtration, not only of the*
World's

World's being made originally by a *supreme intelligent Cause,* but moreover that it depends every moment on *some superior Being,* for the *Preservation* of its *Frame,* and that all the great *Motions* in it are caused by some immaterial *Power,* not having originally impressed a certain *Quantity* of *Motion* upon *Matter,* but perpetually and actually exerting itself every *Moment* in every *Part* of the *World* : which preserving and governing *Power* gives a very noble *Idea* of PROVIDENCE.

Dr. *Cheyne* demonstrates, That *Gravity,* or the *Attraction* of Bodies towards one another, cannot be mechanically accounted for. The *Planets* themselves cannot continue their Motions in their Orbs without it. It is not a Result from the *Nature* of *Matter,* because the Efficacy of *Matter* is communicated by *immediate Contact,* and it can by no means act at a distance. Whereas this Power of *Gravitation* acts at all Distances, without any *Medium* or Instrument for the Conveyance of it, and passes as far as the Limits of the Universe. *Matter* is indeed entirely *passive,* and can't either *tend* or *draw,* with regard unto other Bodies, no more than it can *move itself.* And what is essential to *Matter* cannot be intended or be remitted ; but *Gravity* increases or diminishes reciprocally, as the Squares of the Distances are increased or diminished. 'Tis plain this universal Force of *Gravitation* is the Effect of the *Divine Power* and *Virtue,* by which the Operations of all *material Agents* are preserved. They that press for a *mechanical Account* of *Gravity,* advance a Notion of a *subtile Fluid,* unto the Motion whereof they would ascribe it. But then still those Parts of Matter must be destitute of *Gravity,* which were very unlikely ! And this *Hypothesis* would still remove us but one Step further from *immechanical Principles* ; for the Cause of the Motion of your *subtile Fluid,* this, *Gentlemen,* you must own to be *immechanical.* Since you must admit a *first Cause,* you had as good be sensible of it in this place. 'Tis *He* who does immediately impress on

Matter

Matter this Property. There never was yet afforded unto the World (as my Doctor obſerves) a *Syſtem of Natural Philoſophy* which did not require *Poſtulates,* that are not *mechanically* to be accounted for. The feweſt any one pretends to, are, *the Exiſtence of Matter,* and *the Impreſſion of rectilinear Motions,* and the *Preſervation of the Faculties of natural Agents.* No Man has pretended to fetch from the Principles of *Mechaniſm* an Account for theſe. The *Impreſſion of an attractive Faculty upon Matter,* is no harder a *Poſtulate* than the reſt. It is a *Matter of Fact,* that *Matter* is in poſſeſſion of this Quality. And it can be referred unto nothing, but the Influence of that Glorious O N E, who is the *firſt Cauſe* of all Things.

' Behold, a continual Opportunity for a conſiderate ' and religious Man, to have a *Senſe* of a Glorious ' G O D awaken'd in him! And what is a *Walk with* ' *God,* but that *Senſe* kept alive in every Step of our ' *Walk?* I am continually entertain'd with *weighty* ' *Body,* or *Matter* tending to the *Center of Gravity;* I ' feel it in *my own.* The *Cauſe* of this *Tendency,* 'tis ' the Glorious G O D. *Great G O D, Thou giveſt this* ' *Matter ſuch a Tendency, and thou keepeſt it in its Opera-* ' *tion.* There is no other Cauſe but the *Will* and ' *Work* of the Glorious G O D. I am now effectually ' convinc'd of that antient Confeſſion, and muſt with ' Affection make it, *He is not far from every one of us.* ' When I ſee any thing moving or ſettling that way ' that its *heavy Nature* carries it, I may very juſtly ' think, and I would often form the Thought, *it is* ' *the Glorious G O D, who now carries this Matter ſuch a* ' *way!* When *Matter* ſinks *downward,* my Spirit ſhall ' even *therefore* mount *upward,* in acknowledgment of ' the God who orders it. I will no longer complain, ' *Behold, I go forward, but He is not there, and backward,* ' *but I cannot perceive Him; on the Left-hand, where He* ' *doth work, but I cannot behold Him; He hideth himſelf* ' *on the Right-hand, that I cannot ſee Him.* No, I am
' now

' now taught where to meet with Him, even at *every*
' *turn. He knows the way that I take.* I cannot ftir *for-*
' *ward* or *backward*, but I *perceive* Him in the *Weight*
' of every *Matter;* on the *Left-hand* and on the *Right* I
' fee Him *at work.* My way fhall be to improve this
' as a *weighty* Argument for the Being of a God. I
' will argue from it, *Behold, there is a God, whom I*
' *ought for ever to love, and ferve, and glorify.* Yea, and
' if I am *tempted* to the doing of any wicked thing, I
' may reflect, that it cannot be done without fome
' Action, wherein the *Weight of Matter* operates. But
' then I may carry on the Reflection, *How near am I*
' *to that Glorious* G O D, *whofe Commands I am going to*
' *violate! Matter keeps his Laws; but, O my Soul, wilt*
' *thou break 'em! How fhall I do this Wickednefs, and*
' *therein deny the God, who not only is above, but alfo is*
' *moft fenfibly now exerting His Power in the very Matter,*
' *upon which I make my criminal Mifapplications!'*

¶. Before we go any further, it appears high time
to introduce an Affertion or two of that excellent
Philofopher Dr. *Cheyne*, in his *Philofophical Principles of*
natural Religion. He afferts, and with Demonftration,
(for truly without *that* he afferts nothing!) that there
is no fuch thing as an *univerfal Soul*, animating the
vaft Syftem of the World, according to *Plato;* nor any
fubftantial Forms, according to *Ariftotle;* nor any omnifcient *radical Heat*, according to *Hippocrates;* nor
any *plaftick Virtue*, according to *Scaliger;* nor any *hy-*
larchick Principle, according to *More.* Thefe are mere
allegorical Terms, coined on purpofe to conceal the
Ignorance of the Authors, and keep up their Credit
with the credulous Part of Mankind. Thefe *unintelli-*
gible Beings are derogatory from the Wifdom and Power of the Great G O D, who can eafily *govern* the
Machine He could *create*, by more direct Methods than
employing fuch fubfervient *Divinities;* and indeed
thefe Beings will not ferve the Defign for which we
invent them, unlefs we endow them with Faculties

above

above the Dignity of *secondary Agents.* It is now plain from the moſt *evident Principles,* that the Great GOD not only has the *Springs* of this immenſe *Machine,* and all the ſeveral Parts of it, in his own Hand, and is the *firſt Mover;* but that without His *continual Influence* the whole Movement would ſoon fall to pieces. Yet beſides this, He has reſerved to Himſelf the power of *diſpenſing* with theſe *Laws,* whenever He pleaſes.

My Doctor has made it evident, That it is not eſſential to *Matter* to be either in *Reſt* or in *Motion:* But tho there is in *Matter* a *Vis inertiæ,* by which all Bodies reſiſt, to the utmoſt of their power, any *Change* of their State, whether of *Reſt* or *Motion;* yet this *Vis* is not eſſential to *Matter,* but a *poſitive Faculty* implanted therein by the Author of Nature. It is therefore evident that the Preſervation of a *Body* in *Reſt* or in *Motion* (after the firſt Inſtant) abſolutely depends on the Almighty GOD, as the Cauſe. No part of *Matter* can move itſelf, nor when put into *motion,* is this *Motion* abſolutely eſſential to its Being, nor does depend upon itſelf; and therefore the *Preſervation* of this *Motion* muſt have its Dependance on ſome other Cauſe. But there is no other Cauſe aſſignable beſides the *omnipotent Cauſe,* who preſerves the Being and Faculties of all natural Agents.

Great GOD, on the Behalf of all thy Creatures, I acknowledge in Thee we move and have our Being!

ESSAY XXII. *Of the* WATER.

PURE *Water* is a Fluid void of all Sapor, and ſeems to conſiſt of ſmall, ſmooth, round and porous Particles, that are of equal *Diameters* and equal *Gravities.* There are alſo between them Spaces, that are ſo large, and ranged in ſuch a manner, as to be on all ſides pervious. Their *Smoothneſs* accounts for their ſliding eaſily over the Surfaces of one another. Their *Roundneſs* keeps them from touching one another
ther

ther in more Points than one. So great is their *Poro-sity*, that there is at least forty times as much *Space* as *Matter* in *Water*. For *Water* is nineteen times specifically lighter than *Gold*; but *Gold* will by Pressure let Water thro its Pores, and has doubtless more *Pores* than *solid Parts*.

Dr. *Wainwright* observes, 'The compounding Particles of *Water* are less than those of *Air*; the former will pass thro several Bodies that the latter will not; it will force itself thro the *Skins* of Animals, even after they are dried and converted into Leather. Fasten a strong Rope, of what length you please, to an Hook; at the bottom of the *Cord* hang any *Weight* short of what will break it, tho' ever so great; you will find the Weight will *rise* in *moist* Weather, and *sink* in *dry*. You may also raise the *Weight*, by moistening the sides of the *Cord* with a wet Sponge. Thus a few Particles of Water may overcome any *finite Resistance*, if a *Cord* will bear it. Now since there is but a little Quantity of Water in this Experiment, and this is driven into the sides of the *Cord* with a Force no greater than the Weight of a Cylinder of Air incumbent on the *Water*, therefore the *Water* must act by a Property, whereby its Force is greatly augmented; and this can be no other than that of the *Cuneus* : And the Forces of *Wedges* are to one another reciprocally proportional to the *Angles* their Edges do make. But in *Spheres* the greater or lesser Degree of *Curvity* is to be considered as their *Angles*, when *Spheres* are considered as *Wedges*, and the Degrees of *Curvity* in *Spheres* are reciprocally as their *Radii*. Now the Particles of *Water* being so inconceivably small, much less than those of *Air*, they must, when acting as *Wedges*, have their Powers inconceivably increased, so as to overcome any *finite Resistance*.

If such Power is in a Particle of Water, what is Thy Power, O Thou infinite Maker of that, and all things!

Dr.

Dr. *Cheyne* observes, That the Quantity of *Water* on the outside of our Globe doth daily decrease, part of it being every day turn'd into *Mineral, Vegetable,* and *Animal* Substances, which are not easily dissolved again into their component Parts.

It is a Curiosity demonstrated by *Mariotte,* in his *Du Movement des Eaux,* That a *Jet-d'eau* never will rise as high as its Reservatory, but always fall short of it by a Space, which is the *subduplicate Ratio* of that *Height.*

In the *Congregations* of *Water,* and the *Distributions* of it over our Globe, we cannot but see the wonderful Wisdom and Goodness of our GOD. *The great and wide Sea, wherein are swimming Things innumerable, 'tis full of Thy Riches, O our GOD!* And the Uses of it are marvellous. *The Waters are in the Place which Thou, O our God, hast prepared for them: Thou hast set a Bound that they may not pass over.*

A fanciful and presumptuous Gentleman having made his Exceptions against the Proportion of *Water* to dry Land on our Globe, is well answer'd by Mr. *Keil;* That the Objections proceed from a deep Ignorance of *Natural Philosophy.* For if there were but half the *Sea* that now is, there would be but half the *Vapours;* and we should soon find our miserable want of these.

Mr. *Ray* assures us, That where the bottom of the Sea is not rocky, but Earth, Ouze, or Sand, which is incomparably the greatest part of it, it is by the Motion of the Waters, as far as the Reciprocation of the *Sea* extends to the bottom, every where brought unto a Level; that is to say, it has an *equal and uniform Descent* from the Shores to the Deeps.

That the *Motion of the Water* descends to a good Depth, is proved from the *Plants,* that grow deepest in the Sea: which all generally grow flat, in manner of a *Fan,* and not with Branches on all sides like *Trees:* a thing that is contrived by the Divine Providence, for that the Edges of them do in that posture, with most

ease,

case, cut the Water flowing to and fro. Probably in the greater Depths of the Sea there grow no *Plants* at all; the Bottom is probably too remote for the external *Air* to pass in a sufficient Quantity thither. Nay, we are told that in those *deep Seas* there are *no Fish* at all; their Spawn would be lost there: being lighter than the Water, it will not sink thither; and the Climate there may be too cold for the quickening of it.

According to Mr. *Halley*'s Experiment, *Water* as warm as the *Air* in the Summer, will in *twelve Hours* exhale the *tenth part* of an *Inch*. This Quantity will be found abundantly sufficient for all the *Rains*, and all the *Dews*, and all the *Springs* in the World; and will account for the *Caspian Sea*, and our vast *Canadian* Lakes, being always at a stand; and for the *Current*, said always to set in at the Streights of *Gibraltar*, tho the *Mediterranean Sea* receive so many Rivers. Every *ten square Inches* of the Surface of the Water, yields in Vapour *per diem* [we allow it only for the time the *Sun* is up] a *Cube Inch* of Water. Every Mile will yield 6914 Tons. A square Degree of sixty-nine *English* Miles will yield thirty-three Millions of Tons. If the *Mediterranean* Sea be estimated at forty Degrees long, and four broad, which is the least, the whole *Mediterranean* must lose in Vapours in a Summer's-day at least 5280 Millions of Tons. And yet sometimes the *Winds* lick up the Surface of Water faster than it exhales by the Heat of the Sun. The *Mediterranean Sea* receives nine considerable Rivers. We will suppose each of them to bring down ten times as much Water as the River *Thames*, which they do not; but this will allow for the small Rivulets. The *Thames*, allowing the Water to run after the rate of two Miles an Hour, may yield 20,300,000 Tons *per diem*. Allow as before, and all the nine Rivers bring down 1827 Millions of Tons in a day. This is but little more than a

Third

Third of what is proved to be evaporated out of the *Mediterranean* in twelve Hours time.

The astonishing *Flux* and *Reflux* of the *Sea,* what Benefits it affords unto the World! If the *Ocean* once were stagnated, first all the Places towards the Shore would be turned into a *Mephitis*; and then by degrees it would yet further corrupt, until the whole became as poisonous as the Lake of *Sodom.* The *Fishes* would be first hereby destroyed, and by the poisonful Steams, anon the *Plants* and *Animals* would share in the Destruction. In the *Tide* of the Sea the Waters are lifted up in an Heap, and then let fall again. So the fear'd Corruption is prevented: And how many Conveniences afforded for our *Navigation!* But what? Oh! what the Original of it? Where's the *Zaphnath Paaneah* who shall enlighten us?

On our Globe all Bodies have a Tendency towards the *Center* of it. And such a *Gravitation* there is towards the Center of the *Sun,* and of the *Moon,* and of all the *Planets.* There is cause to suspect that the Force of *Gravity* is, in the Celestial Globes, proportional to the Quantity of Matter in each of them. The *Sun,* for instance, being more than ten thousand times as big as the *Earth,* its *Gravitation,* and the attracting Force of it, is ten thousand times as much as that of the Earth, acting on Bodies at the same Distances.

If our Globe were alone, or not affected by the Actions of the *Sun* and the *Moon,* the Ocean, equally pressed by the Force of *Gravity* towards the Center, would continue in a perfect *Stagnation,* always at the same height, without ever *ebbing* or *flowing.* But it is demonstrated, that the *Sun* and the *Moon* have a like Principle of *Gravitation* towards their Centers, and our Globe is also within the Activity of their Attractions. Whence it will follow, that the Equality of the Pressure of *Gravity* towards the Center will be thereby disturbed. And tho the Smallness of these Forces, in respect of the *Gravitation* towards the Center

ter

ter of the Earth, render them imperceptible, yet the *Ocean* being fluid, and yielding to the leaſt **Force**, by its *riſing* ſhews where there is the leaſt Preſſure upon it, and where it is moſt preſſed, by *ſinking*. Accordingly we ſhall find, that where the *Moon* is perpendicularly either above or below the Horizon, there the Force of *Gravity* is moſt of all diminiſhed, and conſequently that there the *Ocean* muſt neceſſarily ſwell, by the coming in of the Water from thoſe Parts where the Preſſure is greateſt, namely, in thoſe where the *Moon* is near the *Horizon*. The *Sea*, which otherwiſe would be *ſpherical*, upon the Preſſure of the *Moon* muſt form itſelf into a *ſpheroidal* or *oval Figure*, whoſe longeſt Diameter is where the *Moon* is vertical, and ſhorteſt where ſhe is in the Horizon; and the *Moon* ſhifting her Poſition as ſhe turns round our Globe once a day, this *Oval* of *Water* ſhifts with her, occaſioning thereby the two *Floods* and *Ebbs* obſervable in each five and twenty Hours. The *Spring-Tides* upon the *New* and *Full Moons*, and the *Neap-Tides* upon the Quarters, are occaſion'd by the attractive Force of the *Sun* in the *New* and *Full*, conſpiring with the Attraction of the *Moon*, and producing a *Tide* by their *united Forces*. Whereas in the Quarters the *Sun* raiſes the Water where the *Moon* depreſſes, and on the contrary; ſo as the *Tides* are made only by the difference of their *Attraction*. The *Sun* and *Moon* being either conjoin'd or oppoſite in the *Equinoctial*, produce the greateſt *Spring-Tides*. The ſubſequent *Neap-Tides* being produced by the *Tropical Moon* in the Quarters, are always the *leaſt Tides*.

But then from the *Shoalneſs* of the *Water* in many places, and from the *Narrowneſs* of the *Straits*, by which the Tides are in many places propagated, there ariſes a mighty Diverſity, which, without the Knowledge of the Places, cannot be accounted for.

Dr. *Cheyne* has taught me to take notice of one thing more. If our *Earth* had any more than *one Moon* attending

tending it, we should receive probably a Detriment from it, rather than an Advantage. For at the *Conjunction* and *Opposition* with one another, and with the *Sun*, we should have *Tides* that would raise the Waters to the Tops of our Mountains, and in their *Quadratures* we should have no *Tides* at all.

O my Soul, beholding the Moon above, look up to God, who hath so wisely proportion'd her, for the Designs on which He placed her there.

The *Sea* is the grand Fountain of those *fresh Waters*, which supply and enrich the *Earth*, and by convenient Channels are carried back to the place from whence they came; the *perpetui Fontes, vitæque perennis Imago:* How equally are these fresh Waters distributed? How few *Antigua's* in the World? How agreeably are they disposed? And what a prodigious Run have many of the Rivers? The *Danube*, in a sober Account, as *Bohun* computes, runs fifteen hundred Miles in a strait Line from its Rise to its Fall. The *Nile*, according to *Varenius*, allowing for Curvatures, runs three thousand Miles; and the *Niger* two thousand four hundred; the *Ganges* twelve hundred; the *Amazonian* above thirteen hundred *Spanish* Leagues.

¶. 'But is it not high time for us to hear *the Voice* 'of many Waters!

'One celebrating the Bounty of our God unto us 'in the *Water*, so expresses it: *Quo Thesauro vel uni-* 'cum *Elementum Aquæ, si Deus illud in Sanguinem, ut* 'olim *in* Egypto, *converteret, possemus redimere?* The 'Contemplation may be carried unto the Element 'that is next above it.'

An excellent Person, who writes *Augustissimam Naturæ Scholam*, has thus rendred something of it articulate: *O Homo, ne imitare Equos & Mulos, qui me quidem bibunt, sed tantum bibunt. At tu, cui melior est Anima, ita me bibe, ut non tantum bibas, sed benedicentem Deum habeas dum bibis. Habebis autem si agnoscas ipsius Majestatem, eamque colas.*

Long

Long ſince have we been taught ſuch Notes as
theſe. ' *O Lord, how manifold are thy Works! In Wiſdom*
' *haſt thou made them all. The Earth is full of thy Riches.*
' *And ſo is the great and wide Sea, wherein are ſwimming*
' *things innumerable.*'
  ' But can we look on the *Sea*, and not ſee a Picture
' of *a troubleſome World*; ſee and be inſtructed.'

APPENDIX.

§. WE can ſcarce leave the *Water* without ſome
Remarks on our *Fluids*; and we will be
more particularly indebted to Dr. *Cheyne* for hinting
them firſt. How *frugal* is Nature in *Principles,* and
yet how *fruitful* in *Compoſitions* and in *Conſequences!*
The *primary Fluids* are but *four,* *Water* and *Air,* and
Mercury and *Light.* 'Tis but ſeldom that three of
theſe are much compounded with others. 'Tis *Water*
alone, 'tis *Lymph,* that is moſtly the *Baſis* of all other
Mixtures; and it is the Parts of ſolid Bodies floating
in this Fluid that produce all our pleaſant and uſeful
Varieties of Liquors.

  Again, How vaſt the difference between the *ſpeci-*
fick Gravities of our *Fluids!* *Mercury* is about eight
thouſand times heavier than *Air.* *Air* muſt have
choak'd us, if it had been half ſo heavy as *Mercury.*
And yet Mankind, in its preſent Circumſtances of the
Blood-Veſſels, under frequent *Obſtructions,* could not
well have done without ſuch an *heavy Fluid* as *Mer-*
cury.

  Thirdly, All *Fluids* agree in the condition of the
direction of their *Preſſure* upon the ſides of the containing Veſſel. This *Preſſure* is for ever communicated in Lines *perpendicular* to the ſides of the containing Veſſel. This beautiful and uniform Property of
all *Fluids* neceſſarily follows from the *Sphericity* of their
conſtituent Particles.

Our

Our Doctor's Conclusion is as I would have it.
' Now could any thing but the Almighty *Power* of
' God have rounded those infinite numbers of small
' Particles whereof *Fluids* consist? Or could any thing
' but his *Wisdom* have assigned them their true Di-
' mensions, their exact Weights, and required Solidi-
' ties ?'

I beseech you, *Sirs*, by what Laws of *Mechanism*
were all the Particles of the several *Fluids* turned of
differing *Diameters*, differing *Solidities*, differing *Weights*
from one another : but all of the same *Diameters*, and
Solidities, and *Weights* among themselves? *This is the
Finger of God!* It is a just Assertion of Dr. *Grew, The
Regularity of Corporeal Principles shews that they come at
first from a Divine Regulator.*

ESSAY XXIII. *Of the* EARTH.

THE *Lord by Wisdom has founded the Earth.* A
poor Sojourner on the *Earth* now thinks it his
Duty to behold and admire the *Wisdom* of his glorious
Maker there.

The *Earth*, which is the Basis and Support of so
many Vegetables and Animals, and yields the alimen-
tary Particles, whereof *Water* is the Vehicle, for their
Nourishment : *Quorum omnium* (as *Tully* saith well) *in-
credibilis Multitudo, insatiabili Varietate distinguitur.*

The various Moulds and Soils of the Earth declare
the admirable Wisdom of the Creator, in making such
a provision for a vast variety of Intentions. *God said,
Let the Earth bring forth !*

And yet,

Nec vero Terræ ferre omnes omnia possunt.

It is pretty odd ; they who have written *de Arte
Combinatoria*, reckon of no fewer than one hundred
and seventy-nine Millions, one thousand and sixty different sorts of Earth : But we may content ourselves
with

with Sir *John Evelyn's* Enumeration, which is very ſhort of *that*.

However, the *Vegetables* owe not ſo much of their Life and Growth to the *Earth* itſelf, as to ſome agreeable Juices or Salts lodg'd in it. Both Mr. *Boyle* and *Van Helmont*, by Experiments, found the Earth ſcarce at all diminiſhed when *Plants*, even *Trees*, had been for divers Years growing in it.

The *Strata* of the Earth, its *Lays* and *Beds*, afford ſurprizing Matters of Obſervation; the *Objects* lodged in them; the *Uſes* made of them; and particularly the *Paſſage* they give to *ſweet Waters*, as being the *Calanders* wherein they are ſweetned. It is aſſerted that theſe are found all to lie very much according to the Laws of *Gravity*. Mr. *Derham* went far to demonſtrate this Aſſertion.

The *vain Colts of Aſſes*, that *fain would be wiſe*, have cavill'd at the *unequal Surface of the Earth*, have open'd againſt the *Mountains*, as if they were *ſuperfluous Excreſcences*; but *Warts* deforming the Face of the Earth, and Proofs the *Earth* is but an Heap of Rubbiſh and Ruins. *Pliny* had more of Religion in him.

The ſagacious Dr. *Halley* has obſerved, That the Ridges of *Mountains* being placed thro the midſt of their Continents, do ſerve as *Alembicks*, to diſtil freſh Waters in vaſt Quantities for the Uſe of the World: And their *Heights* give a Deſcent unto the *Streams*, to run gently, like ſo many Veins of the *Macrocoſm*, to be the more beneficial to the Creation. The generation of *Clouds*, and the diſtribution of *Rains*, accommodated and accompliſhed by the *Mountains*, is indeed ſo obſervable, that the learned *Scheuchzer* and *Creitlovius* can't forbear breaking out upon it with a *Mirati ſummam Creatoris Sapientiam!*

What *Rivers* could there be without thoſe admirable *Tools of Nature!*

Vapours being raiſed by the *Sun*, acting on the Surface of the *Sea*, as a *Fire* under an Alembick, by ra-

H   refying

refying of it, makes the lighteſt and freſheſt Portions thereof to riſe firſt; which *Rarefaction* is made (as Dr. *Cheyne* obſerves) by the inſinuation of its active Particles among the porous Parts thereof, whereby they are put into a violent Motion many different ways, and ſo are expanded into little Bubbles of larger Dimenſions than formerly they had; and ſo they become ſpecifically lighter, and the weightier *Atmoſphere* buoys them up. The Streams of theſe *Vapours* reſt in places where the Air is of equal *Gravity* with them, and are carried up and down the *Atmoſphere* by the courſe of that Air, till they hit at laſt againſt the ſides of the *Mountains*, and by this Concuſſion are condenſed, and thus become heavier than the Air they ſwum in, and ſo gleet down the rocky Caverns of theſe *Mountains*, the inner parts whereof being hollow and ſtony, afford them a *Baſon*, until they are accumulated in ſufficient Quantities, to break out at the firſt *Crany:* whence they deſcend into Plains, and ſeveral of them uniting, form *Rivulets*; and many of thoſe uniting, do grow into *Rivers*. This is the Story of them; this their *Pedigree!*

Minerals are dug out of *Mountains*; which, if they were ſought only in level Countries, the Delfs would be ſo flown with Waters, that it would be impoſſible to make *Addits* or *Soughs* to drein them. Here is, as *Olaus Magnus* expreſſes it, *Inexhauſta pretioſorum Metallorum ubertas.*

A *German* Writer, got upon the *Mountains*, gives this Account of them: *Sunt ceu tot naturales Fornaces Chymicæ, in quibus Deus varia Metalla & Mineralia excoquit & maturat.*

The *Habitations* and *Situations* of Mankind are made vaſtly the more comfortable for the *Mountains*. There is a vaſt variety of *Plants* proper to the *Mountains:* and many Animals find the *Mountains* their moſt proper places to breed and feed in. *The higheſt Hills a Refuge to the wild Goats!* A Point Mr. *Ray* has well ſpoken to.

They report that *Hippocrates* did uſually repair to the *Mountains* for the *Plants,* by which he wrought the chief of his Cures.

Mountains alſo are the moſt convenient Boundaries to Territories, and afford a Defence unto them. One calls them *the Bulwarks of Nature, caſt up at the Charges of the Almighty; the Scorns and Curbs of the moſt victorious Armies.* The *Barbarians* in *Curtius* were confidently ſenſible of this!

Yea, we may appeal to the Senſes of all Men, whether the grateful Variety of *Hills* and *Dales* be not more pleaſing than the largeſt continued *Plains.*

'Tis alſo a *ſalutary Conformation* of the Earth; ſome Conſtitutions are beſt ſuited *above,* and others *below.*

Truly theſe maſſy and lofty Piles can by no means be ſpared.

Galen, thou ſhalt chaſtize the *Pſeudo-Chriſtians,* who reproach the Works of God. Say! —— *Accuſandi ſanè meâ Sententiâ hic ſunt Sophiſtæ, qui cùm nondum invenire neque exponere Opera Naturæ queant, eam tamen inertia atque inſcitia condemnant.*

Say now, *O Man,* ſay, under the ſweet Conſtraints of Demonſtration, *Great G O D, the Earth is full of thy Goodneſs!*

And Dr. *Grew* ſhall carry on the more general Obſervation for us. 'How little is the Miſchief which 'the *Air, Fire,* or *Water* ſometimes doth, compared 'with the innumerable *Uſes* to which they daily ſerve? 'Beſides the *Seas* and *Rivers,* how many *wholeſome* '*Springs* are there for one that is *poiſonous?* Are the 'Northern Countries ſubject to *Cold?* They have a 'greater plenty of *Furs* to keep the People warm. 'Would thoſe under or near the Line be ſubject to 'Heat? They have a conſtant *Eaſterly Breeze,* which 'blows ſtrongeſt in the Heat of the Day, to refreſh 'them: And with this Refreſhment *without,* they

'have

' have a variety of excellent *Fruits* to comfort and cool
' them *within*. How admirably are the *Clouds* fed with
' Vapours, and carried about with the *Winds*, for the
' gradual, equal, and seasonable watering of most
' Countries? And in those which have less *Rain*, how
' abundantly is the want of that supplied with noble
' *Rivers?*'

Even the subterraneous *Caverns* have their Uses.
And so have the *Ignivomous Mountains*: Those terrible
things are *Spiracles*, to vent the *Vapours*, which else
might make a dismal Havock. Dr. *Woodward* observes,
That tho Places which are very subject unto *Earthquakes* usually have these *Volcano's*, yet without these
fiery Vents their *Earthquakes* would bring more tremendous Desolations upon them.

Those two flammivomous Mountains, *Vesuvius* and
Ætna, have sometimes terrified the whole World with
their tremendous Eruptions. *Vesuvius* transmitted its
frightful Cinders as far as *Constantinople*, which obliged
the Emperor to leave the City; and Historians tell us
there was kept an Anniversary Commemoration of it.
Kircher has given us a Chronicle of what furious things
have been done by *Ætna*; the melted Matter which
one time it poured forth, spreading in breadth six
Miles, ran down as far as *Catanea*, and forced a Passage into the Sea.

Asia abounds in these *Volcano's*. *Africa* is known
to have eight at least. In *America* 'tis affirmed that
there are no less than fifteen, among that vast Chain
of Mountains called the *Andes*. One says, ' Nature
' seems here to keep house under ground, and the
' Hollows of the *Mountains* to be the *Funnels* or *Chim-
' neys*, by which the fuliginous Matter of those ever-
' lasting Fires ascends.'

The *North* too, that seems doom'd unto *eternal Cold*,
has its famous *Hecla*. And *Bartholomew Zenet* found
one in *Greenland*, yet nearer to the Pole; the Effects
whereof are very surprizing.

A

A reaſonable and religious Mind cannot behold theſe formidable *Mountains*, without ſome Reflections of this importance: *Great GOD, who knows the Power of thine Anger?* Or what can ſtand before the powerful Indignation of that God, who can kindle a Fire in his Anger that ſhall burn to the loweſt Hell, and ſet on fire the Foundations of the Mountains!

The *Volcano's* would lead us to conſider the *Earthquakes*, wherein the *Earth* often ſuffers violent, and ſometimes very deſtructive Concuſſions.

The *Hiſtory of Earthquakes* would be a large, as well as a ſad Volume. Whether a *Colluctation of Minerals* in the Bowels of the Earth is the cauſe of thoſe direful Convulſions, may be conſidered: As we know a Compoſition of Gold which *Aqua Regia* has diſſolved; *Sal Armoniack*, and *Salt of Tartar*, ſet on fire, will with an horrible crack break thro all that is in the way. But Mankind ought herein to tremble before the Juſtice of God. Particular *Cities* and *Countries*, what fearful Deſolations have been by Earthquakes brought upon them!

The old ſinking of *Helice* and *Buris*, abſorbed by *Earthquakes* into the Sea, mention'd by *Ovid*, or the twelve Cities that were ſo ſwallow'd up in the Days of *Tiberius*, are ſmall things to what *Earthquakes* are to do on our Globe; yea, have already done. I know not what we ſhall think of the huge *Atlantis*, mentioned by *Plato*, now at the bottom of the *Atlantick* Ocean: But I know *Varenius* thinks it probable, that the Northern Part of *America* was joined unto *Ireland*, till Earthquakes made the vaſt and amazing Separation. Others have thought ſo of *England* and *France*; of *Spain* and *Africa*; of *Italy* and *Sicily*.

Ah, *Sicily!* Art thou come to be ſpoken of? No longer ago than t'other day what a rueful Spectacle was there exhibited in the Iſland of *Sicily* by an *Earthquake*, in which there periſhed the beſt part of two hundred thouſand Souls!

H 3 Yea,

Yea, *Ammianus Marcellinus* tells us, in the Year 365, *Horrendi Tremores per omnem Orbis Ambitum graffati funt.*

O Inhabitants of the Earth, how much ought you to fear the things that will bring you into ill Terms with the Glorious G O D! *Fear,* left the *Pit* and the *Snare* be upon you! Againft all other Strokes there may fome Defence or other be thought on: There is none againft an *Earthquake!* It fays, *Tho they hide in the top of* Carmel, *I will find them there!*

But furely the *Earthquakes* I have met with will effectually inftruct me to avoid the Folly of fetting my Heart inordinately on any *Earthly* Poffeffions or Enjoyments. Methinks I hear Heaven faying, *Surely he will receive this Inftruction!*

A modern Philofopher fpeaks at this rate, ' We do ' not know when and where we ftand upon *good* ' *Ground:* It would amaze the ftouteft Heart, and ' make him ready to die with Fear, if he could fee ' into the *fubterraneous World,* and view the dark Re- ' ceffes of Nature under ground; and behold, that ' even the ftrongeft of our Piles of Building, whofe ' Foundation we think is laid firm and faft, yet are ' fet upon an Arch or Bridge, made by the bending ' Parts of the Earth one upon another, over a prodi- ' gious Vault, at the bottom of which there lies an ' unfathomable Sea, but its upper Hollows are filled ' with ftagnating Air, and with Expirations of ful- ' phureous and bituminous Matter. Upon fuch a ' *dreadful Abyfs* we walk, and ride, and fleep; and ' are fuftained only by an *arched Roof,* which alfo is ' not in all places of an equal Thicknefs.'

Give me leave to fay, I take *Earthquakes* to be very *moving Preachers* unto *worldly-minded Men:* Their Addrefs may be very agreeably put into the Terms of the Prophet; *O Earth, Earth, Earth, hear the Word of the Lord!*

' *Chryfoftom*

‘ *Chryſoſtom* did well, among his other Epithets, to
‘ call the Earth *our Table*; but it ſhall *teach* me as
‘ well as *feed* me : May I be a *Deipnoſophiſt* upon it.

‘ Indeed, what is the Earth but a *Theatre*, as has
‘ been long ſince obſerved ? *In quo Infinita & Illuſtria*,
‘ *Providentiæ, Bonitatis, Potentiæ ac Sapientiæ Divinæ*
‘ *Spectacula contemplanda !* But I muſt not forget that
‘ this *Earth* is very ſhortly to be my *ſleeping-place*; it
‘ has a *Grave* waiting for me : *I will not fear to go*
‘ *down, for thou haſt promiſed, O my Saviour, to bring me*
‘ *up again.*’

A P P E N D I X.

§. HAving arrived thus far, I will here make a
Pauſe, and acknowledge the Shine of Hea-
ven on *our Parts of the Earth,* in the Improvements of
our *modern Philoſophy.*

To render us the more ſenſible hereof, we will
propoſe a few Points of the *Mahometan Philoſophy,* or
Secrets reveal’d unto *Mahomet,* which none of his Fol-
lowers, who cover ſo much of the Earth at this Day,
may dare to queſtion.

The *Winds* ; ’tis an *Angel* moving his *Wings* that
raiſes them.

The *Flux* and *Reflux* of the *Sea,* is cauſed by an
Angel’s putting his Foot on the middle of the *Ocean,*
which compreſſing the Waves, the Waters run to the
Shores ; but being removed, they retire into their
proper Station.

Falling Stars are the *Firebrands* with which the *good
Angels* drive away the *bad,* when they are too ſaucily
inquiſitive, and approach too near the Verge of the
Heavens, to eves-drop the Secrets there.

Thunder is nothing elſe but the cracking of an *Angel’s Whip,* while he flaſhes the dull Clouds into ſuch
and ſuch places, when they want *Rains* to fertilize the
Earth.

Eclipſes

Eclipses are made thus: The *Sun* and *Moon* are shut in a *Pipe*, which is turned up and down; from each Pipe is a Window, by which they enlighten the World; but when God is angry at the Inhabitants of it for their Transgressions, He bids an *Angel* clap to the Window, and so turn the Light towards Heaven from the Earth: for this Occasion *Forms of Prayer* are left, that the Almighty would avert his Judgments, and restore Light unto the World.

The thick-skull'd Prophet sets another *Angel* at work for *Earthquakes*; he is to hold so many *Ropes* tied unto every Quarter of the Globe, and when he is commanded, he is to pull; so he shakes that part of the Globe: and if a City, or Mountain, or Tower, is to be overturned, then he tugs harder at the Pulley, till the Rivers dance, and the Valleys are filled with Rubbish, and the Waters are swallowed up in the Precipices.

May our Devotion exceed the Mahometan *as much as our Philosophy!*

ESSAY XXIV. *Of* MAGNETISM.

SUCH an unaccountable thing there is as *the* MAGNETISM *of the Earth.* A Principle very different from that of *Gravity.*

The Operations of this amazing Principle, are principally discovered in the communion that *Iron* has with the *Loadstone*; a rough, coarse, unsightly Stone, but of more Value than all the *Diamonds* and *Jewels* in the Universe.

It is observed by *Sturmius*, That the *attractive Quality* of the *Magnet* was known to the Antients, even beyond all History. Indeed, besides what *Pliny* says of it, *Aristotle* speaks of *Thales*, as having said, the *Stone* has a *Soul*, ὅτι τὸν σίδηρον κινεῖ· *because it moves Iron.*

It

It was *Roger Bacon* who firſt of all diſcovered the *Verticity* of the *Magnet*, or its Property of pointing towards the *Pole*, about four hundred Years ago.

The Communication of its Vertue to *Iron* was firſt of all diſcovered by the *Italians*. One *Goia* firſt lit upon the Uſe of the *Mariner's Compaſs*, about *A. C.* 1300. After this, the various *Declination* of the *Needle* under different Meridians, was diſcovered by *Cabot* and *Norman*. And then the Variation of the Declination, ſo as to be not always the ſame in one and the ſame place, by *Hevelius*, *Auzot*, *Volckamer*, and others.

The inquiſitive Mr. *Derham* ſays, The *Variation of the Variation* was firſt found out by our *Gellibrand*, *A. C.* 1634.

And he himſelf has added a further Diſcovery; That as the *Common Needle* is continually varying towards the *Eaſt* and *Weſt*, ſo the *Dipping Needle* varies up and down, towards the *Zenith*, or fromwards, with a *magnetick* Tendency, deſcribing a Circle round the Pole of the World, or ſome other Point; a Circle, whereof the *Radius* is about 13 Degrees.

In every *Magnet* there are *two Poles*, the one pointing to the *North*, and the other to the *South*.

The *Poles*, in divers Parts of the Globe, are diverſly inclined towards the *Center* of the Earth.

Theſe *Poles*, tho contrary to one another, do mutually help towards the *Magnet's* Attraction, and Suſpenſion of *Iron*.

If a *Stone* be cut or broke into ever ſo many pieces, there are theſe *two Poles* in each of the *pieces*.

If two *Magnets* are ſpherical, one will conform itſelf to the other, ſo as either of them would do to the *Earth*; and after they have ſo turned themſelves, they will endeavour to approach each other: but placed in a contrary Poſition, they avoid each other.

If a *Magnet* be cut thro the *Axis*, the Segments of the Stone, which before were joined, will now avoid and fly each other.

If

If the *Magnet* be cut by a Section perpendicular to its *Axis*, the two Points, which before were conjoined, will become contrary Poles; one in one, t'other in t'other Segment.

Iron receives Vertue from the *Magnet*, by application to it, or barely from an approach near it, tho it do not touch it; and the *Iron* receives this Vertue variously, according to the Parts of the Stone it is made to approach to.

The *Magnet* loses none of its own Vertue by communicating any to the *Iron*. This Vertue it also communicates very speedily; tho the longer the *Iron* joins the Stone, the longer its communicated Vertue will hold. And the better the *Magnet*, the sooner and stronger the communicated Vertue.

Steel receives Vertue from the *Magnet* better than *Iron*.

A *Needle* touch'd by a *Magnet*, will turn its Ends the same way towards the Poles of the World as the *Magnet* will do it. But neither of them conform their Poles exactly to those of the World; they have usually some *Variation*, and this *Variation* too in the same place is not always the same.

A *Magnet* will take up much more *Iron* when *arm'd* or *cap'd* than it can alone. And if the *Iron Ring* be suspended by the *Stone*, yet the magnetical Particles do not hinder the Ring from turning round any way, to the Right or Left.

The best *Magnet*, at the least distance from a lesser or a weaker, cannot draw to it a piece of Iron adhering actually to a much weaker or lesser Stone; but if it come to touch it, it can draw it from the other. But a weaker *Magnet*, or even a little piece of *Iron*, can draw away or separate a piece of *Iron* contiguous to a better and greater *Magnet*.

In our Northern Parts of the World, the *South Pole* of a *Loadstone* will raise more *Iron* than the *North Pole*.

A

A Plate of *Iron* only, but no other Body interpofed, can impede the Operation of the *Loadſtone*, either as to its attractive or directive Quality.

The Power and Vertue of the *Loadſtone* may be impair'd by lying long in a wrong poſture, as alſo by Ruſt, and Wet, and the like.

A *Magnet* heated *red-hot*, will be ſpeedily deprived of its *attractive* Quality; then cooled, either with the *South Pole* to the *North*, in an horizontal poſition, or with the *South Pole* to the *Earth* in a perpendicular, it will change its *Polarity*; the *Southern* Pole becoming the *Northern*, and *vice verſâ*.

By applying the Poles of a very *ſmall Fragment* of a *Magnet* to the oppoſite vigorous ones of a larger, the Poles of the Fragment have been ſpeedily changed.

Well temper'd and harden'd *Iron* Tools, *heated* by Attrition, will attract Filings of *Iron* and *Steel*.

The *Iron Bars* of *Windows*, which have ſtood long in an erect poſition, do grow permanently *magnetical*; the lower ends of ſuch Bars being the *Northern Poles*, and the upper the *Southern*.

Mr. *Boyle* found *Engliſh Oker*, heated red-hot, and cooled in a proper poſture, plainly to gain a *magnetick* Power.

The illuſtrious Mr. *Boyle*, and the inquiſitive Mr. *Derham*, have carried on their Experiments, till we are overwhelmed with the *Wonders*, as well as with the *Numbers* of them.

That of Mr. *Derham*, and *Grimaldi*, That a piece of well-touch *Iron Wire*, upon being bent round in a Ring, or coiled round upon a Stick, loſes its Verticity; is very admirable.

The Strength of ſome *Loadſtones* is very ſurprizing.

Dr. *Liſter* ſaw a Collection of *Loadſtones*, one of them weighed naked not above a *Dram*, yet it would raiſe a *Dram* and half of *Iron*; but being ſhod, it would raiſe *one hundred and forty and four Drams*. A ſmooth *Loadſtone*, weighing 65 Grains, drew up 14 Ounces; that
is,

is, 144 times its own weight. A *Loadstone* that was no bigger than an Hazel-nut, fetch'd up an huge bunch of Keys.

The *Effluvia* of a *Loadstone* seem to work in a *Circle*. What flows from the *North Pole*, comes round, and enters the *South Pole*; and what flows from the *South Pole*, enters the *North Pole*.

Tho a minute *Loadstone* may have a prodigious force, yet it is very strange to see what a *short Sphere of Activity* it has; it affects not the *Iron* sensibly above an Inch or two, and the biggest little more than a Foot or two. The *magnetick Effluvia* make haste to return to the Stone that emitted them, and seem afraid of leaving it, as a Child the Mother before it can go alone.

On that astonishing Subject, *The Variation of the Compass*, what if we should hear the acute Mr. *Halley*'s Proposals?

He proposes, That our whole Globe should be looked upon as a *great Magnet*, having four *magnetical Poles*, or Points of Attraction, two near each Pole of the Equator. In those Parts of the World which lie near adjacent unto any one of these *magnetical Poles*, the Needle is governed by it; the nearer Pole being always predominant over the remoter. The *Pole* which at present is nearest unto *Britain*, lies in or near the Meridian of the Lands-end of *England*, and not above seven Degrees from the *Artick Pole*. By this *Pole* the Variations in all *Europe*, and in *Tartary*, and in the *North Sea*, are principally governed, tho' with some regard to the other *Northern Pole*, which is in a Meridian passing about the middle of *Calefornia*, and about fifteen Degrees from the *North Pole* of the World. To this the Needle pays its chief respect in all the North *America*, and in the two Oceans on either side, even from the *Azores* Westward, unto *Japan*, and further. The two *Southern Poles* are distant rather further from the *South* Pole of the World; the

one

one is about ſixteen Degrees therefrom, and is under a *Meridian* about twenty Degrees to the Weſtward of the *Magellanick* Streights; this commands the Needle in all the South *America,* in the *Pacifick Sea,* and in the greateſt part of the *Ethiopick Ocean.* The fourth and laſt Pole ſeems to have the greateſt Power and the largeſt Dominions of all, as it is the moſt remote from the Pole of the World; for 'tis near twenty Degrees from it, in the Meridian which paſſes thro *Hollandia Nova,* and the Iſland *Celebes.* This Pole has the maſtery in the South part of *Africa,* in *Arabia,* and the *Red Sea,* in *Perſia,* in *India,* and its Iſlands, and all over the *Indian Sea,* from the *Cape of Good Hope* Eaſtwards, to the middle of the great *South Sea,* which divides *Aſia* from *America.*

Behold, the Diſpoſition of the *magnetical Vertue,* as it is throughout the whole Globe of the *Earth* at this day!

But now to ſolve the *Phænomena!*

We may reckon the external Parts of our Globe as a *Shell,* the internal as a *Nucleus,* or an *inner Globe* included within ours; and between theſe a *fluid Medium,* which having the ſame common Center and Axis of diurnal Rotation, may turn about with our Earth every four and twenty Hours: only this outer Sphere having its turbinating Motion ſome ſmall matter either ſwifter or ſlower than the internal Ball, and a very ſmall difference becoming in length of Time ſenſible by many Repetitions; the internal Parts will by degrees recede from the external, and not keeping pace with one another, will appear gradually to move, either Eaſtwards or Weſtwards, by the difference of their Motions. Now if the exterior Shell of our Globe ſhould be a *Magnet,* having its Poles at a diſtance from the Poles of diurnal Rotation; and if the internal *Nucleus* be likewiſe a *Magnet,* having its Poles in two other places, diſtant alſo from the Axis, and theſe latter, by a ſlow and gradual Motion, change their place

in

in respect of the external, we may then give a reasonable account of the *four magnetical Poles*, and of the *Changes of the Needle's Variations*. Who can tell but the *final Cause* of the Admixture of the *magnetical Matter* in the Mass of the terrestrial Parts of our Globe, should be to maintain the concave Arch of this our Shell? Yea, we may suppose the Arch lined with a *magnetical Matter*, or to be rather one great *concave Magnet*, whose *two Poles* are fixed in the Surface of our Globe? Sir *Isaac Newton* has demonstrated the *Moon* to be more solid than our *Earth*, as nine to five; why may we not then suppose four Ninths of our Globe to be Cavity? Mr. *Halley* allows there may be Inhabitants of the lower Story, and many ways of producing *Light* for them. The Medium itself may be always luminous; or the concave Arch may shine with such a Substance as does invest the Surface of the *Sun*; or they may have peculiar *Luminaries*, whereof we can have no Idea: As *Virgil* and *Claudian* enlighten their *Elysian* Fields; the latter,

Amissum ne crede Diem; sunt altera nobis
Sydera; sunt Orbes alii; Lumenque videbis
Purius, Elysiumque magis mirabere Solem.

The Diameter of the Earth being about eight thousand *English* Miles, how easy 'tis to allow five hundred Miles for the Thickness of the Shell! And another five hundred Miles for a Medium capable of a vast Atmosphere, for the Globe contained within it! —— But it's time to stop, we are got beyond *Human Penetration*; we have *dug* as far as 'tis fit any *Conjecture* should carry us!

It is a little surprizing that the Orb of the Activity of *Magnets*, as Mr. *Derham* observes, is larger or lesser at different times. There is a noble and a mighty *Loadstone* reserved in the Repository at *Gresham*-College, which will keep a Key, or other piece of

Iron,

Iron, fufpended unto another, fometimes the diftance of eight or ten Foot from it, but at other times not above four.

[A *Digreffion,* if worthy to be called fo!]

§. But is it poffible for me to go any further without making an *Obfervation,* which indeed would ever now and then break in upon us as we go along?

Once for all; *Gentlemen Philofophers,* the MAGNET has quite *puzzled* you. It fhall then be no indecent *Anticipation* of what fhould have been obferved at the Conclufion of this Collection, here to demand it of you, that you glorify the infinite Creator of this, and of all things, as *incomprehenfible.* You muft acknowledge that *Human Reafon* is too feeble, too narrow a thing to comprehend the *infinite* God. The Words of our excellent *Boyle* deferve to be recited on this Occafion: ' Such is the *natural Imbecillity* of the *Hu-*
' *man Intellect,* that the moft piercing Wits and excel-
' lent Mathematicians are forced to confefs, that not
' only their own *Reafon,* but that of Mankind, may
' be puzzled and nonplus'd about QUANTITY, which
' is an Object of Contemplation natural, nay, mathe-
' matical. Wherefore why fhould we think it unfit
' to be believed, and to be acknowledged, that in the
' *Attributes* of God [it may be added, *and in His Dif-*
' *penfations towards the Children of Men*] there fhould be
' fome things which our finite Underftandings cannot
' clearly *comprehend?* And we who cannot clearly
' comprehend how in ourfelves two fuch diftant Na-
' tures, as that of a *grofs Body* and an *immaterial Spirit*
' fhould be fo united as to make up *one Man,* why
' fhould we grudge to have our REASON Pupil to an
' *omnifcient Inftructor,* who can teach us fuch things,
' as neither our own mere Reafon, nor any others,
' could ever have difcovered to us?'

I will now fingle out a few plain *Mathematical In-fances,* wherein, Sirs, you will find your fineft *Reafon* fo tranfcended, and fo confounded, that it is to be

hoped

hoped a *profound Humility* in the grand Affairs of our holy *Religion* will from this time for ever *adorn* you.

Mr. *Robert Jenkin* difcourfing on *the Reafonablenefs of the Chriftian Religion,* gives two Inftances *how much we may lofe ourfelves in the Speculation of material things.*

Firft, Nothing feems more evident, than that *all Matter is divifible;* yea, the *leaft Particle of Matter* muft be fo, becaufe it has the Nature and Effence of *Matter:* it can never be fo *divided* that it fhall ceafe to be *Matter.* But then, on the other fide, it is plain, *Matter* cannot be *infinitely divifible;* becaufe whatever is *divifible,* is *divifible* into *Parts;* and no *Parts* can be *infinite,* becaufe no *Number* can be fo. A *numberlefs Number* is a Contradiction; all Parts are capable of being *numbred;* they are *more* or *fewer,* odd or even. It is not enough to fay, that *Matter* is only capable of fuch a *Divifion,* but never can be *actually divided into infinite Parts;* for the Parts into which it is *divifible* muft be *actually exiftent,* tho they be not *actually divided.* And laft of all to fay, thefe Parts of Matter are *indefinite,* but not *infinite,* is only to confefs *we know not what to fay.*

Secondly, We all agree that all the *Parts* into which the *Whole* is divided, being taken together are *equal to the Whole.* But it feems any *fingle Part* is *equal to the Whole.* It is granted, that in any *Circle* a *Line* may be drawn from *every Point* of the Circumference to the *Center.* Suppofe the Circle to be the *Equator,* and a million leffer Circles are drawn within the *Equator,* about the fame *Center,* and then a *right Line* drawn from *every Point* of the *Equator* to the Center of the Globe; every fuch *right Line* drawn from the *Equator* to the *Center,* muft of neceffity cut thro the million *leffer Circles,* about the fame *Center:* confequently there muft be the fame number of Points in a Circle a million of times lefs than the *Equator,* as there is in the *Equator* itfelf. The *leffer Circles* may be multiplied into as many as there are *Points* in the *Diameters;* and ſo the *leaſt Circle* imaginable may have *as many Points* as the greateſt; that is, be as big as the greateſt, as big as one that is millions of times as big as itſelf.

Yet more; What will you ſay to this? Let a *Radius* be moved as a *Radius* upon a *Circle*; 'tis a Caſe of **Dr.** *Grew's* propoſing: whether we ſuppoſe it *wholly* moved, or but *in part*, the Suppoſition will bring us to an *Abſurdity*; if it be in a part *movent*, and in a part *quieſcent*, it will be a *curve Line*, and no *Radius*; if it be wholly *movent*, then it moves either *about* or *upon* the Center; if it moves *about* it, it then comes ſhort of it, and ſo again is no *Radius*: it cannot move *upon* it, becauſe all motion having parts, there can be no motion upon a *Point*.

More yet; We cannot conceive how the *Perimeter* of a Circle, or other *curve Figure*, can conſiſt without being infinitely *angular*; for the *parts* of a *Line* are *Lines*: But we cannot conceive how thoſe Lines can have, as here they have, a different direction, and therefore an inclination, without making an *Angle*. And yet if you ſuppoſe a *Circle* to be *angular*, you deſtroy the Definition of a *Circle*, and the Theorems depending on it.

Once more; I will offer a Caſe of my own. The Line on which I am now writing is a *Space* between *two Points*; it will be doubtleſs allowed me, that my Pen in paſſing over this Line, from the one point unto the other, muſt *paſs over the half of the Line before it paſſes over the whole*; and ſo the *half* of the remaining half, and ſo the half of the quarter that remains: ſo ſtill the half of the remaining ſpace, the *half before the whole*; and yet when it comes to execution, you find it is not ſo. If the Poſition you allowed me had been true, my Pen would not have reach'd unto the *end* of the *Line* before the *End* of my *Life*; or in a Term wherein it might have written ten Books as big as old *Zoroaſter's*, or more Manuſcripts than ever were in the *Alexandrian* Library.

I   It

It is then evident, that all Mankind is to this day in the dark as to the *ultimate Parts* of *Quantity,* and of *Motion.*

Go on my learned *Grew,* and maintain [who more fit than one of thy *recondite Learning?*] *that there is hardly any one thing in the World, the Essence whereof we can perfectly comprehend.* But then to the *natural Imbecillity* of R E A S O N, and the *moral Depravations* of it, by our Fall from God, and the Ascendant which a corrupt and vicious *Will* has obtain'd over it, how much ought this Consideration to warn us against the Conduct of an *unhumbled Understanding* in things relating to the *Kingdom of God?* I am not out of my way, I have had a *Magnet* all this while *steering* of this **Digression**: I am now returning to *that.*

¶. God forbid I should be, *Tam Lapis ut Lapidi Numen inesse putem.* To fall down before a *Stone,* and say, *Thou art a God,* would be an *Idolatry,* that none but a Soul more senseless than a *Stone* could be guilty of. But then it would be a very agreeable and acceptable *Homage* unto the Glorious G O D, for me to see much of Him in such a wonderful *Stone* as the M A G N E T. They have done well to call it the *Loadstone,* that is to say, the *Lead-stone: May it lead me unto Thee, O my God and my Saviour! Magnetism* is in this like to *Gravity,* that it leads us to G O D, and brings us very near to Him. When we see *Magnetism* in its Operation, we must say, *This is the Work of God!* And of the *Stone,* which has proved of such vast use in the Affairs of the *Waters that cover the Sea,* and will e'er long do its part in bringing it about that the *Glory of the Lord shall cover the Earth,* we must say, *Great God, this is a wonderful Gift of Thine unto the World!*

I do not propose to exemplify the *occasional Reflections* which a devout Mind may make upon all the *Creatures* of God, their *Properties,* and *Actions,* and *Relations;* the *Libri Elephantini* would not be big enough to
contain

contain the thousandth part of them. If it were lawful for me here to pause with a particular *Exercise upon the Loadstone*, my first Thoughts would be those of the holy *Scudder*, whose Words have had a great Impression on me ever since my first reading of them in my Childhood: 'An upright Man is like a *Needle* touch'd ' with the *Loadstone*; tho he may thro boisterous ' *Temptations* and strong *Allurements* oftentimes look ' towards the Pleasure, Gain and Glory of this *present* ' *World*, yet because he is truly touch'd with the ' sanctifying Spirit of God, he still inclineth *God-ward*, ' and hath no Quiet till he stand *steady towards Heaven*.' —— However, to animate the Devotion of my *Christian* Philosopher, I will here make a Report to him. The ingenious *Ward* wrote a pious Book, as long ago as the Year 1639, entitled, *Magnetis Reductorium Theologicum*. The Design of his Essay, is, to *lead* us from the Consideration of the *Loadstone*, to the Consideration of our SAVIOUR, and of his incomparable *Glories*; whereof the *Magnet* has in it a notable Adumbration. In his Introduction he has a Note, worthy to be transcribed here, as religiously asserting the Design, of which our whole Essay is a Prosecution. *Hic præcipuus & potentissimus Creaturarum omnium Finis est, cum Scalæ nobis & Alæ fiunt, quibus Animæ nostræ suprà Dumeta & Sterquilinia Mundi hujus volitantes, faciliùs ad Cœlum ascendunt, & ad Deum Creatorem aspirant.* For what is now before us, if our *Ward* may be our Adviser; *Christian*, in the *Loadstone* drawing and lifting up the *Iron*, behold thy *Saviour* drawing us to himself, and raising us above the secular Cares and Snares that ruin us. In its ready *communication* of its Vertues, behold a shadow of thy *Saviour* communicating his holy Spirit to his chosen People; and his *Ministers* more particularly made Partakers of his *attractive Powers*. When *Silver* and *Gold* are neglected by the *Loadstone*, but coarse *Iron* preferred, behold thy *Saviour* passing over the *Angelical World*, and chusing to take *our Na-*

ture

ture upon him. The *Iron* is alfo undiftinguifhed, whether it be lodged in a fine Covering, or whether it be lying in the moft fqualid and wretched Circumftances; which invites us to think how little *refpect of Perfons* there is with our *Saviour.* However, the *Iron* fhould be *cleanfed,* it fhould not be *rufty*; nor will our *Saviour* embrace thofe who are not fo far *cleanfed,* that they are at leaft *willing to be made clean,* and have his *Files* pafs upon them. The *Iron* is at firft *merely paffive,* then it *moves* more feebly towards the *Stone*; anon upon Contact it will fly to it, and exprefs a marvellous Affection and Adherence. Is not here a Picture of the Difpofitions in our Souls towards our Saviour? It is the Pleafure of our Saviour to work by *Inftruments,* as the *Loadftone* will do moft when the Mediation of a *Steel Cap* is ufed about it. After all, whatever is done, the whole *Praife* is due to the *Loadftone* alone. But there would be *no end,* and indeed there fhould be *none,* of thefe Meditations! —— Our *Ward* in his Dedication of his Book to the King, has one very true Compliment. *Hoc aufim Majeftati tuæ bonâ fide fpondere; fi unicus unicum poffideres, Mundi totius te facile Monarcham efficeret.* But what a Great KING is He, who is the Owner, yea, and the Maker of all the *Magnets* in the World! *I am a Great KING, faith the Lord of Hofts, and my Name is to be feared among the Nations!* May the *Loadftone* help to carry it to them.

ESSAY XXV. *Of* MINERALS.

OPERUM *Dei Cognitienem* (fays my dear *Arndt*) *quilibet ex fincero erga Deum amore & gratitudine, fibi acquirere ftudeat, ut fciat, quæ Deus noftri caufa creaverit.* He fmiles at the trifling *Logicians,* who, *totam ætatem inter inanes Subtilitates tranfigentes,* wholly taken up with *Trifles,* overlook the glorious Works of God.

Our *Earth* is richly furnifhed with a Tribe of *Minerals,* called fo becaufe dug out of *Mines*; and becaufe cause *dug*, therefore also called *Fossils*. Many things to be written of these, ought to have a *Nimok* in the Margin!

The *adventitious Fossils*, which are but the *Exuviæ* of *Animals*, have been erroneously thought a sort of *peculiar Stones*. These must be excluded.

But then the *Natives of the Earth* are to be found in a vast variety. The inquisitive **Dr.** *Woodward* has prepared us a noble *Table* of them.

There are near twenty several sorts of *Earth*. Of these, besides the *Potter's Earth*, and the *Fuller's Earth*, how exceedingly useful is the *Chalk* to us! 'Tis a πολύχρηϛον.

There are above a dozen several sorts of *Stones*, that are found in *larger* Masses.

What *Vessels*, what *Buildings*, what *Ornaments*, do these afford us; especially the *Slate*, the *Marble*, the *Free-stone*, and the *Lime-stone?*

How helpful the *Warming-stone?*

How needful the *Grind-stone* and *Mill-stone?*

To the *Service* of our Maker we have so many Calls from the *Stones* themselves, [for if *Men* should be silent at proclaiming the Glory of God, the *very Stones would speak*] that a learned and a pious *German* so addresses us: *Audis tibi loquentes Lapides; tu ne sis Lapis in hac parte, sed ipsorum Vocem audi, & in illis Vocem Dei.*

The *Whetstone* gives me a particular Admonition, which I have somewhere met with: *Multi multa docent alios, quæ ipsi præstare nequeunt.* The worst Motto for a *Divine* that can be! *Lord, save me from it!*

How astonishing the *Figures*, which **Dr.** *Robinson* and **Mr.** *Ray* report, as naturally delineated upon several kinds of *Stones*; almost every thing in Nature described in them, so as could not be out-done by any Sculptor or Painter! The *Colaptice*, such as no *Human Skill* could arise to!

Yea,

Yea, in *Stones* there has been fometimes found fo much of an *Human Shape*, that every thing really in it has been aftonifhed at it. *Zeiler* and *Kircher* mention fome famous *Rocks*, which fo refemble *Monks*, that all People call them fo. *Olaus Wormius* was Poffeffor of a large *Stone*, which had exactly the Head, Face, Neck and Shoulders of a *Man*. *Monconnys* and others relate the feveral *Parts* of a Man, which many *Stones* have exactly exhibited. *Oh! how happy we, if Men and Stones had lefs Refemblance!*

There are many forts of *Stones* found in *leffer Maffes.*

Of thefe there are many who do *not* exceed the hardnefs of *Marble.*

Seven or eight of thefe are of an *indeterminate Figure.*

Twice as many have a *determinate Figure.*

Among thefe the Wonders of the *Ofteo-colla*, to join and heal our *broken Brones.*

But then there are others which *do* exceed *Marble* in hardnefs.

To this Article belong thofe that are ufually called *Gems* or *precious Stones.*

[*Pebbles* and *Flints* are of the *Agate-kind.*]

Some of thefe are *opake.*

Three of the opake have a Body of *one Colour.*

Here the Wonders of the *Nephritick Stone!*

Three of the *opake* have *different* Colours mixed in the fame Body.

Here the Wonders of the *Blood-ftone!*

Some are *pellucid.*

Two with *Colours changeable*, according to their different pofition in the Light.

Nine or ten with *Colours permanent.*

Some are *diaphanous.*

Two *yellow* (or partaking of it.)

Three *red.*

Three *blue.*

Two *green.*

Four *without any Colours.*

'But

' But an excellent Writer obferving, *Deus eft Figu-*
' *lus Lapidum,* carries on his Obfervation, That the
' God who makes *precious* as well as *common Stones,* has
' made *Men* with as much of a *Difference,* and not al-
' together without fuch a *Proportion.*'

' Good God, *Thy heavenly Graces in the Soul are brighter*
' *Jewels than any that are dug out of the Earth!* A poor
' Man may be adorn'd with thefe; thofe who are fo,
' *they fhall be mine, faith the Lord, in the Day when I*
' *make up my Jewels.*'

' How often have I feen a Jewel in the *Snout of a*
' *Swine!*'

' And how many *Counterfeits* in the World!'

There are feven forts of *Salts* to be met withal.

But the *Salt* of our *Table,* of how much confequence
this to us! The Ufes of it are too many to be by any
reckoned: Very many are well known to all. To
which add the Experience which *Bickerus* affirms the
Army of the Emperor *Charles* V. had, that they muft
have perifh'd on the *African* Shore, if they had not
found a Grain of *Salt* in their Mouths; an Antidote
not only againft *Thirft,* but *Hunger* too.

He deferves to be herded with the Creatures, which
Animam habent pro Sale, who fhall be fo *infipid* an Animal, as to be infenfible that the Benefits of *Salt* call
for very great Acknowledgments. *My God, fave me*
from what would render me unfavory Salt!

There are three liquid *Bitumens,* fix or feven folid.

There are about a dozen *metallick Minerals. Mercury*
is one of thefe, but how aftonifhing an one! The Particles whereof how fmall, how fmooth, how folid!
The Corpufcles of it have Diameters much lefs than
thofe of *Air;* yea, than thofe of *Water;* and not much
greater than thofe of *Light* itfelf!

At laft we come to *Metals; Iron,* with its Attendants; *Tin, Lead, Copper, Silver* and GOLD.

' I fhall not confider the Reafons which moved
' *Cardan* to affert that *Metals* have a *Soul;* but I am
' fure

' fure that I myfelf have a *Soul*, and am one that is
' *reafonable*; if fo, what can be more agreeable to me,
' than a Confideration which I find hinted by a curi-
' ous Writer of *natural Theology:* We fhould admire
' the *Munificence* of one who would beftow a confide-
' rable Quantity of enriching *Metals* upon us. But
' then how much caufe have we to adore the *Munifi-*
' *cence* of our bountiful G O D, who has enrich'd us
' with *Metals* in fo vaft a Quantity, and with fo much
' Profufion from His *hidden Treafures! Quotufquifque*
' *eft qui non videt, quid Ratio officii fui poftulat?*'

How amazingly ferviceable is our *Iron* to us! In our
mechanical Arts, in our *Agriculture*, in our *Navigation*,
in our *Architecture*; in *all*, I fay, *all* our Bufinefs! What
a *fordid Life* do thofe *Barbarians* lead, who are kept ignorant of it! Unthankful for this, *O Man*, you deferve
Heaven fhould become as *Iron* over you.

It is from G O D that the *Metals* of moft neceffary
Ufes are the moft plentiful; others that may be better fpared, there is a rarity of them.

That one fingle *Metal*, Iron, as Dr, *Grew* obferves,
it fets on foot above an hundred forts of manual Operations.

Tho the *Love of Money* be the *Root of all Evil*, yet
the ingenious Dr. *Cockburn* has difcourfed very juftly
on the vaft Importance whereof the Ufe of *Money* is to
Mankind. And indeed where the Ufe of *Money* has
not been introduced, Men are brutifh and favage, and
nothing that is good has been cultivated.

There is a furprizing Providence of GOD in keeping up the Value of *Gold* and *Silver*, notwithftanding
the vaft Quantities dug out of the Earth in all Ages,
ever fince the Trade begun of *effodiuntur Opes*; and fo
continuing them fit Materials to make *Money* of.

Among the marvellous Qualities of *Gold*, its *Ducti-*
lity deferves to have a particular Notice taken of it.

The *Wire-drawers*, to every 48 Ounces of *Silver*,
allow one of *Gold.* Now *two Yards* of the fuperfine
Wire

Wire weigh a *Grain.* In the Length of 98 Yards there are 49 Grains of Weight. A single Grain of *Gold* covers the said 98 Yards. The 10000th part of a *Grain* is above one third of an Inch long, which yet may be actually divided into ten; and so the 100000th part of a *Grain of Gold* may be visible without a *Microscope.*

It is a marvellous thing that *Gold,* after it has been divided by corrosive Liquors into *invisible Parts,* yet may presently be so precipitated, as to appear in its own *golden Form* again.

But, as Dr. *Grew* observes, the same *Immutability* which belongs to the Composition of *Gold,* much more belongs to the *Principles* of *Gold,* and of all other Bodies, when their Composition is destroyed. *Dampier,* an ingenious Traveller all round the Globe, has an Observation; *I know no Place where Gold is found, but what is very unhealthy.*

' Possessor of *Gold!* Beware lest the Observation be
' verified in the *unhealthy* Influences of thy *Gold* upon
' thy *Mind;* and lest the *love* of it betray thee into
' many *foolish and hurtful Lusts,* which will drown thee
' in *Destruction and Perdition.*'

' The *Auri sacra Fames* is the worst of all Distem-
' pers.'

My God, I bless Thee; I know something that is better than fine Gold, something that cannot be gotten for Gold, neither shall Silver be weighed for the Price thereof.

If *Gold* could speak, it would rebuke the *Idolatry* wherewith Mankind adores it, in much such Terms as I find a devout Writer assigning to it. *Non Deus sum, sed Dei Creatura; Terra mihi Mater. Ego servio tibi, ut tu servias Creatori.*

¶. ' Finally, The antient Pagans not only worship-
' ped the *Host of Heaven,* [justly called *Zabians*] but
' whatsoever they found *comfortable* to Nature, they
' also *deified,* even, *Quodcunque juvaret.* The River
' *Nilus* too must at length become a Deity; yea, *Nas-*
' *cuntur in bortis Numina.*'

' And

' And according to *Pliny, a Man that helps a Man*
' *becomes a God.*'

' *God* fave us from the Crime ftigmatiz'd by our
' Apoftle, *to adore the Creatures more than the Creator* !
' By no means let us be as *Philo* fpeaks, Κοσμὸν μαλλὸν
' ἢ κοσμοποιον θαυμάσαντες, *more admiring the World, than*
' *the Maker of the World.*'

' We will glorify the G O D who has beftowed
' things upon us ; *for the Silver is mine, and the Gold is*
' *mine, faith the Lord of Hofts.*'

E S S A Y XXVI. *Of the* VEGETABLES.

THE Contrivance of our moft Glorious Creator,
in the VEGETABLES growing upon this Globe,
cannot be wifely obferved without Admiration and
Aftonifhment.

We will fingle out fome Remarkables, and glorify
our G O D !

Firft, In *what manner* is *Vegetation* performed ? And
how is the Growth of *Plants* and the Increafe of their
Parts carried on ? The excellent and ingenious Dr.
John Woodward has, in the way of nice Experiment,
brought this thing under a clofe Examination. It is
evident that *Water* is neceffary to *Vegetation* ; there is
a *Water* which afcends the Veffels of the *Plants*, much
after the way of a *Filtration* ; and the Plants take up a
larger or leffer Quantity of this Fluid, according to
their Dimenfions. The much greater part of that
fluid Mafs which is conveyed to the Plants, does not
abide there, but exhale thro them up into the *Atmofphere.* Hence Countries that abound with *bigger
Plants* are obnoxious to greater Damps, and Rains,
and inconvenient Humidities. But there is alfo a *terreftrial Matter* which is mixed with this *Water*, and
afcends up into the *Plants* with the *Water.* Something
of this Matter will attend *Water* in all its motions,
and ftick by it after all its Percolations. Indeed the

Quan-

Quantity of this *terrestrial Matter*, which the Vapours carry up into the *Atmosphere*, is very *fine*, and not very *much*, but it is the truest and the best prepared *vegetable Matter*; for which cause it is that *Rain-Water* is of such a singular Fertility. 'Tis true there is in *Water* a *mineral Matter* also, which is usually too scabrous, and ponderous, and inflexible, to enter the Pores of the *Roots*. Be the *Earth* ever so rich, 'tis observed little good will come of it, unless the Parts of it be loosened a little, and separated. And this probably is all the use of *Nitre* and other *Salts* to Plants, to loosen the Earth, and separate the Parts of it. It is this *terrestrial Matter* which fills the *Plants*; they are more or less nourished and augmented in proportion, as their *Water* conveys a greater or lesser quantity of proper *terrestrial Matter* to them. Nevertheless 'tis also probable that in this there is a variety; and all Plants are not formed and filled from the same sort of *Corpuscles*. Every *Vegetable* seems to require a *peculiar and specifick Matter* for its Formation and Nourishment. If the Soil wherein a Seed is planted, have not all or most of the Ingredients necessary for the *Vegetable* to subsist upon, it will suffer accordingly. Thus *Wheat* sown upon a Tract of Land well furnish'd for the Supply of that *Grain*, will succeed very well, perhaps for divers Years, or, as the Husbandman expresses it, *as long as the Ground is in heart*; but anon it will produce no more of that *Corn*; it will of some other, perhaps of *Barley*: and when it will subsist this no more, still *Oats* will thrive there; and perhaps *Pease* after these. When the Ground has lain fallow some time, the *Rain* will pour down a fresh Stock upon it; and the care of the *Tiller* in manuring of it, lays upon it such things as are most impregnated with a Supply for *Vegetation*. It is observ'd that *Spring-water* and *Rain-water* contain pretty near an equal charge of the *vegetable Matter*, but *River-water* much more than either of them; and hence the Inundations of *Rivers* leave upon their
Banks

Banks the faireſt Crops in the World. It is now plain that *Water* is not the *Matter* that compoſes *Vegetables*, but the *Agent* that conveys that *Matter* to them, and introduces it into the ſeveral parts of them. Where-fore the plentiful proviſion of this Fluid ſupplied to all Parts of the Earth, is by our *Woodward* juſtly celebra-ted with a pious Acknowledgment of that *natural Providence* that ſuperintends over the Globe which we inhabit. The Parts of *Water* being exactly ſpherical, and ſubtile beyond all expreſſion, the Surfaces perfectly polite, and the Intervals being therefore the largeſt, and ſo the moſt fitting to receive a *foreign Matter* into them, it is the moſt proper Inſtrument imaginable for the Service now aſſign'd to it. And yet *Water* would not perform this Office and Service to the *Plants*, if it be not aſſiſted with a due quantity of *Heat*; *Heat* muſt concur, or *Vegetation* will not ſucceed. Hence as the *Heat* of ſeveral *Seaſons* affords a different face of things, the ſame does the *Heat* of ſeveral *Climates*. The *hotter* Countries uſually yield the *larger Trees*, and in a great-er variety. And in *warmer* Countries, if there be a remiſſion of the *uſual Heat*, the Production will in pro-portion be diminiſh'd.

That I may a little contribute my *two Mites* to the illuſtration of the way wherein *Vegetation* is carried on, I will here communicate a couple of Experiments late-ly made in my Neighbourhood.

My Neighbour planted a Row of Hills in his Field with our *Indian Corn*, but ſuch a Grain as was colour'd *red* and *blue*; the reſt of the Field he planted with Corn of the moſt uſual Colour, which is *yellow*. To the moſt *Windward-ſide* this Row infected *four* of the next neighbouring Rows, and part of the fifth, and ſome of the ſixth, to render them colour'd like what grew on itſelf. But on the *Leeward-ſide* no leſs than ſeven or eight Rows were ſo colour'd, and ſome ſmal-ler impreſſions were made on thoſe that were yet fur-ther diſtant.

The

The same Neighbour having his Garden often robb'd of the *Squashes* growing in it, planted some *Gourds* among them, which are to appearance very like them, and which he distinguish'd by certain adjacent marks, that he might not be himself imposed upon; by this means the Thieves 'tis true found a very *bitter Sauce,* but then all the *Squashes* were so infected and embitter'd, that he was not himself able to eat what the Thieves had left of them.

That most accurate and experienc'd Botanist Mr. *Ray* has given us the *Plants* that are more commonly met withal, with certain characteristick Notes, wherein he establishes *twenty-five Genders* of them. These *Plants* are to be rather stiled *Herbs.*

But then of the *Trees* and *Shrubs,* he distinguishes *five Classes* that have their *Flower* disjoined and remote from the *Fruit,* and as many that have their *Fruit* and *Flower* contiguous.

How unaccountably is the *Figure* of *Plants* preserved? And how unaccountably their *Growth* determined? Our excellent *Ray* flies to an intelligent *plastick Nature,* which must understand and regulate the whole Oeconomy.

Every particular *part* of the *Plant* has its astonishing Uses. The *Roots* give it a Stability, and fetch the Nourishment into it, which lies in the Earth ready for it. The *Fibres* contain and convey the Sap which carries up that Nourishment. The *Plant* has also larger Vessels, which entertain the proper and specifick Juice of it; and others to carry the Air for its necessary respiration. The outer and inner *Bark* defend it from Annoyances, and contribute to its Augmentation. The *Leaves* embrace and preserve the *Flower* and *Fruit* as they come to their explication. But the principal use of them, as *Malpighi,* and *Perault,* and *Mariotte,* have observed, is, to concoct and prepare the *Sap* for the Nourishment of the *Fruit,* and of the whole *Plant;* not only that which ascends from the Root, but also

what

what they take in from without, from the Dew, and from the Rain. For there is a *regress* of the *Sap* in Plants from above downwards; and this descendent Juice is that which principally nourishes both Fruit and Plant, as has been clearly proved by the Experiments of Signior *Malpighi* and Mr. *Brotherton.*

How agreeable the *Shade* of *Plants,* let every Man say that *sits under his own Vine, and under his own Fig-tree!*

How charming the Proportion and Pulchritude of the *Leaves,* the *Flowers,* the *Fruits,* he who confesses not, must be, as Dr. *More* says, *one sunk into a forlorn pitch of Degeneracy, and stupid as a Beast.*

Our Saviour says of the *Lillies* (which some, not without reason, suppose to be *Tulips*) *that* Solomon *in all his Glory was not arrayed like one of these.* And it is observed by *Spigelius,* that the Art of the most skilful Painter cannot so mingle and temper his *Colours,* as exactly to imitate or counterfeit the *native* ones of the *Flowers* of *Vegetables.*

Mr. *Ray* thinks it worthy a very particular Observation, that *Wheat,* which is the best sort of Grain, and affords the wholesomest Bread, is in a singular manner patient of both Extremes, both Heat and Cold, and will grow to maturity as well in *Scotland,* and in *Denmark,* as in *Egypt,* and *Guiney,* and *Madagascar.* It scarce refuses any Climate. And the exceeding *Fertility* of it is by a Pagan *Pliny* acknowledged as an Instance of the Divine Bounty to Man, *Quod eo maxime Hominem alat;* one Bushel in a fit Soil, he says, yielding one hundred and fifty. A *German* Divine so far plays the Philosopher on this Occasion, as to propose it for a Singularity in *Bread,* that *totum Corpus sustentat, adeo, ut in unicâ Bucellâ, omnium Membrorum totius externi Corporis, nutrimentum contineatur, illiusque Vis per totum Corpus sese diffundat.* A Friend of mine had *thirty-six Ears* of Rye growing from *one Grain,* and on *one Stalk.*

But

But of our *Indian Corn*, one Grain of *Corn* will produce above a *thouſand.* And of *Guiney Corn*, one Grain has been known to produce *ten thouſand.*

The *Anatomy of Plants*, as it has been exhibited by the incomparable Curioſity of Dr. *Grew*, what a vaſt *Field of Wonders* does it lead us into!

The moſt inimitable *Structure* of the Parts!

The particular *Canals*, and moſt adapted ones, for the conveyance of the lymphatick and eſſential Juices!

The *Air-Veſſels* in all their curious Coylings!

The *Coverings* which befriend them, a Work unſpeakably more curious in reality than in appearance!

The ſtrange Texture of the *Leaves*, the angular or circular, but always moſt orderly Poſition of their *Fibres*; the various *Foldings*, with a *Duplicature*, a *Multiplicature*, the *Fore-rowl*, the *Back-rowl*, the *Tre-rowl*; the noble Guard of the *Films* interpoſed!

The *Flowers*, their Gaiety and Fragrancy; the *Perianthium* or *Empalement* of them; their curious Foldings in the *Calyx* before their Expanſion, with a *cloſe Couch* or a *concave Couch*, a *ſingle Plait* or a *double Plait*, or a *Plait* and *Couch* together, or a *Rowl*, or a *Spire*, or *Plait* and *Spire* together; and their luxuriant Colours after their *Foliation*, and the expanding of their *Petala!*

The *Stamina*, with their *Apices*; and the *Stylus* (called the *Attire* by Dr. *Grew*) which is found a ſort of *Male Sperm*, to impregnate and fructify the Seed!

At laſt the whole Rudiments and Lineaments of the *Parent-Vegetable*, ſurprizingly lock'd up in the little compaſs of the *Fruit* or *Seed!*

Gentlemen of Leiſure, conſult my illuſtrious Doctor, peruſe his *Anatomy of Plants*, ponder his numberleſs Diſcoveries; but all the while conſider that rare Perſon as inviting you to join with him in adoring the *God of his Father*, and the God who has *done theſe excellent things*, which ought to be *known in all the Earth.*

Signior

Signior *Malpighi* has maintain'd it with cogent Arguments, that the whole *Plant* is actually in the *Seed*; and he answers the grand Objection against it, which is drawn from a degeneracy of one Plant sometimes into another. One of his Answers is, *Ex morboso & monstroso affectu, non licet inferre permanentem statum à Natura intentum.*

But there is no Objection to be made against *Ocular Observation.* Shew us, *Lewenhoeck*, how it is? He will give us to see, a small Particle no bigger than a Sand, contain the *Plant*, and all belonging to it, all actually in that *little Seed*; yea, in the *Nux vomica* it appears even to the naked Eye, and in an astonishing Elegancy! Dr. *Cheyne* expresses himself with good assurance upon it: 'We are certain that the Seeds of Plants are 'nothing but *little Plants* perfectly formed, with Bran-'ches and Leaves duly folded up, and involved in '*Membranes*, or surrounded with *Walls* proper to de-'fend them in this tender state from external Injuries; 'and *Vegetation* is only the unfolding and extending 'of these Branches and Leaves, by the force of Juices 'raised by *Heat* in the slender Tubes of the Plant.'

Those *capillary Plants*, which all the Antients, and some of the Moderns, have taken to be destitute of *Seeds*, are by *Bauhinus* and others now pronounced *Spermatophorous.* Mr. *Ray* says, *Hanc Sententiam verissimam esse Autopsia convincit.*

Fr. Cæsius claims to be the first who discovered the *Seeds* of these *Plants*, with the help of a *Microscope.* One Mr. *Cole* has prosecuted the Observation, and is astonished at the small Dimensions of the *Seeds.* The *Boxes* or Vessels that hold the *Seeds* are not half, perhaps not a quarter, so big as a Grain of Sand : and yet an *hundred Seeds* are found in one of these *Tantam Plantam è tantillo Semine produci attentum Observatorem merito in Admirationem rapiat!*

Sir *Thomas Brown* observes, That of the Seeds of *Tobacco* a thousand make not one Grain; (tho *Otto de*
Gueric,

Gueric, as I remember, says, fifty-two Cyphers with one Figure will give the Number of those, which would fill the Space between us and the Stars!) A Plant which has extended its Empire over the whole World, and has a larger Dominion than any of all the *Vegetable* Kingdom.

Ten thousand Seeds of *Harts-tongue* hardly make the Bulk of a *Pepper-corn.* But now, as Dr. *Grew* notes, the Body, with the Covers of every Seed, the ligneous and parenchymous Parts of both, the Fibres of those Parts, the Principles of those Fibres, and the homogeneous Particles of those Principles, being but moderately multiplied one by another, afford an hundred thousand millions of Atoms formed in the Space of a *Pepper-corn.* But who can define how many more!

The Uses of *Trees* in various Works were elegantly celebrated, as long ago as when *Theophrastus* wrote his fifth Book of the *History of Plants.*

And what *stately Trees* do sometimes by their glorious *Height* and *Breadth* recommend themselves to a more singular Observation with us! The *Cabbage*-tree an hundred and forty or fifty Foot high, as if it were aspiring to afford a Diet to the Regions above us; how noble a Spectacle!

The *Trees* which are found sometimes near twenty Foot, or perhaps more, in circumference, what capacious *Canoes* do they afford, when the Traveller makes them change their Element? Near *Scio* there is an Island called *Long-Island,* and on this Island (as *Jo. Pitts* tells us) there is a Tree of a prodigious bigness; under it are *Coffee-houses,* and many Shops of several Intentions, and several Fountains of Water; and it has near forty Pillars of Marble and of Timber to support the Branches of it. It is a Tree famous to a Proverb all over *Turkey.*

Even the most *noxious* and the most *abject* of the *Vegetables,* how useful are they! As of the *Bramble* Dr. *Grew* notes, *If it chance to prick the Owner, it will*

K *also*

alfo tear the Thief. *Olaus Magnus* admires the Benefits which the *rotten Barks* of *Oaks* give to the Northern People, by the *Shine*, with which they do in their long Nights direct the Traveller. And Dr. *Merret* celebrates the *Thiftles*, and the *Hop-firings*, for the *Glafs* afforded by their Afhes!

The *frugal Bit* of the old *Britons*, which in the bignefs of a *Bean* fatisfied the moft hungry and thirfty Appetite, is now thrown into the Catalogue of the *Res deperditæ.*

The peculiar Care which the great God of Nature has taken for the Safety of the *Seed* and *Fruit*, and fo for the Confervation of the *Plant*, is by my ingenious *Derham* confidered as a loud Invitation to His Praifes.

They which dare fhew their Heads all the Year, how fecurely is their *Seed* or *Fruit* lock'd up in the Winter in their *Gems*, and well cover'd with neat and clofe *Tunicks* there!

Such as dare not expofe themfelves, how are they preferved under the Coverture of the *Earth*, till invited out by the kindly Warmth of the Spring!

When the *Vegetable Race* comes abroad, what ftrange Methods of Nature are there to *guard* them from Inconveniences, by making fome to lie down proftrate, by making others, which were by the Antients called *Æfchynomenæ*, to clofe themfelves up at the Touch of Animals, and by making the moft of them to fhut up under their guard in the cool of the Evening, efpecially if there be foul Weather approaching; which is by *Gerhard* therefore called, *The Countryman's Weather-wifer!*

What various ways has Nature for the *fcattering* and the *fowing* of the *Seed!* Some are for this end winged with a light fort of a *Down*, to be carried about with the *Seed* by the Wind. Some are laid in fpringy cafes, which when they burft and crack, dart their Seed to a diftance, performing therein the part of an Husbandman. Others by their good Qualities invite themfelves

felves to be fwallowed by the Birds, and being fertiliz'd by paffing thro their Bodies, they are by them transferred to places where they fructify. *Theophraftus* affirms this of the *Mifletoe*; and *Tavernier* of the *Nutmeg.* Others not thus taken care for, do, by their Ufefulnefs to *us*, oblige us to look after them.

It is a little furprizing, that *Seeds* found in the *Gizzards* of *Wild-fowl*, have afterwards fprouted in the Earth; and *Seeds* left in the *Dung* of the *Cattel.* The Seeds of *Marjoram* and *Strammonium*, careiefly kept, have grown after feven Years.

How nice the provifion of Nature for their Support in *standing* and *growing*, that they may keep their Heads above ground, and adminifter to our Intentions! There are fome who ftand by their own Strength; and the ligneous parts of thefe, tho' like our Bones, yet are not, like them, inflexible, but of an elaftick nature, that they may dodge the Violence of the Winds: and their Branches at the top very commodioufly have a tendency to an hemifpherical Dilatation, but within fuch an Angle as makes an Æquilibration there. An ingenious Obferver upon this one Circumftance, cannot forbear this juft Reflection: *A vifible Argument that the plaftick Capacities of Matter are govern'd by an all-wife and infinite Agent, the native Strictneffes and Regularities of them plainly fhewing from whofe Hand they come.* And then fuch as are too weak to ftand of *themfelves*, 'tis wonderful to fee how they ufe the Help of their *Neighbours*, addrefs them, embrace them, climb up about them, fome twifting themfelves with a ftrange *convolving* Faculty, fome catching hold with *Clafpers* and *Tendrels*, which are like Hands to them; fome ftriking in rooty *Feet*, and fome emitting a natural *Glue*, by which they adhere to their Supporters.

But, Oh! the glorious *Goodnefs* of our GOD in all thefe things! Lend us thy Pen, O induftrious *Ray*, to declare a little of it. *Plantarum ufus latiffimè patet, & in omni Vitæ parte occurrit. Sine illis cautè, fine illis commode,*

mode, non vivitur; at nec vivitur omnino: quæcunque ad victum necessaria sunt, quæcunque ad Delicias faciunt, è locupletissimo suo Penu abunde subministrant. Quanto ex iis Mensa innocentior, mundior, salubrior, quam ex Animalium Cæde & Laniena! Homo certè Naturâ Animal carnivorum non est; nullis ad Prædam & Rapinam armis instructum; non Dentibus exertis & serratis, non Unguibus aduncis. Manus ad Fructus colligendos, Dentes ad mandendos comparati. Non legimus ei ante Diluvium Carnes ad esum concessas. At non victum tantum nobis suppeditant, sed & Vestitum, & Medicinam, & Domicilia, aliaque Ædificia, & Navigia, & Supellectilem, & Focum, & Oblectamenta Sensuum Animique. Ex his Naribus Odoramenta & Suffumigia parantur: Horum Flores inenarrabili Colorum & Schematum Varietate & Elegantia Oculos exhilarant, & suavissima Odorum quos expirant Fragrantia, Spiritus recreant. Horum Fructus, Gulæ illecebræ Mensas secundas instruunt, & languentem Appetitum excitant. Taceo Virorem Oculis Amicum, quem per Prata, Pascua, Agros, Sylvas spatiantibus objiciunt; & Umbras quas contra Æstum & Solis Ardores præbent.

Indeed all the *Plants* in the whole *Vegetable Kingdom* are every one of them so *useful*, as to *rise up* for thy Condemnation, *O Man, who dost little Good in the World.* But sometimes the *Uses* of one *single Plant* are so many, so various, that a wise Man can scarce behold it without some *Emulation* as well as *Admiration*, or without some wishing, that if a *Metamorphosis* were to befal him, it might be into one of these. *Plutarch* reports, that the *Babylonians* out of the *Palm-tree* fetch'd more than three hundred several sorts of Commodities.

The *Coco-tree* supplies the *Indians* with Bread, and Water, and Wine, and Vinegar, and Brandy, and Milk, and Oil, and Honey, and Sugar, and Needles, and Thread, and Linnen, and Clothes, and Cups, and Spoons, and Besoms, and Baskets, and Paper, and Nails; Timber, Coverings for their Houses; Masts, Sails, Cordage, for their Vessels; add, Medicines for their

Dis-

Difeafes; and what can be defired more? This is more expreffively related in the *Hortus Malabaricus,* publifhed by the illuftrious *Van Draakenftein.*

The *Aloe Muricata* yields the *Americans* all that their Neceffities can call for. *De la Vega* and *Margrave* will inform us how this alone furnifhes them with Houfes and Fences, and Weapons of many forts, and Shoes, and Clothes, and Thread, and Needles, and Wine, and Honey, and Utenfils that cannot be numbred. *Hernandes* will affure us, *Planta hæc unica, quicquid Vitæ effe poteft neceffarium facile præftare poteft, fi effet rebus humanis modus.*

What a furprizing Diverfity from the *Cinnamon-tree!*

Some will have the *Plantane* to be the *King of all Fruit,* tho the Tree be little more than ten Foot high, and raifed not from *Seed,* but from the *Roots* of the old ones. The *Fruit* a delicate Butter, and often the whole Food that a whole Family will fubfift upon.

Among the *Ufes* of *Plants,* how furprizing an one is that, wherein we find them ufed for *Cifterns,* to preferve Water for the needy Children of Men!

The *Dropping-tree* in *Guiney,* and on fome Iflands, is inftead of *Rains* and *Springs* to the Inhabitants.

The *Banduca Cingatenfium,* at the end of its Leaves has long Sacks or Bags, containing a fine limpid Water, of great ufe to the People when they want Rains for eight or ten Months together.

The *wild Pine,* defcrib'd by Dr. *Sloane,* has the Leaves, which are each of them two Foot and an half long, and three Inches broad, fo inclofed one within another, that there is formed a large Bafon, fit to contain a confiderable quantity of Water (*Dampier* fays, the beft part of a Quart) which in the rainy Seafon falling upon the utmoft parts of the fpreading Leaves, runs down by Channels into the Bottle, where the Leaves bending inwards again, come fo clofe to the Stalk, as to hinder the Evaporations of the Water. In the

moun-

mountainous, as well as in the dry and low Woods, when there is a scarcity of Water, this *Reservatory* is not only necessary and sufficient for the nourishment of the Plant itself, but it is likewise of marvellous advantage unto Men and Birds, and all sorts of Insects, who then come hither in Troops, and seldom go away without Refreshment.

What tho there are *venomous Plants?* An excellent *Fellow of the College of Physicians* makes a just Remark: ' *Aloes* has the Property of promoting *Hæmorrhages;* ' but this Property is good or bad, as it is used; a ' *Medicine* or a *Poison* : And it is very probable that ' the most dangerous *Poisons,* skilfully managed, may ' be made not only *innocuous,* but of all other Medi- ' cines the most *effectual.*'

What admirable Effects of *Opium* well *smegmatized!* Even *poisonous Plants,* one says of them, It may be reasonably supposed that they draw into their visible Bodies that malignant *Juice,* which, if diffused thro the other *Plants,* would make them less wholesome and fit for Nourishment.

In the *Delights* of the *Garden* 'tis not easy to hold a Mediocrity. They afford a Shadow for our *celestial Paradise.* The King of *Persia* has a *Garden* called *Paradise upon Earth.* The antient *Romans* cultivated them to a degree of *Epicurism.* Some confined their *Delights* to a single *Vegetable,* as *Cato,* doting on his *Cabbage.* The *Tulipists* are so set upon their gaudy Flower, that the hard Name and Crime of a *Tulipomania,* is by their own Professors charged upon them; a little odd the Humour of those Gentlemen, who affected Plantations of none but *venomous Vegetables.*

But finally, the vast Uses of *Plants* in *Medicine,* are those which fallen and feeble Mankind has cause to consider, with singular Praises to the merciful God, who so pities us under the sad Effects of our Offences.

Among the eighteen or twenty thousand *Vegetables,* we have ever now and then a single one, which is a
Polychrest,

Polychreſt, and almoſt a *Panacæa;* or at leaſt ſuch an
one as obliges us to ſay of it, as Dr. *Morton* ſpeaks of
the *Cortex Peruvianus;* 'tis *Antidotus in Levamen Ærum-
narum Vitæ humanæ plurimarum divinitus conceſſa.* And,
*In Sanitatem Gentium proculdubio a Deo optimo maximo
condita.*

Among the Antients there were ſeveral Plants that
bore the Name of *Hercules,* —— called *Heracleum,* or
Heraclea; probably, as *Le Clerc* thinks, to denote the
extraordinary Force of the Plants, which they compared
to the Strength of *Hercules.*

Cabbage was to the *Romans* their grand *Phyſick,* as
well as *Food,* for ſix hundred Years together.

Mallows has been eſteemed ſuch an *univerſal Medicine,* as to be called *Malva Omnimorbia.*

Every body has heard,

> *Cur moriatur homo cui Salvia creſcit in hortis ?*

The *ſix favourite Herbs* diſtinguiſh'd by Sir *William
Temple* for the many Uſes of them, namely, *Sage,* and
Rue, and *Saffron,* and *Alehoof,* and *Garlick,* and *Elder,*
if they were more frequently uſed, would no doubt
be found vaſtly beneficial to ſuch as place upon *Health*
the Value due to ſuch a *Jewel.*

The *French* do well to be ſuch great Lovers of *Sor-
rel,* and plant ſo many Acres of it; it is good againſt
the *Scurvy,* and all ill Habits of Body.

The Perſuaſion which Mankind has imbib'd of *Tobacco*
being good for us, has in a ſurprizing manner prevail'd !
What incredible Millions have *ſuck'd in* an Opinion,
that it is an *uſeful* as well as a *pleaſant* thing, for them
to ſpend much of their Time in drawing thro a Pipe
the *Smoke* of that lighted Weed ! It was in the Year
1585, that one Mr. *Lane* carried over from *Virginia*
ſome *Tobacco,* which was the firſt that had ever been
ſeen in *Europe;* and within an hundred Years the
ſmoking of it grew ſo much into faſhion, that the very

Cuſtoms

Customs of it brought *four hundred thousand Pounds a Year* into the *English* Treasury.

It is doubtless a *Plant* of many Virtues. The *Ointment* made of it is one of the best in the Dispensatory. The Practice of *smoking* it, tho a great part of them that use it might very truly say, *they find neither Good nor Hurt by it;* yet it may be fear'd it rather does more *Hurt* than *Good.*

' May God preserve me from the indecent, ignoble,
' criminal *Slavery,* to the mean Delight of *smoking a*
' *Weed,* which I see so many carried away with.
' And if ever I should *smoke* it, let me be so wise as
' to do it, not only with *Moderation,* but also with
' such Employments of my Mind, as I may make that
' Action afford me a Leisure for !'

Methinks *Tobacco* is but a poor *Nepenthe,* tho the Takers thereof take it for such an one. It is to be feared the *caustick Salt* in the *Smoke* of this Plant, convey'd by the *Salival Juice* into the Blood, and also the *Vellication* which the continual use of it in *Snuff* gives to the *Nerves,* may lay Foundations for Diseases in Millions of unadvised People, which may be commonly and erroneously ascribed to some other Original.

It is very remarkable, that our compassionate God has furnish'd all Regions with *Plants* peculiarly adapted for the relief of the *Diseases* that are most common in those Regions. 'Tis Mr. *Ray*'s Remark, *Tales Plantarum Species in quacunque Regione a Deo creantur, quales Hominibus & Animalibus ibidem natis maxime conveniunt.*

Yea, *Sclenander* affirms, that from the Quantity of the *Plants* most plentifully growing in any place, he could give a probable Guess what were the *Distempers* which the People there were most of all subject to.

Benerovinus has written a Book, on purpose to shew that every Country has every thing serving to its Occasions, cafions, and particularly *Remedies* for all the Diftempers which it may be afflicted with.

Can we be any other than charmed with the Goodnefs appearing in it, when we fee the *Plants* every where ftarting out of the *Earth*, and hear their courteous Invitation, *Feeble Man, I am a Remedy, which our gracious Maker has provided for thy Feeblenefs*; *take me, know me, ufe me, thou art welcome to all the Good that is to be found in me!*

Yea, fuch are the Virtues of the *Vegetable World*, that it is no rare thing to fee a whole Book written on the Virtues of one fingle *Vegetable*.

How long is *Rofenbergius* on the *Rofe*, in his *Rhodologia!* *Whitaker* will have the *Vine* to be the *Tree of Life*, in his Treatife on the Blood of it. *Alfted* has entertained us with a yet greater variety on that *Plant of Renown*.

I was going to mention the *Anatomia Sambuci*, written by a *German* Philofopher.

But I prefently call to mind fuch a vaft Number of Treatifes publifhed, each of them on one *fingle Vegetable*, by the *Naturæ Curiofi* of *Germany*, that a *Catalogue* would be truly too tedious to be introduced.

If the *Coral* may pafs for a *Vegetable*, *Garencieres* has obliged us with a whole Treatife upon it.

But then we have one *far-fetch'd* and *dear-bought* Plant, on which we have fo many Volumes written, that they alone almoft threaten to become a *Library*. T E A is that charming Plant. Read *Pecklinus's* Book *de Potu Theæ*, and believe the medicinal and balfamick Virtues of it; it ftrengthens the *Stomach*, it fweetens the *Blood*, it revives the *Heart*, and it refrefhes the *Spirits*, and is a Remedy againft a World of Diftempers. Then go to *Waldfchmidt*, and you'll find it alfo to brighten the *Intellectuals*. When *Profe* has done its part, our *Tate* will bring in *Verfe* to celebrate the fovereign Virtues of it.

In-

Innocuos Calices, & Amicam Vatibus Herbam
Vimque datam Folio.

At laſt it ſhall be the very Θεά of the Poet.

Whilſt T E A, our Sorrows ſafely to beguile,
Sobriety and Mirth does reconcile :
For to this Nectar we the Bleſſing owe,
To grow more wiſe as we more chearful grow.

There is a Curioſity obſerved by Mr. *Robinſon* of
Ousby, that ſhould not be left unmentioned ; it is, that
Birds are the *natural Planters* of all ſorts of *Trees* ; they
diſſeminate the *Kernels* on the Earth, which brings
them forth to perfection. Yea, he affirms, that he
hath actually ſeen a great Number of *Crows* together
planting a Grove of *Oaks* ; they firſt made little Holes
in the Earth with their Bills, going about and about,
till the Hole was deep enough, and then they dropt
in the *Acorn*, and cover'd it with Earth and Moſs. At
the time of his writing, this young Plantation was
growing up towards a *Grove of Oaks*, and of an height
for the *Crows* to build their Neſts in.

In *Virginia* there is a Plant called *The James-Town-*
Weed, whereof ſome having eaten plentifully, turn'd
Fools upon it for ſeveral Days ; one would blow up a
Feather in the Air, another dart Straws at it ; a third
ſit ſtark naked, like a Monkey, grinning at the reſt ;
a fourth fondly kiſs and paw his Companions, and
ſnear in their Faces. In this frantick State they were
confined, leſt they ſhould kill themſelves, tho there
appear'd nothing but Innocence in all their Actions.
After eleven Days they return'd to themſelves, not
remembring any thing that had paſs'd.

My Friend, a *Madneſs* more ſenſleſs than that with
which this *Vegetable* envenoms the Eaters of it, holds
thee in the ſtupefying Chains thereof, if thou doſt not
behold

behold in the whole *Vegetable Kingdom* such Works of the glorious Creator, as call for a continual Admiration.

¶. It is a notable Stroke of Divinity methinks which *Pliny* falls upon, *Flores Odoresque indiem gignit Natura, magna (ut palam est) Admonitione hominum.*

' The Man began to be cured of his *Blindness,* who
' could say, *I see Men, like Trees, walking.* That Man
' is yet perfectly *blind* who does not *see Men, like Trees,*
' first *growing* and *flourishing,* then *withering, decaying,*
' *dying.*'

' The *Rapæ Anthropomorphæ,* and some other *Plants,*
' that have grown with much of an *Human Figure,* to
' be fancied on them, have been *odd things.* But there
' are Points wherein all *Plants* will exhibit something
' of the *Human Figure.*'

' The *Parts* of *Plants* analogous to those in an *Hu-*
' *man Body,* are notably enumerated by *Alsted* in his
' *Theologia Naturalis.* The Analogy between their
' States and ours would be also as *profitable* as *reasona-*
' *ble* a Subject of Contemplation.'

' And I hope the *Revival* of the *Plants* in the *Spring*
' will carry us to the Faith of our own *Resurrection*
' *from the Dead.*'

' And of the *Recovery* which the *Church* will one day
' see from a *Winter* of *Adversity*; the *World* from a
' *Winter* of *Impiety*: The *Earth* shall one day be filled
' with the *Fruits of Righteousness,* however barren and
' horrid may be the present Aspect of it.'

' A Man famous in his day (and in ours too) thought
' himself well accommodated for devotionary Studies,
' tho he says, *Nullos se aliquando Magistros habuisse nisi*
' *Quercus & Fagos.*'

' I will hear these *Field-Preachers,* their loud Voice
' to me from the *Earth,* is the same with what would
' be uttered by *Angels flying thro the midst of Heaven*;
' *Fear God, and glorify him!*

' One

' One thus articulates the Vegetable Sermons : *Ecce*
' *nos, O increduli filii hominum, nuper mortui eramus, at*
' *nunc reviximus. Vetus noſtrum Corpus ac Veſtimentum*
' *depoſuimus, & novæ Creaturæ faſtæ ſumus. Facite vos*
' *nunc aliquid ſimile.* And again, *Dum in hac miſerrima*
' *Vitâ eſtis, nolite de Corpore eſſe ſolliciti ; noſtri memores*
' *eſtote, quas Creator honeſtiſſime coloratis Veſtibus induit,*
' *quotannis per tot Millenarios, jam inde ab exordio Mundi.*
' And once more, *Ecce vires noſtræ, non nobis ipſis, ſed*
' *vobis deſerviunt. Non noſtro Bono floremus, ſed veſtro.*
' *Imo Divina Bonitas vobis floret per nos, ut dicere poſſitis,*
' *Dei Benignitatem in nobis florere, ſuoque Odore ſuaviſſimo*
' *vos recreare.*'

' A famous *German* Doctor of Philoſophy declares,
' that he found it impoſſible for him to look upon the
' *Vegetable World* without thoſe Acclamations, *Pſalm*
' cxxxix. 6. *The Knowledge of theſe things is too wonder-*
' *ful for me, it is high, I cannot attain to it.*'

' The pious *Arndt* obſerves, that every Creature is
' enſtamp'd with Characters of the Divine Goodneſs,
' and brings Teſtimonies of a good Creator. Our *Vine*
' ſo calls upon us, *Scias, O homo, hanc Liquoris mei Sua-*
' *vitatem, qua Cor tuum recreo, a Creatore meo eſſe.* Our
' *Bread* ſo calls upon us, *Vis iſta, qua famem ſublevo, a*
' *Creatore meo, & veſtro mihi obtigit.* It is a Saying of
' *Auſtin's, Deum Creaturas ſingulas guttula Divinæ ſuæ*
' *Bonitatis aſperſiſſe, ut per illas homini bene ſit.*'

' A devout Writer treats us with ſuch a Thought
' as this : Our God is like a tender Father, who,
' when the Infant complies not preſently with his
' Calls, allures him with the Offer of pleaſant *Fruits*
' to him. Not that the Child ſhould ſtop in the Love
' of the *Apple,* the *Plumb,* the *Pear,* but be by the
' *Fruits* drawn to the Love and Obedience of the *Fa-*
' *ther* that gives them. Our heavenly Father calling
' on us in his *Word,* gives us alſo *Rain from Heaven,*
' *and fruitful Seaſons,* to engage our Love and Obe-
' dience. *Quæ ſanè Beneficia aliud nihil ſunt, quam tot*

' *manus & Nuncii Dei, parati ad ipsum Deum nos dedu-*
' *cere, illiusque amorem altius animis nostris insinuare, ut*
' *ipsum tandem Datorem in Creaturis & Donis suscipere*
' *discamus.*'

' Among other Thoughts of Piety upon the *Vege-*
' *table World,* some have allow'd a room for this; the
' strong Passion in almost all Children for *Fruit*; ——
' by tendring *Fruits* to them, you may draw them to
' any thing in the World. May not this be a lasting
' *Signature* of the *first Sin,* left upon the Minds of our
' Children! An Appetite for the *forbidden Fruit.* When
' we see our Children greedy after *Fruits,* a remem-
' brance and repentance of *that Sin* may be excited in
' us.'

Add this: *Quid prodest ope Creaturarum vivere, si Deo non vivitur?*

A good Thought of a *German* Writer:
Sol & Luna, totusque Mundus Sydereus, luce sua Deum collaudunt. Terra Deum laudat, dum viret & floret. Sic Herbæ & Flosculi Opificis sui Omnipotentiam & Sapientiam commendant Odore, Pulchritudine, & Colorum varia Pictura: Aves Cantu & Modulatione; Arbores Fructibus; Mare Piscibus; omnes Creaturæ laudant Deum, dum illius mandata exequuntur. Colloquuntur nobiscum per divinitus ipsis insitas Proprietates, manifestantes opificem suum, & exhortantes nos ad ipsum laudandum.

ESSAY XXVII. *Of* INSECTS.

WE are hastening into the *Animal World.* Here we soon find a Tribe vastly numerous, called by *Aristotle* Ἔντομα, and by *Pliny* therefore *Insecta,* be-cause of their having certain Incisures and Indentings about their Bodies.

The *French* Philosopher does well to rebuke us for calling these *imperfect Animals,* for they want no Parts, either *necessary* or *convenient* for them; they are *complete* in their Kind, and the Divine Workmanship is asto-nishing!

niſhing! *Pliny* ſhall here correct us, *In his tam parvii atque nullis, quæ Ratio, quanta Vis, quam inextricabilis perfectio!*

Even the poor *Ephemeron*, whoſe whole Period of Life is but ſix or ſeven Hours, who is bred and born, and lives, and goes thro all his Operations, and expires, and goes into his Grave, all within this little Period, muſt not be thrown into a Claſs of *imperfect Animals*; nor may it be ſaid of it, that it is *made in vain*.

We enjoy an excellent *Ray*, who in his *Methodus Inſectorum* has diſtinguiſh'd to us the ſeveral Kinds of *Inſects*.

Of *Inſects*, there are ſome which do *not change* their Form.

Some of theſe Ἀμετἀμὸρφωτα are *without Feet*; theſe are either *terreſtrial*, produced *on* the Earth or *in* the Earth, (whereto *Snails* may be referred) or within the *Bowels* of Animals; or elſe *aquatick*, whereof ſome are *greater*, which have a peculiar way of moving, by firſt fixing their *Head* on the Ground, and then drawing up their *Tail* towards it; ſome are *leſſer*, having a different way of crawling; and among theſe there are both *round* ones and *flat* ones.

But then there are ſome *having Feet*.

There are *Hexapoda*, or ſix-footed ones; of theſe there are ſome *terreſtrial* ones, both of a *larger* ſort, and of a *ſmaller*: of the *ſmaller*, there are about *five* which moleſt the Bodies of other living Creatures; and as many that give not that Moleſtation. There are other *aquatick* ones.

There are alſo *Octapoda*, or eight-footed ones; of theſe there are ſome that have a *Tail*, as the *Scorpion*; and ſome that have none, as the *Spider*; whereof one ſort ſpins no Web; three ſorts are *Spinſters*. To theſe add the *Ticks*, and the *Mites*.

Yea, there are *Teſſareskaidecápoda*, or fourteen-footed ones; particularly the three ſorts of *Aſelli*. More
than

than so, there are *twenty-four-footed* ones, whose eight Fore-Feet are lesser ones, and sixteen Hinder-Feet are larger ones.

More than this, there is a sort of *thirty-footed* ones: but as being tired with specified Numbers for the Feet of these curious things, the rest we call *Polypoda*, or many-footed ones; of these there are some on the *Land*, and others in the *Water*.

Of *Insects*, there are others who do *undergo a Change*. Tho *Squammerdam* (who has given the best Account of these) observes, that this is improperly affirmed of these Μέ]αμορφέμενα, since there is no real *Transformation* of these, but only an Explication of the Parts of the Animal, which were before latent in *Miniature*, and like the Plant in the Seed.

Of these there are some, in whose Transmutation there is no *Rest* or *Stop* between the old and the new Form, and who don't lose their Motion at the time of their shifting the *Pellicula*. And there are some, in whom the *Vermiculus* leaving the former Shape of the *Nympha*, with which it appeared in the Egg, and subsisted without Food, now beginning to feed, hath its Parts visibly increased and stretched out, and takes the Form of a new *Nympha*, which is not without motion, and from thence becomes a *Flyer*.

To the former *Species* of Transmutation there belong many sorts, thirteen at least; to the second a vast multitude more. And among the rest, the multitudinous Armies of *Butterflies*, which being divided into *diurnal* and *nocturnal*; of the former sort alone there is about *fifty* several Kinds observed in *England*.

There is a third *Species* of Transmutation, which is a sensible Change from a *Vermiculus* to a *flying Insect*, but yet with a sensible *Rest* or *Stop* between one Form and the other. The *Flesh-Flies* belong to this, and so do some other Kinds.

Before we go any further, we will make a pause upon an Observation, thus expressed by Mr. *Barker* in his

his *Natural Theology*; for it is upon a Matter which occurs in the View of all Creatures, that now remain for our Contemplation; yea, the *Vegetables* too have themselves exemplified it. ' Whence is it that those
' two natural Principles of *Self-Preservation* and *Self-*
' *Propagation*, are so inviolably founded in the Nature
' of all living Creatures, even those that have *no Rea-*
' *son*, as well as those that have; both which are ne-
' cessary to the Subsistence of the Universe? May not
' we hence easily argue, that surely this was done *in-*
' *tentionally* for such an *End*? And if *intentionally*, then
' it is done by *Reason*; and if by *Reason*, it must be by
' His *Reason* that first made this Universe.'

Dr. *Gorden* adds to the Assurances which all the Inquisitive before him have given us, that no *Insects* are bred of *Corruption*, but all *ex Ovo*.

He also observes, that the Females of all *Flies* put their Spawn in or near those places where the *Eruca's*, which are hatch'd out of them, are to have their *Food*.

He observes likewise, that there is a kind of *Gluten*, by which the Females fasten their *Eggs* to the bearing Buds of Trees, at such a rate, that the *Rain* cannot wash them off.

And he observes, that these *Eggs* will not be hurt by the greatest *Frost* that can happen.

Mr. *Andry* in his Book, *De la Generation de Vers dans le corps de l'Homme*, takes notice of a Mistake in the Antients, who denied *Breath* to the *Insects* on the score of their wanting *Lungs*; for *Insects* have a greater number of *Lungs* than other Animals. The Antients also thought that the *Insects* had no *Blood*, because many of them had not a *red Liquor* like ours; but this too was a Mistake, 'tis not the *Colour*, but the *Intent* of the *Liquor* that is to be considered in this Case. It was likewise the Belief of the Antients, that the *Insects* had no *Hearts*; whereas our Microscopes now convince us of the contrary. And the *Silk-worms* particularly have a
con-

continued Chain of *Hearts*, from the Head almost to the extremity of the Tail. And it is the number of *Lungs* and *Hearts* that occasions those *Insects* to give signs of Life a long while after they are divided into several parts.

Mr. *Poupart* affirms, that the *Earth-worms* and the *Round-tail'd Worms*, which are found in the *Intestines* of Animals, as also *Snails* and *Leeches*, are *Hermophrodites*; but such *Worms* as become *Flies* are not so, rather they are of no Sex, but are *Nests* full of Animals.

The *spontaneous Generation* of *Insects* has at last been so confuted by *Redi*, and *Malpighi*, and *Squammerdam*, and our excellent *Ray*, and others, that no Man of Sense can any longer believe it. Indeed such a *spontaneous Generation* would be nothing less than a *Creation*. That all Animals are generated of *Parent Animals*, is a thing so cleared up from Observation and Experiment, that we must speak of it in the Language of those who have lately writ of it, *Nous croyons absolument.* And of their *Generation* any other way, we cannot but use the Language of Dr. *Lyster*, *Non inducor ut credam.* If an *Insect* may be *equivocally generated*, then, as Dr. *Robinson* justly enquires, *why not sometimes a Bird, yea, a Man? Or why no new Species of Animals now and then? For there is as much Art shewn in the Formation of those, as of these.* Dr. *Cheyne* assures us, nobody now-a-days, that understands any thing of Nature, can so much as imagine, that any Animal, how abject soever, can be produced by an *equivocal Generation*, or without the Conjunction of Male and Female *Parents*, in the same or in two different Individuals. And there are very few who have considered the Matter, but what own that every *Animal* proceeds from a præ-existent *Animalcule*, and that the *Parents* conduce nothing but a convenient *Habitation* to it, and suitable *Nourishments*, till it be fit to be trusted with Light, and capable of enjoying the Benefits of the Air. There is nothing in the *Animal Machine*, but an inconceivable number of branching and winding *Canals*, filled with Liquors

L

of

of different natures, going a perpetual round, and no more capable of producing the wonderful Fabrick of another Animal, than a thing is of making itself. There is besides in the *Generation* of an Animal, a necessity that the *Head, Heart, Nerves, Veins* and *Arteries*, be formed at the same time, which never can be done by the motion of any Fluid, which way soever moved.

Great *G O D, Thou art the Father of all things; even the Father of Insects, as well as the Father of Spirits : And Thy Greatness appears with a singular Brightness in the least of Thy Creatures!*

Concerning *Frogs* generated in the *Clouds*, there has been a mighty Noise; the *Thunder* scarce makes a greater! But Mr. *Ray* says well, it seems no more likely than *Spanish* Gennets begotten by the *Wind*, for that has good Authors too. He adds, *He that can swallow the raining of Frogs, hath made a fair Step towards believing that it may rain Calves also; for we read that one fell out of the Clouds in* Avicen's *Time. Fromondus*'s Opinion, that the *Frogs* which appear in great multitudes after a Shower, are not indeed generated in the Clouds, but are coagulated of *Dust*, commix'd and fermented with *Rain-water*, is all over as impertinent. It is very certain that *Frogs* are of two different Sexes, and have their spermatick Vessels; and their Copulation is notorious (*per integrum aliquando Mensem continuata*) and after the Spawn must be cast into the Water, where the Eggs lie in the midst of a copious Gelly; then must appear a Feetless *Tadpole*, in which Form it must continue a long while, till the Limbs be grown out, and it arrives to the perfect Form of a *Frog*. To what purpose all this, if your way, Gentlemen, [*Fromendus*, and the rest] may suffice?

Frogs appearing in such multitudes upon *Rains*, do but come forth upon the Invitation which the agreeable Vapor of *Rain-water* gives to them. And for some such reason we are commonly entertain'd with such
Armies

Armies of them in the cool *Summer-Evenings,* that we wonder where they have been lurking all the Day. Monfieur *Perrault,* upon the Diffection of the *Falling-Frogs,* which the *equivocal Gentlemen* fo teaze us with, found their *Stomachs* full of Meat, and their *Inteflines* of Excrement. The inquifitive Mr. *Derham,* on his meeting with *Frogs* in a prodigious Number, crofting a fandy Way juft after a Shower, purfued the Matter with his ufual Exactnefs, and he foon found the Colony iffue from an adjacent Pond, who having pafs'd thro their *Tadpole-State,* and finding the Earth moiftned for their March, took the opportunity to leave their old *Latibula,* where they had now devour'd their proper Food, and feek a more convenient Habitation. Or what if we fuppofe them, at leaft in their Spawn, fetch'd up into the *Clouds* by the *Sun,* and kept there till grown into the State wherein they fall down from thence, as it has been affirmed they have on Veffels at Sea?·

As to the *Worms* and other Animals bred in the Inteftines of Man and Beaft, it is Dr. *Robinfon's* Remark, *I think it may be proved, that the vaft variety of Worms found in almoft all the Parts of different Animals, are taken into the refpective Bodies by Meats and Drinks.*

Even the *Maggots* which grow in the Back of the common *Caterpillar,* are by their Parents lodg'd there, as a proper Apartment for them.

The *Toads* found in the midft of *Trees,* nay, and of *Stones,* when they have been fawn afunder, no doubt they grew of a *Toad-Spawn,* which fell into that Matter before the Concretion thereof.

The vulgar Opinion, that the *Heads* or *Clothes* of uncleanly People do breed *Lice,* or that *Mites* are bred in *Cheefe,* Mr. *Ray* notes, is a *vulgar Error :* he affirms, that all fuch Creatures are produced of *Eggs* laid in fuch places by their *Parents;* Nature has endued them with a wondrous Acutenefs of Scent and Sagacity, whereby they can, tho far diftant, find out fuch pla

L 2   ces,

ces, and make towards them; and tho they seem so slow, yet it has been found that in a little time they will march a considerable way to find out a convenient Harbour. Here Mr. *Ray* makes a *Pause of Religion*; says he, 'I cannot but look upon the strange 'Instinct of this noisome and troublesome Creature 'the *Louse*, of seeking out foul and nasty Clothes to 'harbour in, as an Effect of Divine Providence, de- 'sign'd to deter Men and Women from Sordidness 'and Sluttishness, and provoke them to *Cleanliness*. 'God himself hates *Uncleanness*, and turns away from 'it, [*Deut.* xxiii. 12, 13, 14.] But if God requires, 'and is pleased with *Bodily Cleanliness*, much more is 'He so with the *Pureness* of the *Mind*. *Blessed are the* 'pure in Heart, for they shall see God!'

The *Eyes* of *Insects* have in them what is very admirable! Their great necessity for accurate Vision is, in the reticulated *Cornea* of their Eyes, admirably provided for; it is a most curious piece of Lattice-work, in which every *Foramen* is of a lenticular nature, and enables the Creature to see every way without any Time or Trouble; probably every *Lens* of the *Cornea* has a distinct Branch of the Optick Nerve ministring to it.

Spiders are mostly octonocular; some, as Mr. *Willoughby* thought, *senocular*. *Flies* are *multocular*, having as many Eyes as there are Perforations in their *Cornea*. The greatest part of the Head of that prædatious Insect, the *Dragon-Fly*, is possessed by its *Eyes*.

Tho we say, *As blind as a Beetle*, Mr. *Leuenhoeck* has discover'd at least *three thousand Eyes* in the *Beetle*.

Insects have their *Antennæ*, by which they not only cleanse their *Eyes*, but also *guard* them; their Eyes being fitted mostly to see *distantial Objects*, these *Feelers* obviate the Inconvenience of their too rashly running their Heads against Objects that may be very near to them.

And

And many of them are, as Mr. *Derham* observes, most surprizingly beautiful.

The Mechanism in those that *creep* is most exquisitely curious.

What can exceed the *Oars* of the *Amphibious Insects*, that *swim* and *walk*? Their hindmost Legs are made most nicely, with commodious flat Joints, and Bristles on each side thereof towards the ends, serving for *Oars* to swim; and nearer the Body are two stiff *Spikes*, to enable them to walk, as they have occasion.

An incomparable provision is made in the *Feet* of such as walk or hang on smooth Surfaces; divers of these, besides their acute and hooked *Nails*, have also skinny *Palms* on their Feet, which enable them to stick on Glass, and other smooth Bodies, thro the Pressure of the *Atmosphere*.

The great Strength and Spring in the *Legs* of such as *leap*, is very notable; and so are the well-made *Feet* and strong *Talons* of such as *dig*.

Admirable the Faculty of some that cannot fly, to convey themselves with Speed and Safety, by the help of their *Webs*, or some other Artifice that renders their Bodies lighter than the Air! How pleasantly do the *Spiders* dart out their *Webs*, and *sail* away by the help thereof; whereof Dr. *Lyster* and Dr. *Hulse* were some of the first who made a discovery? There seems to be an hint of their *darting* in *Aristotle*, and in *Pliny*; but the Antients knew nothing of their *sailing*. Some other little Animals may have their ways of *Conveyance* as unknown to us, as heretofore has been that of the *Spiders*; Creatures found in very new Pits, and Holes in the Tops of Houses, where they were never bred by any *equivocal Generation*. The *green Scum* on the Surface of stagnating Waters, which is nothing but prodigious Numbers of Animalcules; how come they there? And when gone, where do they go?

What can be better contriv'd than the *Legs* of *Insects*, most incomparably fitted for the intended Service?

Or

Or than their *Wings*, diftended and ftrengthned with
the fineft *Bones,* and thefe cover'd with the lighteft
Membranes, whereof fome are adorned with the moft
beautiful *Feathers;* for the elegant Colours of *Moths*
and *Butterflies* are owing to neat *Feathers* on their
Wings, that are fet in Rows with great Exactnefs,
and all the good Order imaginable? And fome
are provided with *Articulations,* for their *Wings* to be
withdrawn, and folded up in Cafes, and again readily fpread abroad upon occafion : *Scarabs* and other that
have *Elytra,* are thus accommodated. That their Body may be kept fteady and upright, there is the admirable Artifice of *Pointels* and *Poifes,* under thofe who
have no more than *two Wings,* (whereas the *four-wing'd*
ones have no fuch things :) Thefe *Poifes* in the bipen-
nated Infects are for the moft part little *Balls,* that are
fet at the top of a flender Stalk, which they can move
every way at pleafure to obviate *Vacillations.* If one
of the *Poifes* be cut off (or if the *four-winged* have loft
one of their fecondary or auxiliary Wings) the Infect
will fly as if one fide over-balanc'd the other, till it
fall to the ground.

How *minute,* but how aftonifhingly *curious,* muft be
the Joints, the Mufcles, the Tendons, and the Nerves,
neceffary to perform the Motions of thefe marvellous
Creatures! Thefe things concur even in the *fmalleft*
Animalcules, and fuch as cannot be feen without our
Microfcopes.

When *Galen* had admired the Skill, *quod declarant
Opifices cum in Corporibus parvis aliquid infculpant,* in-
ftanced in the *Phaeton* in a *Ring,* where the Legs of
the *Horfes* were no bigger than thofe of a *Gnat,* he yet
very juftly cries out, their Make did not come up to
thofe of a *Gnat: Major adhuc alia quædam effe videtur
Artis ejus, qui Pulicem condidit, Vis atque Sapientia;* and
is amazed that *Ars tanta in tam abjectis Animalibus ap-
pareat.*

Among

Among the celebrated Pieces of Human Art, there was the *Cup* that *Oſwald Nerlinger* made of a *Pepper-corn*, that held twelve hundred little Ivory Cups, all gilt on the Edges, and having each of them a Foot, and yet afforded room for four hundred more. But our *Derham* juſtly celebrates the more ſtupendous Art, which *plainly manifeſteth the Power and Wiſdom of the infinite Contriver of the inimitable Fineries* in the Bodies of our little *Inſects;* they muſt have *Eyes*, a *Brain*, a *Mouth*, a *Stomach*, and *Entrails*, and other Parts of an Animal Body, as well as *Legs* and *Feet :* and all theſe muſt have their neceſſary *Nerves* and *Muſcles;* all theſe are cover'd with an agreeable *Tegument*, whereof how neat the *Imbrications* and other Fineries! All this Curioſity many times lying in a Body much ſmaller than the ſmalleſt *Grain* of Sand. A *Drop of Water* is a ſort of an *Ocean* to them! Mr. *Derham* in a *Drop* of the *green Scum* upon Water, a *Drop* no bigger than a *Pin's-head*, ſees no fewer than an hundred friſking about. How vaſtly many more in a *Drop* of *Pepper-water*! How vaſtly many, many, many more, in a Drop of the *Leuenhoeckian* Examination! Dr. *Harris* affirms, that not only in *black Pepper-water*, but alſo in Water wherein *Barley* and *Oats*, but eſpecially *Wheat*, hath been ſteeped for about four or five Days, he hath ſeen prodigious Numbers of them. *Great G O D, we are amazed!*

The *Jews* have a fooliſh Notion, tho advanc'd by a Rabbi *Solomon*, (upon the *Egyptian* Plague of *Lice*) *Quod Diabolus non dominatur ſuper Creaturam, quæ Grano Hordei ſit minor.* Indeed a Man who by *Humility* ſhrinks himſelf into leſs than the *light Duſt of the Balance*, may take the comfort of the Notion. But then in *Philoſophy* what a mighty Army of Animals leſs than a *Barley-corn* are found under the Dominion of the glorious GOD, who alſo has all the *Devils* as much under His Command as the leaſt of theſe. I have read of a *Flea* in a *Chain*, *Beelzebub* is no more before the Almighty Maker of the *Flies*, and all the other *Insects*.

The *Sagacity* observable in the generality of *Insects*, for their Provision against the Necessities of the *Winter*, is never enough to be admired.

Some having fed and bred themselves up to the Perfection of their *Vermicular State* in the Summer Months, then retire to a Place of Safety, and there throw off their *Nympha*, and put on their *Aurelia-state* for all the Winter, in which they have no occasion for any Food at all; this is done by all the *Papilionaceous*, as well as divers other Tribes.

Others, in their most perfect State, are able to subsist in a kind of *Torpitude*, without any Food at all; being at no *Action*, they are at no *Expence*, but can lie and sleep whole Months without any Sustenance. 'Tis remarkable that it is not any Stress of Weather which drives them into their intended Retirement, but they go to it in the *proper Season*, towards the end of Summer. 'Tis also remarkable, that every *Species* betakes itself to a convenient Receptacle, whereof there is a vast variety, where the *Frost* cannot come at them.

There are others who need *Food* in the Winter, and it is astonishing to see what a Foresight their glorious Creator has given them to lay up accordingly.

One of these Providers is the B E E, reckon'd by *Aristotle* among the Ζᾶα Πολιτικὰ, or *Civil People*. Prepare now for a Scene of Wonders! Every Colony of *Bees* has a *King*, whereof *Pliny* gives this true Description: *Omnibus semper forma egregia, & duplo quam cæteris major, Pennæ breviores, Crura recta, Ingressus celsior, in Fronte macula quodam Diademate candicans, multum etiam Nitore a vulgo differunt.* This majestical *Bee* has a *Sting*, which he can use without losing it; but his Majesty rarely finds occasion for it. The *common Bees* (which have their four *Wings* and six *Legs*) are divided into *Bands*, which have their *Officers*, all working for the Good of the Whole, and as long as they live. But then

then there are *Drones*, which are bigger than they, and are Servants and Nurses under the *Honey-Bees*, in the hatching of their Brood. A *Bee*, as *Rusden* observes, the first day of his flying abroad is an exquisite *Chymist*, or at least a diligent Purveyor and Collector of the *Honey-dews*, provided by Heaven for him on the Leaves of the Plants in the Field, which he lays up in convenient *Cells*, and there preserves it in a Covering of *Wax*, as foreseeing that a Winter is coming. How indefatigable the Pains of these industrious and marvellous Creatures! If they have *no King*, they pine, they die, they yield themselves a Prey to Robbers; but they will not bear *two*. *Butler* observes, they abhor *Polyarchy*, as well as *Anarchy*. Their King oppresses none, is a Benefactor to all; so their Loyalty to him is inviolate. His Place of Abode makes a Court a noble Retinue of *Bees* attends him.

—— *Rege incolumi Mens omnibus una est,*
Amisso rupere fidem. ——
Ille operum custos; illum admirantur; & omnes
Circumstant fremitu denso, stipantque frequentes,
Et sæpe attollunt humeris, & Corpora bello
Objectant, pulchramque petunt per Vulnera mortem.

They have the *Orders* of their *King* for all the Work they do; and they never *swarm* without his *Orders*. The chief cause of their *Swarm* is the want of room. He usually goes himself with them, as in view of a more flourishing State, and leaves his decaying and unpleasant Kingdom, with the noisome old Combs, to such Successors as he has left alive. If the old one dies in his going forth, they return home to the Prince whom they had relinquish'd. And the King sometimes gives his Consent to a *second Swarm*, tho there be no lack of room, out of his respect to some of his Royal Lineage. In their *Hives* they are mighty just to one another, tho the fear of being robb'd makes

makes them kill any Strangers that break in upon them. *Colonies* are fometimes engaged in Wars; the *King* ufually orders the Battel, and animates them with his *Voice*, and like a General, for whofe Defence they unanimoufly expofe themfelves : They neither give nor take any *Quarter*, and they diftinguifh one another by their *fmelling*. Spurt any thing among them that may make them *fmell all alike*, and their *Hoftility* ceafeth. The King is the only *Male* among the *Bees*. Each particular Cell in the *Honey-comb* is a Matrix. The King walks from one Cell to another, and injects a Seed into each of them; the *Honey-Bees* mix with it a *generative Matter*, which they have lodg'd there, and add Water to it, and cover it with *Wax*, which is not opened till the young Bee opens its way out of it. The *Drones* are alfo begotten by the King in like manner, but on a *generative Matter* fomething different, and in *deeper Cells*. The *Drones* are for no purpofe, but only to lie at home clofe to the *Combs*, where the *young Bees* are breeding, and hatch the young Brood, as a *Capon* does the Eggs affign'd to him. Hence the time for breeding the *Drones* is deferr'd till near the fall of the *Honey-Dews*, becaufe they would have the ufe of them at as little charge of feeding as they can. But fuch is the Nature of the *Drones*, that if the *Bees* do not kill them, as they generally do, when they can be no further ferviceable, they do by the Coldnefs of the Seafon in *September* die of them- felves.

But now how many *moral Inftructions* would the *Commonwealth of Bees* afford to a Mind willing to be *inftructed* of God, by the Miniftry of this *myfterious Infect* ! Honeft *Purchas* has with an Imitation of it ga- ther'd no lefs than three Centuries of them ; and yet thefe are but a few of the things which thefe *aculeated Preachers* would advife us of : I will fingle out but this one peculiar Document from them for myfelf, which
Pliny

Pliny takes notice of : *Nullus Apibus, si per Cœlum licuit, Otio perit Dies.*

Another of thefe Providers is the A N T, whereof the Wife-Man fays, they are *exceeding wife; a People not ftrong, yet they prepare their Meat in the Summer.*

Sir *Edward King* having been curious in examining their Generation, wonders to find them lying in Multitudes on their Eggs (which they induftrioufly gather together) by way of Incubation. He wonders to fee them in the Morning bringing them up towards the top of the Bank, and for the moft part on the South-fide of it ; but at Night, efpecially if it be cool, or likely to rain, you may dig a Foot before you can find them. Indeed all is wonderful !

There is the *Field-Ant* and the *Wood-Ant ;* the *Field-Ant* feeds upon fmall Seeds. They have their *Leaders* and *Rulers,* which they follow along their little *Paths* in exact Order, and return the fame way *;* they all go out light, but all return home heavy laden, with their *Burdens* on their Backs. The *Wood-Ant* feeds upon Leaves. You may fee fometimes great *Paths* made by them, three or four Inches broad, and as beaten as the High-ways ; they march ftoutly under fuch Loads, that you cannot fee their Bodies ; a *Path* looks perfectly *green* with them.

In two Months of the Year they take *Wing,* and fly abroad in the warm Sun, to take their Pleafure, after the *Fatigue* of their *Labour* is over.

And how unparallel'd the Tendernefs, the Diligence, the Forecaft of this little Animal, for the Safety of their *young ones !* A ςεγὴ, that filled *Squammerdam* with an unfpeakable Pleafure at the view thereof ; *Non fine Jucunditate fpectabam !* 'Tis very diverting to fee how they carry about their *young ones,* and expofe themfelves to any *Dangers,* rather than leave their *young ones* expofed ; and how they remove them from one place to another, as they find occafion.

Some-

Sometimes the *Ants* in the *Indies* will have Neſts moſt artificially placed between the Limbs of huge *Trees*, and theſe Neſts as big as an *Hogſhead*; here is their *Winter Habitation*.

They will ranſack ſtrangely for Proviſions, and in mighty Troops, which all follow wherever the foremoſt goes.

Excellently well Mr. *Derham* hereupon: ' That the ' great *Wiſdom* diſcernible in this little *Animal*, is ow- ' ing to the Infuſions of the great Conſervator of the ' World, is evident; becauſe either this *Wiſdom* and ' *Forecaſt* is an Act of the Animal itſelf, or of a Being ' that hath *Wiſdom*: but the Animal being *irrational*, ' 'tis impoſſible it can be its *own Act*, but it muſt be ' deriv'd or receiv'd from ſome *wiſe Being*. And who! ' —— What can that be, but an infinite L O R D, ' and Conſervator of the World!'

An *Ant-hill*, 'tis a Seat of a very curious Contrivance. *Johnſton* makes it an Article of his *Thaumatography*, and ſays very truly, *Vix ullius Urbis artificioſior Structura*. If you read the Deſcription of the *quadrangular City*, four Foot long, and a Foot wide, the Streets wiſely laid out, the convenient Granaries provided, the Civility of the Citizens to one another, as *Aldrovandus* has given it, you would ſee nothing in any *Strabo* more entertaining.

I wonder not that the Wiſdom of God ſends me thither: *Go to the Ant, thou Sluggard*; may I *learn her Ways and be wiſe*!

But we are paſſing into a Theme, whereon there is *no end of the Wonders!* The Care of the *Inſects* about their *Off-ſpring*.

Singular their Providence for their Young, in finding or making fit Receptacles for their *Eggs* or *Seed*, where they may enjoy a ſufficient Incubation, and have ready an agreeable and ſufficient Food for their Education.

They

They to whom *Flesh* is proper Food, lay their Sperm in *Flesh*; from which Nursery of *Maggots*, *S. Redi* has for ever banish'd the old Whimsey of *anomalous Generation*, by incontestable Experiments.

Others, to whom the Fruits or Leaves of the *Vegetables* are a *Food*, find a Repository there.

Some take this *Tree*, some take that *Herb*; and one Family still always the same.

If the *Cochineel* were not accommodated with a Fruit like a *Prickle-Pear*, which opens after the Flower which protected it is by the Heat of the Sun scorched away, when the small *red Insects* are come to maturity, and would die and rot for want of more Food, if the *Indians* did not now come to shake them out; *Gentlemen*, where would you be supplied with your so much esteemed *Scarlet*?

Others require a greater degree of Warmth in their Lodging, and those look out the *Bodies* of *larger Animals*, that they may be lodged there. Many, if not most sorts of *Birds*, have their *Lice* in their Feathers; and several sorts of *Beasts* have peculiar *Lice* in their Hairs, all distinct from the two sorts wherewith *Man* is infested. It has been pretended that the *Ass* is free, and an odd reason assigned for it; but it has been rather supposed from a Passage in *Aristotle*, the *Chronology* whereof won't well suit with the *odd Reason* I refer to.

Some work themselves into the very *Scales* of the *Fishes*. There *Lumbricus innascitur, qui debilitat*; it was observed as long ago as the Days of the *Stagyrite*. They find them even in the *Stomach* of *Cod-fish*.

The *Sheep* complains of them in his *Nose*; the *Kine* have them on their Backs; the *Horses* in their *Guts*.

Those in the *Heads* of *Deer* are often mentioned by antient Writers.

Worms of many Yards long are bred in the *Legs* of *Men*, and in other Parts of their Bodies; in their *Tongues*, their *Gums*, and their *Noses*, as 'tis reported

in

in our *Philosophical Transactions*; in their *Eyes*, and their *Eyebrows*, as in the *German Ephemerides*. *Mouffet* and *Tyson* will set before you what Worms the *Stomach* and *Bowels* of *Men* have often breeding in them. Lately in my Neighbourhood a poor Man reaching to vomit, a monstrous *Worm* thrust up one end of itself, which the Man seizing on, fell to pulling of it, as a Fisherman hales up his Line, and pull'd till the *Worm* lay in an enormous heap; whence being drawn into its length and measured, the *Worm*, in the full extent of it, made about *one hundred and fifty Foot long.* I may say, *Hisce ipse vidi Oculis.* Yea, Dr. *Lyster* affirms true *Caterpillars* to have been vomited from thence. And Mr. *Jessop* affirms true *Hexapods* to have been also thrown up with a *Vomit.* Entertain unquestionable Accounts from *Germany*, and you will see *Toads*, and *Frogs*, and *Lizards*, cast up from an Human *Stomach*, no doubt from the drinking of their Spawn. The *Livers* and *Kidneys* of Animals have had their *Worms* : yea, *Verzascha* has found them (without a Metaphor) in the *Brains* of *Men* ; probably they were laid in the *Laminæ* of the *Nostrils*, and gnawed their way into the *Brains* thro the *Os Cribriforme.*

Wierus found them divers times in the *Gall-Bladder* of Persons whom he had opened. In divers *Fevers* the Blood has been found strangely *vermiculated*, as *Kircher* and several others have upon Examination reported ; [so *one Worm kills another !*] *Verminous* Collections are found in the *Small-Pox*, as *Lange* and *Borellus* testify ; and in *pocky Scabs* there are incredible Multitudes of them.

Others who make themselves *Nests* by Perforations in the *Earth*, or in some *Wood*, or in *Combs* of their own building ; 'tis admirable to see how they lay in, and seal up the Provisions that will be necessary for their young ones there. So divers *Ichneumons* carry in *Maggots*, which they take from the Leaves of Trees, which

which they fagacioufly put up clofe into their Nefts. *Ariftotle* fays they carry in *Spiders* too.

Their *Nidification* is aftonifhing! When their *Eggs* are on the Leaves of Plants, or other Materials on the *Land,* how commodioufly are they laid! Always carefully *glued* on, with one certain End lowermoft, and handfome Juxta-pofitions.

When in the *Water,* in what beautiful *Rows!* In a *gelatine Matter* fo faften'd, as to prevent its Diffipation.

Single out but *Pliny's* Inftance of the *Gnat,* a contemptible Animal, the Story of his Proceedings would give you a thoufand Aftonifhments!

They who muft perforate hard Bodies, to make their Lodgings there, have their Legs, Feet, Mouth, yea, their whole Bodies, very ftrangely accommodated to the Service.

But for them who build or fpin their *Nefts,* their Art, as Mr. *Derham* expreffes it, *juftly bids defiance to the moft ingenious Artift among Men fo much as tolerably to copy them.* The geometrical *Combs* of fome, the terreftrial *Cells* of others; the *Webs,* the *Nets,* the *Cafes,* of divers. A Bifhop of *Paris* long fince obferved, *Nafcitur Aranea cum Lege, Libro, & Lucernâ;* the very *Spider* knows its Leffon.

There is a *natural Glue* afforded by the Bodies of feveral to confolidate their Work. The *Wafps* have this, as well as the *Tinea Veftivora,* the *Cadew-worm,* and feveral others; what *Goedart* alfo obferves of his *Eruca,* this can be by fome darted out at pleafure, and woven into filken Balls. Mr. *Boyle* mentions an *oval Cafe* of a *Silk-worm,* which a Gentlewoman of his Acquaintance drawing out all the *filken Wire* that compofed it, found it above *three hundred Yards,* and yet weighed no more than *two Grains and an half.* That wondrous Infect the *Silk-worm!* It has no *Eyes,* but how fine its Performances. Let the *Hiftoria Singularis* of them, written by *Libavius,* be perufed, it will be found a Collection of Wonders. *Good God, fhall thy*

Silk-worm

Silk-worm adorn me, and shall he not instruct me too! There is another Worm, which would at least learn this of him, to spin out of his own Bowels, from his own Experience and his own Meditation, such things as may be useful to those to whom they shall be communicated. But, O *vain Person*, proud of the *silken Attire* that is rustling upon thee; is it possible that in a little *Worm* thy *Pride* should find a Nourishment!

There are others of these little Animals which make Nature itself serviceable to their Purpose, and make the Vegetation of *Trees* and *Herbs* the Means of building their little Habitations. They build in the *Galls* and *Balls* of the *Oak*, the *Willow*, the *Briar*, and other Vegetables, and are furnished with a *Piercer*, to prosecute their Business. Among these we will single out what the *Ichneumon-Fly* does to the Leaf of the *Nettle.* The Parent-Insect, with a stiff setacious Tail, terebrates the Rib of the Leaf when tender, and makes way for its *Egg* into the very Pith or Heart thereof, and probably lays in therewith some Juice of its Body, which will pervert the regular Vegetation of it. From this Wound arises a small *Excrescence*, which (when the *Egg* is hatch'd into a *Maggot*) grows bigger as the *Maggot* increases, and swells on each side the Leaf, between the two Membranes, and extends itself into the parenchymous part thereof, till it is grown as big as two Grains of *Wheat.* In this Mansion there lies a small, white, rough *Maggot*, which turns to an *Aurelia*, and afterwards to a very beautiful, green, small, *Ichneumon-Fly*.

A peculiar Artifice, and so far out of the reach of any mortal Understanding, that here must be, as Mr. *Derham* justly pauses upon it, *the Concurrence of some great and wise Being, that has from the beginning taken care for the Good of the Animal!* The Formation of these *Cases* is quite beyond the Cunning of the *Animal* itself, but it is the Act partly of the *Vegetable*, and partly of some *Virulency* in the Juice or Egg of the

† Animal

Animal repofited on the *Vegetable*; which *Malpighi*, in his Defcription of the *Fly* bred in *Oaken-Galls*, has notably confirm'd to us. *Erunt Plantarum Tumores, morbofæ Excrefcentiæ, vi depofiti Ovi à turbata Plantarum compage, & vitiato humorum Motu excitatæ, quibus inclufa Ova & Animalcula, velut in Utero foventur & augentur; donec manifeftatis firmatifque propriis partibus, quafi exoriantur novam exoptantia auram.*

It is a juft Thought of one well skill'd in *Cofmology*, That *Men* themfelves, and much more *other Creatures*, may do many things which aptly ferve to fome *certain End* whereof they have no confideration. Creatures may be directed and conftrained by a *ftrong Fancy* which they have of fuch and fuch Works, and of Actions that belong to them. Well, but who has imprinted it? It is the Great GOD, who will have *fuch Works* to be done. *Great GOD, fhall we contrive what Service of thine thy nobler Creature M A N may thereby be helped to!* My excellent Philofopher concludes: *The Divine Reafon runs like a Golden Vein through the whole Leaden Mine of Brutal Nature.*

There is one thing more to be added: That the Numbers of *Infects* and *Vermin* may not be too offenfive to us, Providence has ordained many Creatures, efpecially fuch as are in fuperior Orders, to make it their bufinefs to deftroy them, efpecially when their Increafe grows too numerous and enormous. As in the *Indies,* where they are fometimes exceedingly punifhed with *Ants,* there is the *Urfus Formicarius,* whofe very bufinefs is to devour them. Hideous Armies of *Worms* do fometimes vifit my Country, and carry whole *Fields* of Corn before them, and climbing up Trees, leave them as bare as the middle of *Winter.* Our *wild Pidgeons* make this the *Seafon* of their *Defcent,* and in prodigious Flocks they fall upon thefe Robbers, and clear the Country of them.

The *Deftruction* and *Death* of *Animals* does proclaim the *Fame* of the Divine *Wifdom* in adjufting of it!

M   The

The *Locusts*, that have sometimes proved so devouring a *Plague*, do also prove a *Dish* to the People that suffer from them. In *A Voyage round the World*, I read, That in the *East-Indies*, when these Creatures come in great Swarms to devour their Fruits and Herbs, the Natives take them with Nets, and parch them over the fire in an earthen Pan, on which their Wings and Legs would fall off, and their Head and Backs turn red, but their *Bodies* being full, would eat *moist* and *sweet* enough, and their *Head* a little crackle in one's Teeth; a Dish that People might subsist upon: tho the Condition of the *Acridophagi*, mentioned by *Diodorus*, and by *Strabo*, would not encourage one to be confin'd to it.

Even the more noxious *Insects* and *Vermin* are such, that we may consider in them *the Finger of God!* The *Sufferings* they inflict upon us, may be considered as the *Scourges* of God upon us for our Miscarriages, and be improved as Excitations to *Repentance.* I have read somewhere a Passage to this purpose: ' I would carry
' on the Matter to so much of *Watchfulness*, in my ap-
' prehending Opportunities for *Thoughts of Repentance*,
' that the Provocations that may happen to be given
' to my *Bodily Senses* at any time, shall provoke such
' *Thoughts* in my Soul. —— If I happen to lodge
' where any *Insect* or *Vermin* assaults me, it shall *hum-*
' *ble* me. I will think *I have been one among the Enemies*
' *of God in the World. These uneasy Creatures are part of*
' *the Armies which the Lord of Hosts employs, and with some*
' *Contempt, against his Enemies!*'

The *Worms* which, especially in places where the *salt* and *fresh* Water meets, do in such horrid Swarms eat into the Bottoms of our *Ships*, and render them even like *Honey-combs*; the Coasts that are not infested with them, ought to acknowledge the Favour of Heaven in it; and the Merchant and Mariner that suffers by them, ought to consider *what Rebuke of Heaven up-*

on

on their Dealings or Doings may lie at the bottom of such a Calamity!

How wretched would our Condition be, if we were conftantly infefted with *Flies,* like the poor *winking People* of *New-Holland* in the *Eaft-Indies!* To be exempted from the Mifchiefs which the *Juftice* of God fometimes *inflicts* on People that do not acknowledge Him, 'tis what calls for our Acknowledgments of His *Goodnefs.*

If the *Lord of Hofts* pleafe to fingle out from his *Armies,* whereof *there is no Number,* no other *Legions* than thofe of *Infects,* even thofe *Velites* commanded by Him, how would they *embitter,* and even *extinguifh* our Lives! *Locufts* alone make whole Nations tremble: *Worms* have deftroyed *Kings;* and *Flies* have fcattered *Kingdoms.*

But then the reverfe: O *Cantharides,* how many Millions of Lives are continually faved by your *epifpaftick* Applications! *GOD is to be acknowledged in the Good which is done by a poor green Fly to the Children of Men!*

Honeft Mr. *Terry* tells us, That among the *Perfees* in the *Eaft-Indies* they profefs this Devotion: That the firft Creature of *Senfe* and of *Ufe* which they behold in a Morning, they employ ftill as a Remembrancer to them all the Day following, to draw up their Thoughts in *Thankfgiving* to the Almighty *God,* who hath made fuch a Creature for our Service.

My God, fhall the Pagan rife up and condemn the Chriftian! If we fhould not, from the View of thy Creatures have our Hearts drawn up to thy Praifes, we fhould to our confufion find it fo!

¶ ' For what E N D S are all thefe little Creatures
' made? Moft certainly for great E N D S, and for
' fuch as are worthy of a G O D!'

' The exquifite Artifice which is confpicuous in the
' *Make* of thefe Creatures, does proclaim a marvellous
' and matchlefs *Wifdom* in the *Maker* of them; and
' *Wifdom* will *make nothing in vain.*'

' Tho

' Tho the more *special Uses* of these Creatures be as
' yet unknown to us, the *only wise God* sends to us
' this Advice concerning them: *What I do thou know-*
' *est not now, but thou shalt know hereafter.*'

' However, this we *know N O W*; for these and all
' Creatures this E N D is great enough, *that the Great*
' *God therein beholds with pleasure the various and curious*
' *Works of His Hands.* Behold a sufficient E N D, as
' well for a *World* as for a *Worm*, that the infinite
' God may with delight *behold His own Glories* in the
' Works which His Hands have wrought. *My Rea-*
' *ders*, let us come to a Consort in the Doxology, *0*
' *Lord, thou hast created all things, and for thy Pleasure*
' *they are and were created!* The Great God has con-
' trived a mighty *Engine*, of an Extent that cannot be
' measured, and there is in it a Contrivance of won-
' drous *Motions* that cannot be *numbred.* He is infi-
' nitely gratified with the View of this *Engine* in all
' its *Motions*, infinitely grateful to Him so glorious a
' Spectacle! when it becomes grateful to *us*, then we
' come into some Communion with Him. I will
' esteem it a sufficient E N D for the whole Creation
' of God, *that the Great Creator may have the Gratifica-*
' *tion of beholding His own admirable Workmanship.* And
' I will esteem it a part of the Homage I owe to His
' Eternal Majesty, to be satisfied in such an E N D as
' this.'

' I will transfer this *Meditation* to the Exercises
' which are to fill a *Life of Piety.* Have I not *Reason*
' enough, *Motive* enough, to abound in all the Exer-
' cises of a *pious Life*, even the most *secret* of them, and
' a Guard upon the *Frames* and *Thoughts* of my Heart
' within me? *The Great G O D is the Beholder of my*
' *whole Behaviour, He knows the way that I take; and I*
' *chuse the things that please Him in what I am now a do-*
' *ing.*'

§. Finding myself now entred into the *Animal*
World, I will take this opportunity to insert and pur-
sue

sue an Observation of the acute Dr. *Cheyne*; which is, That the *Production of Animals* is a thing altogether *inconsistent* with the *Laws of Mechanism*. from whence I infer, that it must be from something *superior* to them.

For first, the *Blood* is by the Force of the *Heart* squeezed from the *left Ventricle*, thro the *Arteries*, to the Extremities of the Body, and is thence returned by the *Veins* into the right Ventricle, thence by the *Arteria Pulmonalis* into the *Lungs*; from the Lungs by the *Vena Pulmonalis* again into the *right Ventricle*. The *Motion of the Heart* is caused by the *nervous Juices* mixing with the Blood, in the *muscular* part thereof; and these *nervous Juices* are both derived from the Blood, and forced into the *muscular* part of the Heart, by the Motion of the *Heart* itself, the Texture of the containing Vessels, and perhaps by the Pulsation of the *Arteries* upon the Nerves of the Brain. Here now, the *Heart* is the cause of the *Motion of the Blood* in the *Arteries*; and the *Motion of the Blood* in the *Arteries* urging their Juices thro the Nerves, is the cause of the *Motion of the Heart*: which is a plain Circulation of Mechanical Powers, a *Perpetuum Mobile*, a thing unknown to Nature! An *Epicurean* cannot contrive a *Water-Machine*, wherein the *Water* should move the *Machine*, and the *Machine* move the *Water*, and the same *Water* continually return in a *Circle* to move the *Machine*.

Great GOD, it is thy immediate Influence on the Powers of Nature in me that keeps my Heart in motion. Oh! that I may love thee and serve thee with all my Heart! In thee I live! To glorify thee, should be the Business of my Life!

Again, In all *Animals* how *small*, how *fine* the Organs! How indefinite the *Number* of them! *Sensation* is performed by the mediation of *Organs* arising from the *Brain*, and continued thro the part affected. Now there is not the least imaginable solid part of the *Vessels* or *Muscles* but what we find sensible; wherefore

the

the Number of *Organs* that convey *Sensation* must be inconceivable! *Nutrition* is also performed by *Organs*, thro which a Supply is conveyed to the place to be nourished. Now there is *no Part* of the Body but what may be *increased* or *lessened*; so then in every *individual Point* of the Body there is the Termination of *Organs*, thro which a *Nourishment* may be conveyed. Furthermore, the *Canals* do all augment, and may all decay; and therefore every assignable part of these *Canals* must be the Termination of some *secretory Duct*, separating a *Fluid* fit for the repairing of their Losses, and these again must have others to repair their Losses; and how shall we conceive where to stop? Moreover, the most exquisite *Glasses* can discover nothing in the several parts of the Vessels and Muscles, but *Canals* amazingly slender; the better the Glasses, the more of these *capillary Pipes* are discovered. In short, all the *solid* Parts of the Body are nothing but either *Tubes* to convey some *Fluid*, or *Threads* in Bundles, tied by others that surround them, or going from one Fibre to another, or spread into thin Membranes; but each of these how *inconceivably* minute! the *Doctor* does not scruple to say, *infinitely!*

O infinitely Great GOD, I am astonished! I am astonished! For all those things hath my Hand made, saith the Lord.

ESSAY XXVIII. *Of* REPTILS.

LET us now handle the *Reptils*, which are a sort of *Animals* that rest one part of their Body on the Earth, while they advance the other forward.

In our way of doing it we shall *take up Serpents, and it shall not hurt us.*

Concerning the meanest of these, namely, the *Earthworm*, Dr. *Willis* makes this Remark: *Lumbricus terrestris, licet vile & contemptibile habeatur, Organa Vitalia, necnon*

necnon & alia Viscera, & Membra Divino artificio admi-rabiliter fabrefacta sortitur.

And the *spiral Motion* of it is admired as well as de-scribed by Dr. *Tyson.*

The Motion of *Reptils* is extremely curious.

Their *Food* and their *Nest* lies in the next Clod, Plant, or Hole; or they can long bear Hunger and Hardship.

So their *sinuous Motion,* perform'd with as much Art as what is in the *Legs* or *Wings* of other Creatures, and as curiously provided for, is found sufficient for the conveying of them.

There is abundance of *geometrical* Neatness and Niceness in the Motion of *Serpents*; their *annular Scales* lie cross their Belly, contrary to what those in the Back and the rest of the Body do: the Edges also of the *foremost Scales* lie over the Edges of the *following Scales*; and every Scale has a *distinct Muscle,* one end of which is tack'd to the middle of the Scale, the other to the upper Edge of the following Scale.

The *Snails* have neither Feet nor Claws, but they creep with an undulating motion of their Body; on which Dr. *Lyster* has written: and by a *Slime* emitted from their Body, they adhere to all Kinds of Super-ficies.

The *motive* Parts of *Caterpillars* are admirably con-trived, not only to serve their progression, but for ga-thering of their Food.

The *Spine,* and *Muscles* co-operating with the Spine, in such as have Bones; and the *annular* and other Muscles in such as have none; are incomparable Con-trivances.

The *Magnitude* whereto some *Serpents* have grown, is prodigious. *Bochart* will astonish you with a Colle-ction of Relations found in Antiquity concerning *Ser-pents*, and particularly *Dragons*, of a most enormous Magnitude. *Gesner* too will quote us Authors for

some

some so big, that the little Book I am now writing will afford no room for them.

Yea, *Suetonius* affirms, that one was exposed by *Augustus*, which was no less than fifty Cubits long. *Dio* comes up with him, and affirms, that in *Hetruria* there was one that was fourscore and five Foot long, which, after he had made fearful Devastations, was kill'd with a Thunderbolt. *Strabo* out-does him, and affirms, that in *Cœlo-Syria* there had been one which was an hundred Foot long, and so thick, that a couple of Men on horseback, on each side of him, could not see one another. Yea, one that was an hundred and twenty Foot long, was kill'd near *Utica* by the Army of *Regulus.* Well might *Austin* say of these dreadful Animals, *Majora non funt super Terram.*

Tho, if I might be allowed the Benefit of a *Metaphor*, I would say, *I have known where to find a greater than all of these!* But,

Ye Dragons, whose contagious Breath
Peoples the dark Retreats of Death,
Change your dire Hissings into heavenly Songs,
And praise your Maker with your forked Tongues.

> 'Tis what occurs in my Lord *Roscommon's* Paraphrase on Psalm cxlviii.

The *poisonous Tribes* have been made an Objection against the Divine Providence, as being destructive to the rest of the World.

The *Poison* of a *Viper* is found by Dr. *Mead*, on a microscopial Examination, *a parcel of small Salts, nimbly floating in the Liquor, but quickly changed, and shot out into Chrystals, of an incredible Tenuity and Sharpness, with something like 10 Knots here and there, from which they seemed to proceed:* it lies in a *Bag* in the *Gums*, at the upper-end of the *Teeth*; these Teeth are tubulated, for the conveyance of the *Poison* into the Wound which they make. *Galen* says, Mountebanks did use to stop

these

these Perforations of the *Teeth*, before they would let Spectators behold the *Vipers* to bite them.

Let it be confidered, that the venomous Creatures have their great *medicinal Ufes*; we fee a *Treacle* fetch'd out of a *Viper*; the *Viper's* Flesh cures *Leprofies*, and obftinate Maladies. The *Gall* of a *Rattle-fnake* (which we take out of him in the more early Months of his yearly appearance, and work into *Troches* with *Chalk* or *Meal*) is a rich *Cordial* and *Anodyne*, for which purpofe I have often taken it, and given it: it invigorates the Blood into a mighty *Circulation*, when fatal Suppreffions are upon it; it is highly *alexipharmick*, and cures *Quartan-Agues*. And yet this *Rattle-fnake*, fuch a venomous Wretch, that if he bite the Edge of an *Axe*, we have feen the bit of *Steel* that has been bitten, come off immediately, as if it had been under a *Putrefaction*.

The very Steam of the *Serpents* in the famous *La Grotta delli Serpi*, at *Saffa* in *Italy*, celebrated by *Wormius* from *Kircher*, and ftrangely difcovered by a *Leper* happening to fleep there, does wondrous things.

Moreover, *ubi Virus, ibi Virtus*; 'tis obferved, the bruifed *Flefh* of the *venomous* Creatures applied to their *Bites*, cures the *Venom* of them.

But, as Mr. *Derham* obferves, ' There would be ' no Injuftice in God for to make a Set of fuch noxious ' Creatures, as Rods and Scourges, to execute the ' Divine Chaftizements on finful Men.' He adds, ' I ' am apt to think, that the Nations which know not ' God are the moft annoyed with thofe noxious *Reptils*, and other pernicious Creatures.'

There is a ftrange Story related and afferted by *Franzius*, That *Anno Chrifti* 1564, vaft Armies of *Serpents* appeared in *Hungary*, and occupied their Fields of Corn; and when the People were with a particular Contrivance by Fire going to deftroy them, one who was bigger than the reft lifting up his Head, articulately cried out, *Nolite hoc facere, quia non noftro Arbitrio,*

trio, fed a Deo huc miffi fumus, ad perdenaas Segetes. If the Story fhould be but a *Fable,* yet the *Moral* is wife and good.

It may be they that have been thought *venomous,* have not had in them fo much *Venom* as has been thought for. Sir *Theodore Mayern* laughs at the Poifon of a *Toad,* and fays, 'tis no worfe than a *Frog;* he had himfelf without mifchief eaten feveral.

There is one Mr. *Robinfon* of *Cumberland,* who offers it as a probable Conjecture, that the *venomous Creatures* lick up the Venom of the *Earth,* which, if it were diffufed, might be more dangerous than their *Bite* or *Sting.*

The fame Gentleman obferves concerning the *crawling Worm,* which is defpifed, as the moft ufelefs among all the Creatures of God, that the Earth abounds with a grofs, fat, luxuriant *Slime* at the time when thefe Vermin are engendred, and thefe Vermin then feed upon it; this, if it were not fuck'd up, and contracted into the Bodies of thefe diminutive *Animals,* but were diffufed thro the Grafs and Herbage, would occafion *Murrains* in Beafts, and perhaps *Difeafes* in Men, whofe Diet is much upon Herbage.

A Worm now makes a paufe, and adores the Divine Workmanfhip appearing in the Conftitution of his Brethren!

What amazing Effects follow on the Bite of the *Tarantula!* The Patient is taken with an extreme difficulty of *breathing,* and heavy Anguifh of *Heart,* a difmal Sadnefs of *Mind,* a *Voice* querulous and forrowful, and his *Eyes* very much difturbed. When the violent Symptoms which appear on the firft Days are over, a continual *Melancholy* hangs about the Perfon, till by dancing, or finging, or change of Age, the poifonous Impreffions are extirpated from the Blood, and the Fluid of the Nerves: but this is an Happinefs that rarely happens; nay, *Baglivi,* this wicked *Spider's* Countryman, fays, *there is no Expectation of ever being perfectly cured.* Many of the Poifoned are never well but

but among the *Graves*, and in *solitary places*; and they lay themselves along upon a *Bier*, as if they themselves were *dead:* like People in despair, they will throw themselves into a *Pit*; *Women*, otherwise chaste enough, will cast away all Modesty, and throw themselves into very exposing and indecent Postures; they love to be toss'd in the Air, but some will be mightily pleased with rolling themselves, like *Swine*, in the Dirt; and others cannot be pleased except they be soundly drubb'd on their hinder Parts. There are some Colours agreeable to them, others offensive, especially *Black*; and if the Attendants have their Clothes of ungrateful Colours, they must retire out of their sight. The *Musick* with the *Dancing* which must be employ'd for their Cure, continues three or four Days; in this vigorous Exercise they *sigh*, they are full of Complaints; like Persons in drink, they almost lose the right use of their Understanding: they distinguish not their very Parents from others in their treating of them, and scarce remember any thing that is past. Some during this Exercise are mightily pleased with *green Boughs*, of *Reeds* or *Vines*, and wave them with their Hands in the Air, or dip them in the Water, or bind them about their Face or Neck; others love to be handling *red Cloths* and *naked Swords*. And there are those who, upon a little intermission of the *dancing*, fall a digging of Holes in the *Ground*, which they fill with *Water*, and then take a strange satisfaction in rolling there. When they begin to *dance*, they call for *Swords*, and act the *Fencers*; sometimes they are for a *Looking-glass*, but then they fetch many a deep Sigh at the beholding of themselves. Their Fancy sometimes leads them to *rich Clothes*, to Necklaces, to Fineries, and a variety of *Ornaments*; and they are highly courteous to the By-standers that will gratify them with any of these things; they lay them very orderly about the place where the Exercise is performed, and in *dancing*

cing please themselves with one or other of these things by turns, as their troubled Imagination directs them.

How miserable would be the Condition of Mankind, if these Animals were common in every Country! But our compassionate God has confined them to one little Corner of *Italy*; they are existing elsewhere, but no where thus venomous, except in *Apulia*. *My God, I glorify thy Compassion to sinful Mankind, in thy Restraints upon the Poisons of the* Tarantula!

But who can behold the Dispositions of the poor *Tarantulates*, and not behold at the same time with Horror, a lively Exhibition of the *Follies* whereto *vicious People* are dispesed? Perhaps the Thought well pursued would give such an Illustration of the *Venom* that besools, depraves, and enslaves *vicious People*, as to lead us into some very right Notions of the Methods, wherein the *evil Spirits*, to whose Conduct they have resign'd themselves, do, thro a just Judgment of God, operate upon them.

Vicious People, if you are not so *Tarantulated*, that it will fright you to look into a *Looking-glass*, bethink yourselves, and in the Condition of the Miserables that are stung with a *Tarantula*, behold as in a *Looking-glass* your own Behaviour and Confusion.

¶. ' That the *least* and the *worst* of the Creatures
' may do *Man* the Service of leading him to God, a
' renowned Writer has demonstrated, in singling out
' the Example of a *Toad*. A Gentleman saying, that
' in every one of the *Creatures* he could see Invitations
' to the *Praises* of G O D, one ask'd him, What! in
' a *Toad? Quomodo in Bufone potes laudare Deum?* He
' made this good Answer, *This*; *That a good God has
' advanced me above the Baseness and Venom of that con-
' temptible Animal!*'

' The Bishops who in their Travel to the Council
' of *Constance*, found a poor Country-man in the Tears
' of *Praises* to God at the sight of a *Toad*, were struck
' into

‘ into juſt Reflections, whereof this was one, *Surgunt*
‘ *Indocti, & rapiunt Cœlum.*’

ESSAY XXIX. *Of the* Fishes.

THE *Fiſhes of the Sea ſhall declare to thee!*
Let us become *Divers*, and viſit the *watery
World* ; there we ſhall ſee, as Mr. *Derham* truly ſays,
*a various, a glorious, an inexhauſtible Scene of the Divine
Power, Wiſdom, and Goodneſs.*

The *Variety* of the Creatures that are the *Inhabitants
of the Waters* is very conſiderable. *Pliny* in the ele-
venth Chapter of his thirty-ſecond Book reckons up
one hundred and ſeventy-ſix Kinds of them : indeed
he is very ſhort in his Account. Our Chriſtian *Pliny,*
the excellent *Ray*, raiſes the Number of the *Fiſhes* to
five hundred, excluding the *Shell-fiſh* ; but of the *Shell-
fiſh* more than ſix times the Number, and yet he
thinks there may be but half the Species of the *Fiſhes*
yet known to us.

If you’ll believe *Pliny* and Company, *Vera eſt vulgi
Opinio, Quicquid naſcitur in parte Naturæ ulla, & in
Mari eſſe, præterque multa quæ nuſquam alibi.*

Mr. *Willoughby* ſays *Ariſtotle*’s Diviſion of the *Fiſhes*
is the beſt, [better than *Rondelerius*’s] into three
Kinds, the *cetacious*, the *cartilaginous*, and the *ſpinous.*

He gives us a Catalogue of *ninety-three* ſeveral ſorts
of our *Engliſh Fiſhes.*

The *Shape* of their Bodies, long and ſlender, or elſe
very thin, is admirably accommodated to their Action
of *ſwimming*, wherein they are to *divide the Waters.*

The *Air-bladder*, wherewith moſt of the *Fiſhes* are
furniſhed ; this is what cannot be beheld without
Aſtoniſhment ! By this they poiſe their Bodies, and
keep them equiponderant to the Water ; without it
they would fall to the bottom, and lie groveling there,
as it has been found, when that *Wind-bladder* has been
broken. By *contracting* or *dilating* this Bladder, they are
able

able to fink or to raife themfelves at their pleafure, and continue in any depth of Water they pleafe.

Fifhes are *fenfible* of *Sounds*, but whether they *hear*, or only *feel* the *Sounds*, is very much difputed. *Athanafius Kircher* obferves, That tho the *Fifhes* that have *Lungs* have alfo *Ears*, yet by what *Organs* the hearing of the reft is performed, *à nemine adhuc penitus exploratum eft.*

Their *Fins*, made of griftly *Spokes*, connected by Membranes, like our *Fans*, and furnifhed with *Mufcles* for motion, thefe do partly ferve them for progreffion, but chiefly to hold the Body upright : when thefe are cut off, as they were by *Borelli*, they waver to and fro, and when they die, their Belly turns upwards.

The great Strength, by which they dart themfelves forward with an incredible Celerity, lies in their *Tails*; almoft the whole mufculous part of their Bodies is beftowed upon *them*, to affift the Vibration thereof. How *Fifhes* row themfelves by their *Tails*, and other Curiofities relating to *fwimming*, you may read in *Borelli's* ingenious Difcourfe *de motu Animalium.*

It is remarkable to fee how *Fifhes* have the *Center of Gravity* always placed in the fitteft part of their Bodies, which is a Point of great Confideration in their fluid Element.

Confider the *Food* of thefe Animals; they neither *chew* their Meat in their Mouths, nor *grind* it in their Maws : but in their *Stomach* they are furnifhed with a *diffolvent Liquor*, which does corrode their Food, and reduce it, Skin and Bones and all, into a *Chylus* or *Cremor*; and yet it is very marvellous, the Tafte can perceive in this Liquor nothing of *Acidity :* it will manage Flefh as *Aqua-fortis* does Metals, and yet no fenfible *Sharpnefs* in it !

But where fhall they find their Food ? *Lord, thefe wait all upon thee, that thou mayft give them their Meat in due Seafon : what thou giveft them, they gather; thou openeft*
thine

thine Hand, they are filled with Good. How rich a *Promptuary* is this unlikely Element! From the largeſt *Leviathan* which *playeth in the Seas,* to the ſmalleſt *Mite* in the Lakes and Ponds, all are plentifully provided for; as is manifeſt (which Mr. *Derham* notes) from *the Fatneſs of their Bodies, and the Gaiety of their Aſpects and Actions.*

There is a Germination of divers *aquatick Plants* in the Waters; the Waters are alſo a ſort of a *Matrix* to many Animals, particularly *Inſects,* not only ſuch as are peculiar to the Waters, but alſo many pertaining to the Air and the Land; who, by their near alliance to the Waters, delight in being about them, and ſo become a Prey to the Inhabitants thereof. Dr. *Schuyl* mentions the Horror of the *Water turned into Blood* at *Leyden,* from nothing but the infinite Swarms of *Pulices* upon it; beſides theſe, what mighty Shoals do we find of *leſſer* Animals there, which the *greater* feed upon!

What a vaſt Supply of our Food have we in *ſucking the Abundance of the Seas?* How many Millions of the *Fiſh* are every Year fetch'd out of their Element, and interr'd in the hungry Bowels of *Men?* Some of theſe very delicious, particularly the *White-fiſh,* whereof ſuch infinite Shoals in the vaſt Lakes of the *North America,* which has this very ſingular Property, that all ſorts of *Sauces* do but ſpoil it; it is always eaten, either boil'd or broil'd, without any manner of Seaſoning.

You, *Gentlemen,* who think your own Country of *England* worth viſiting with your *Travels,* as methinks you ſhould before you go abroad, find the little River *Trent* in *Staffordſhire* affording *thirty* ſeveral ſorts of *Fiſhes;* you'll be ready to affirm of it, as the *Hungarians* do of their *Tibiſcus,* two parts are *Water,* the third is *Fiſh.*

My God, when in our Neceſſities we ask of our Father a Fiſh, our heavenly Father feeds us, how agreeably, how plentifully!

As

As the *smallest* Animals are bred in the Waters, witness those in *Pepper-water*, so are the *largest*; those of the *cetaceous* Kind are there.

Pliny mentions the *Balænæ* of the *Indian Sea*, which were nine hundred and sixty Foot long; and he mentions *Whales* that were six hundred Foot long, and three hundred and sixty broad, which came into a River of *Arabia*. In the second Chapter of his ninth Book he offers a Reason why the *largest Animals* are bred in the Sea.

But I love to pass from him to a more trusty and modern *Pliny*, our industrious *Ray*; and we will now see something of his Remarks upon these *Belluæ Marinæ*: The *Tail* in these has a different position from what it has in all other *Fishes*; it lies parallel to the Horizon in these, and it is perpendicular in the rest; hereby it supplies the use of the hinder pair of *Fins*, which these Creatures lack; and it serves both to raise and sink their Body at their pleasure. It is necessary that these Creatures frequently ascend to the top of the Water to *breathe*, and therefore they should be furnished with an Organ, by which their ascent and descent might be facilitated. The turning of their Bodies in the Water they perform like the *Birds*, by the motion of one of their *Fins*, while the other is quiescent. It is very remarkable that their whole Body is compass'd round with a copious *Fat*, which we call *the Blubber*, whereby their Bodies are poised, and rendred equiponderant to the Water, and the Water also is kept off at some distance from the *Blood*, the immediate Contact whereof might else have had some chilling force upon it; it serves likewise, as our Clothes do for us, to keep the *Fish warm*, in reflecting the hot Steams of their Body, and so redoubling the Heat thereof: hence they can abide the greatest Cold of the *Northern Seas*, to which they chiefly resort, not only for the Quiet which they enjoy there, but because the *Northern Air*, which is more fully charged with the

Particles

Particles which we ſuppoſe to be *nitrous*, and that are
the Aliment of Fire, is fitteſt of all to maintain their
vital Heat in that Activity, which may be ſufficient
for to move ſuch an unwieldy Bulk as theirs.   The
ſtupendous Magnitude of theſe Animals! Thou *Antitype*
thereof, among the *Poets* which adorn our Age, de-
ſcribe them to us.

> *While the vaſt Whale takes in the Deep his place,*
> *Prince of the Waters and the finny Race;*
> *Rolling in Sport, the Billows he removes,*
> *And, like a floating Iſle, the Ocean ſhoves:*
> *Now in his weedy Court he lies at eaſe,*
> *Now ſpouts againſt the Skies exhauſted Seas.*

And yet one ſays very well concerning him; he is
minima quædam operum Dei, particula ac velut mica.
   Let what I gave you of the *nine hundred and ſixty
Foot* paſs for a *Plinyiſm*; and ſo what *Baſil* in his *Hexa-
emeron* reports of *Whales* equal in bigneſs to the greate-
eſt Mountains, let the Cenſure of *Brierwood* paſs upon
it, as *an intolerable Hyperbole:* We will write more ſo-
ber things.   Paſſing by what *Ælian* affirms of the
Whale being five times beyond the largeſt *Elephant*,
we find *Rondeletius* aſſigning him ſometimes *thirty-ſix
Cubits* of length, and *eight* of height.   *Dion* is a grave
as well as an old Writer, and he reports a *Whale* coming to Land out of the *German Ocean* ſixty Foot in
length, twenty in breadth.   But *Geſner*, a later, affirms
a *Whale* to have landed near our *Tinmouth-Haven*, in
the Year 1532, which was *ninety Foot* in length, and
the breadth of his Mouth ſix Yards and an half, and
his Belly of ſuch a compaſs, that one ſtanding on the
Fiſh, and ſlipping into his Belly, very narrowly eſcap'd
being drown'd there.
   But then, if we may take *Hartenius* for a Voucher,
among the *twenty* ſeveral Kinds of *Whales* by him enumerated, he reckons one ſort that is *thirty Ells* long,

N   and

and hath more than *seventy Teeth*, so large as to make
Handles of Knives and other Instruments. He reckons
another sort that is *forty Ells* long, and overwhelms
Vessels that come in his way. He proceeds to some
eighty Ells long, and some of *ninety*.

All these proclaiming the *Grandeur* of their *Great
Creator!*

Even in the *cold Sea* too, what a *Warmth* of Parental
Affection do the *old ones* express for their *young ones*,
and how distinguishing! When the *Seals* are hundreds
of thousands of them lying in a Bay coming out of the
Sea, they bleat like Sheep for their Young; and tho
they pass thro hundreds, yea, thousands of other
young ones before they come to *their own*, yet they
will suffer none but *their own* to suck them. *Even the
Sea-Monsters draw out the Breast, they give suck to their
young ones. Monstrous Parents, that are without natural
Affection!* These Inhabitants of the *Sea* with open
Mouth cry out against you.

¶ 'I remember a *Crassus*, of whom 'tis reported,
'that he so tamed a *Fish* in his Pond, as to make him
'come to him at his calling him; verily, I shall have
'a Soul deserving *his Name*, and be more stupid than
'the *Fish*, if I do not hear the Calls which the *Fish*
'give to me to glorify the God that made them; and
'who has in their *Variety*, in their *Multitude*, in their
'*Structures*, their *Dispositions* and *Sagacities*, display'd
'his Glories. The *Papists* have a silly and foolish Le-
'gend of their St. *Anthony* preaching to the *Fishes*; it
'will be a Discretion in me to make the reverse of the
'*Fable*, and hear the *Fishes* preaching to me, which
'they do many Truths of no small importance. As
'*mute* as they are, they are *plain* and *loud* Preachers;
'I want nothing but an *Ear* to make me a profitable
'Hearer of them.'

'It is a good Wish to be *in virtute Delphinus*, to use
'the Dispatch of the quick *Dolphin* in all good Pur-
'poses.'

'Tho

' Tho 'tis the *way of the Sea* for the *greater to devour
' the leffer,* and the Wifdom of Heaven is confpicuous
' in it; yet I deprecate this *way of all the Earth :* for
' indeed the *Fiſh,* who devour not thoſe of their own
' particular Kind, therein condemn the curſed *Rapa-
' city* too often ſeen among the Children of Men.'

' To *catch Fiſh* is an *Employment* whereby many ſup-
' port themſelves, a *Diverſion* wherewith many refreſh
' themſelves; in managing this *Fiſhery* what an oppor-
' tunity for many uſeful Reflections! In the *Means of
' Good* beſtow'd upon us, the Glorious-One does *Retia
' Salutis pandere.* How happy we, if taken in the *Nets
' of Salvation!* We are ſo when effectually perſuaded
' to the embracing of our Saviour, and of his Reli-
' gion.'

' Alas! the Miniſters of the Goſpel now *fiſh,* not
' with *Nets,* but with *Rods* ; and after long *angling,*
' and *baiting,* and *waiting,* how few are taken!'

' In the *Temptations* to *Sin* and *Vice* which are offer'd
' to me, I ſee the *Hooks* with which the Deſtroyer
' propoſes to *take* me, that I may be thrown into the
' *Perdition of ungodly Men. My God, let not the Satanick
' Baits have any Power over me!'*

' How *ſuddenly* is the *Fiſh* caught and killed, and
' with what a Surprize, when the poor Animal has
' not the leaſt thought of ſuch a Fate coming upon
' him! One moment *ſporting, taken* the next; *he*
' pull'd away, *his Fellows* not at all regarding it! He
' was a wiſe Man who long ſince took notice of this;
' *Man knoweth not his Time: As the Fiſhes that are taken
' in an evil Net, ſo are the Sons of Men. My God, help
' me to think ſeriouſly of Death every day, as not knowing
' but it may be my dying-day.'*

' At our *Tables* we are now welcome to all the *Fiſh*
' we can fairly come at, whether they have any *Fins*
' or *Scales* or no; but methinks it gives a *ſpecial reliſh*
' to the *Diſh,* 'tis a *Diſh* which my admirableS aviour
' *ſometimes taſted of.'*

ESSAY

ESSAY XXX. *Of the* FEATHERED.

THE BIRDS now invite us to *ſoar* and *ſing* with them in the Praiſes of our God.

Theſe ought immediately to follow the *Fiſhes*, not only for the *Order* of their *Creation*, but alſo becauſe, as *Baſil* notes, there is a Συγγένεια τοῖς πετ]ομένοις πρὸς τι᾽ νῆκ]α, *Volantibus Affinitas cum Natantibus.*

Theſe are either *Land-Fowl* or *Water-Fowl*. Of the *Land-Fowl* ſome have *crooked Beaks* and *Talons*, whereof ſome are *carnivorous*, called *Birds of Prey.*

And ſome are alſo *frugivorous*, called by the general Name of *Parrots.*

Others have their *Bills* and *Claws* more *ſtreight*; of which there are ſome of a *larger* Size, which cannot fly at all.

Some are of a *middle* Size, and have either a *bigger* or *longer Bill*; ſome whereof do feed promiſcuouſly, ſome only on *Fiſh*, ſome on *Inſects*: or a *ſmaller* and *ſhorter Bill*, whereof ſome have a *whiter Fleſh*, others a *blacker.*

Some are of a *leſſer* Size, called the *ſmall Birds*; which are either the *ſoft-beak'd*, that feed moſtly on *Worms* or *Flies*; or the *hard-beak'd*, that feed moſtly on *Seeds.*

The *Water-Fowl* are either ſuch as *frequent* the Waters for their Food, theſe are all *cloven-footed*, and generally have *long Legs*, and thoſe *naked* for a good way above the Knees, that they may the more conveniently wade in the Waters; or they are ſuch as do *ſwim* in the Waters, the moſt of theſe are *whole-footed*: ſome have but *three Toes* on a Foot, but moſt of them *four*; theſe either all connected by intervening *Membranes*, or more uſually with the *back Toe looſe*. Moſt *Water-Fowls* have a *ſhort Tail.*

In *Birds* the Shape and Make of their Body is incomparably adapted to their *Flight*; *before* ſharp, to
pierce

pierce and make their way thro the Air, and then ri-
sing to their *full Bulk* by gentle degrees.

Their *Feathers*, how artificially placed, for facilitating the motion of their Body! Being placed any other
way than what they are (as they would have been if
meer *Chance* had placed them) they would have gathered *Air*, and been an Incumbrance to the Passage
of their Body thro the *Air*; whereas in the neat *Order*
wherein they are now placed, they are like a Boat
new dress'd and clean'd, making its Passage thro the
Waters. At the same time they have the Security of
an admirable *Cloathing* in them, with a soft and warm
Down next to their Body, but those next to the
Weather of stronger Consistence, and closed most curiously. And then there is a most surprizing Accession to all this in the Art with which those Animals
do *preen* and *dress* their *Feathers*, and the wondrous
Oil-bag with which they are for this purpose accommodated. There is usually one *Gland* (Mr. *Willoughby*
sometimes found a couple) in which there are divers
little *Cells*, ending in two or three larger ones, which
lie under the Nipple of the *Oil-bag*; this Nipple is
perforated, and being press'd or drawn by the Bird's
Bill or Head, emits a liquid *Oil* in some, an unctuous
Grease in others, which being employ'd on their *Feathers*, contributes to their *nimble gliding* thro the Air.

How commodiously their *Wings* are placed! They
that fly much, or have most occasion for their *Wings*,
have them in the very best part imaginable, to balance
their Body in the Air, and give them a swift progression. Alter their *Equipoise*, by cutting a *Wing*, or
hanging a *Weight*, and how they reel! Such as have
as much occasion for *swimming* as for *flying*, have their
Wings therefore set a little out of the *Center* of their
Body's Gravity; and for such as have more occasion
for *diving* than for *flying*, these for that reason have
their *Legs* more backward, and their *Wings* more forward.

The

The incomparable Curiosity of every *Feather*! The *Shaft*, hollow below, that it may be the stronger and the lighter; above a *Pith* filling it, which is also both strong and light; the *Strength* marvellous! The *Vanes*, how nicely gauged! broader on one side, narrower on the other, in both contributing to the progressive motion of the Fowl, and closeness of the *Wing*. The *Vanes* of the *Flag-feathers* of the Wing, the *Edges* of the exterior bending downwards, of the interior upwards, by which means they lie close to one another when the Wing spreads, and not one *Feather* misses its *full Impulse* on the Air; yea, the very *sloping* of the Tips of these Feathers is a *Nicety* to be wondred at.

Let an Eye assisted with Glasses view the *textrine Art* of the *Plumage*, and, as Mr. *Derham*, who has given us a more particular Account of it, justly says, it will be found so exquisite, that *it cannot be viewed without Admiration!*

'My P E N, thou art fetch'd from the *Wing* of a
'Bird; thou wast one of the *Feathers*, which thou art
'now writing of! How surprizing an *Engine*! How
'surprizing, how extensive, how powerful thy *Opera-*
'*tions* in the World! Never shall my *Pen* be employ-
'ed in any thing but the Service of the glorious God,
'to whom I am indebted for it.'

Admirable the *Apparatus* of the strong, but light *Bones* in the *Wings*! The *Joints* which move so as to answer all Occasions! The Strength of the *pectoral Muscles* in *Birds* is greater than in any things not made for *flying*. *Borelli* observes, that the *pectoral Muscles* in *Men* are very small, and they don't come up to the fiftieth part of all the *Muscles*; but in *Birds* the *pectoral Muscles* are very *large, & æquant, imo excedunt, & magis pendent, quam reliqui omnes Musculi ejusdem Avis simul sumpti.* For which cause our *Willoughby* observes, that if Men would propose to prosper in their vain Project for *flying*, their *Wings* must be fastned not to their

Arms,

Arms, but their *Legs,* the *Muscles* being much ſtronger there.

The *Tail* of the Bird, which has been thought a ſort of a *Rudder,* 'tis proved by *Borelli* that this is the leaſt *uſe* of it; but it ſerves wonderfully to aſſiſt the *Aſcent* and the *Deſcent* of the Bird in the Air, and obviate the *Vacillations* of the Body and Wings.

The *Flight* performed according to the ſtricteſt Rules of *Mechaniſm!* The untaught Artiſt gives a motion to his Wings, than which the acuteſt Mathematician could not give one more agreeable.

Blind Philoſopher, canſt thou ſee no G O D in all of this?

View next the *Feet* and *Legs,* which miniſter to their other motion.

Both of them very light, for their eaſier *Tranſportation* thro the Air.

In *Water-Fowl* how exactly do their *Feet* and *Legs* correſpond to their way of living! Some of them have their *Legs* pretty long, that they may wade in the Waters, in this caſe their *Legs* are without Feathers a good way above their Knees, which is a Conveniency; their *Toes* alſo are all broad: and in the *Mudſuckers* two of the *Toes* are ſomewhat joined, that they may not eaſily ſink in walking upon boggy places. Thoſe that are *whole-footed,* or have their *Toes webbed* together, have their *Legs* generally ſhort, which for *ſwimming* is moſt convenient; and it is pretty to ſee how artificially they gather up their *Toes* and *Feet* when they go to take their Stroke, and as artificially again extend or open their *Feet* when they drive themſelves forward in the Waters.

Rapacious Birds, as they have *hooked Beaks,* thus they have ſtrong, and ſharp, and pointed *Talons,* fitted for the *Rapine* they are ſo intent upon, and for the tearing the *Fleſh* that falls into them; and, as our *Willoughby* and *Ray* obſerve, they have robuſt and brawny *Thighs,* for ſtriking down their Prey.

By

By the way; of this Kind there is a fort of *white Crows* (we muſt believe ſome who tell us this!) which they call *King-Carrion-Crows*; and it is affirmed, that when a great number of *Crows* are aſſembled about a Carcaſe, if a *King-Carrion-Crow* be among them, he falls on firſt, and none of the reſt will taſte the leaſt Morſel till he has fill'd his Belly, and is withdrawn. I hope theſe *Crows* do no hurt by breaking in upon a Paragraph that is treating upon other Matters, eſpecially if they effectually teach us, that the want of *good Manners* will never want a Condemnation.

Birds that climb, as the *Wood-pecker* Kind are, how fitted for the purpoſe! Their *Thighs* very ſtrong, their *Legs* very ſtrong, but yet very ſhort; their *Toes*, two forwards, two backwards, and ſo cloſely joined, that they may firmly lay hold on the Tree: an hard and a ſtiff *Tail*, bending downwards, on which they lean, and ſo bear themſelves up in climbing.

How conveniently are the *Legs* of *Birds* curved, for their eaſy perching, and rooſting, and reſt! And to help them up upon their Wings in taking their Flight, and then to be ſo tuck'd up to the Body, as not to obſtruct the Flight!

It is admirable that ſuch *Birds* as are *Fin-toed* are naturally directed and carried to the *Water*, and fall to ſwimming there; thus *Ducklings*, tho hatch'd and led by an *Hen*, when they come near a Pond of *Water*, in they go, tho they never ſaw ſuch a thing before, and tho the *Hen* clucks and calls, and is in a mighty Agony to keep them out, as *Pliny* expreſſes it, with *Lamenta circa Piſcinæ ſtagna, mergentibus ſe pullis, Natura duce.*

There is a conſiderable Obſervation of *Ariſtotle*, πτηνὸν μόνον ἰδέιν. There is no *Flyer* but what has *Feet* as well as *Wings*, a power of *walking* or *creeping* on the Earth; 'tis becauſe there is not always a ſufficient Food to be had for them in the *Air*, nor could the *Birds* take any reſt, for without Feet they could not perch on the Trees; and if they lit on the ground,

they

they could not again eaſily raiſe themſelves; and where could they ſit, hatch, and breed their Young? The Story of the *Bird of Paradiſe*, received even by the Learned in the former Age, is now found a *Fable;* that Bird has *Legs* and *Feet*, and thoſe great and ſtrong, and armed with *Talons*, as being a *Bird of Prey.*

The *Bill* of Birds, how ſuited for gathering *Food*, and other Uſes?

The *Eye*, how commodiouſly ſituated! (It is, by the way, a thing ſo remarkable, that nothing leſs than Aſtoniſhment can be the reſult of the Obſervation; that the *Fowls* in their Tribes have their *Centinels*, eſpecially in the Night. The Watchfulneſs of the *Scart* is true to a *Proverb:* One, by ſurprizing the *Centinel*, has caught three hundred in a Night.)

And the *Ear*, which would obſtruct the Flight of it, were it like that of other Animals; the *inner Ear*, largely deſcribed by Mr. *Derham*, is a Contrivance that is a very amazing one.

Willis admires the Points wherein the *Brain* of Birds and *Fiſhes* agrees, differing from the *Brain* of *Man* and *Beaſts.*

To *Steno* there appears *Elegans Artificis liberè agentis indicium*, in the Bifurcation of the *Aſpera Arteria* in *Birds*, which is not in other Animals, and which fits them for their *ſinging.*

In the *Swan* particularly, *Bartholin* celebrates it, as being *admirandæ Structuræ*, by which means it may continue half an Hour under Water without any danger of choaking.

Read *Blaſius* and *Coiter*, and admire the *Tongue* of the *Wood-pecker*, eſpecially the ſharp, horned, bearded *Point*, and the *glewy Matter* at the end of it, the better to ſtab and ſtick into the little *Maggots*, and to draw them out of the Wood.

The ſeveral ways the *Birds* have of purveying for their *Food*, call for our Conſideration as we go along: but how can they be conſidered without ſome ſurprize

of

of Pleasure at the view thereof. Among all these, that of the *Man-of-War Bird*, mention'd by *Dampier*, is very singularly diverting. He sees a Bird called a *Booby*, and flying at him, gives him a *Blow*, which causes him immediately to disgorge the *Fish* he has in his *Crop*; and this he seizes on, perhaps before it can in its fall reach the Earth or Water. ' 'Tis in effect ' what *Men* do to one another, when the Justice of ' Heaven uses them to make *Seizures* on one another's ' Possessions. Have not the *French* in the late and long ' Wars, been *Men-of-War Birds*, on our *English* Nation!'

Wonderful the Provision in the *Bill*, for the *judging* of the *Food!* It has peculiar *Nerves* for the purpose. These are smaller and less numerous in them that have the assistance of their *Eye*: but they are more numerous and thickly branched about, to the very end of the *Beak*, in such as hunt for their Food out of sight, in *Water*, in *Mud*, or under Ground. *Flat-billed Birds*, as Mr. *Clayton* and Dr. *Moulen* have observed, they that *grope* for their Meat have three Pair of *Nerves* that come into their Bills, whereby they accurately distinguish what may be proper for their Food.

Shall we stop a Moment, and consider how useful the *carnivorous* Birds of Prey become, even in prosecuting their voracious Inclinations? If the number of *lesser Birds* were not by their means lessened into such a Proportion, those *lesser Birds* would *overstock their feeding*; and then also, should those *lesser Birds*, which are so numerous, die of Age, they would leave their *Carcases* to rot upon the Ground, and their *Stink* would corrupt the Air, and become insupportable.

Dr. *Grew* observes, both *Birds* and *Beasts* having one common use of *Spittle*, are therefore furnish'd with the *parotid Glands*, which help to supply the Mouth with it; but the *Wood-Pecker*, and other *Birds* of that Kind, because they prey upon *Flies* which they catch with their *Tongue*, therefore in the room of the said *Glands*, they have a couple of *Bags* filled with a *viscous*

Humour;

Humour; a fort of natural *Bird-lime,* which being by fmall *Canals,* like the *Salival,* brought into their Mouths, they dip their *Tongues* in it; and with the help thereof, they attack and mafter their Prey.

Pafs from the *Mouth,* to its near Ally the *Stomach.* 'Tis admirable in its *Duplicity;* one to *foften,* another to *digeft!* Admirable in its *Variety,* fuited unto a diverfe *Diet: membranous* in fome that are *carnivorous; mufculous,* with a Strength agreeable, where *Grain* muft undergo a Comminution!

The *Gizzard* has a Faculty of *grinding;* to which purpofe the *Bird* fwallows rough *Stones,* which when grown fmooth, it throws up again as ufelefs. **Dr.** *Harvey* fays, this *grinding* may be heard in *Eagles* and fome other *Fowls,* if you lay your Ear clofe to them when their *Stomachs* are empty.

In *Birds* there is no *Maftication* or *Comminution* of the Meat in the Mouth; but in fuch as are not carnivorous, it is immediately fwallowed into the *Crop* or *Craw,* or at leaft a kind of *Ante-Stomach,* (which **Mr.** *Ray* obferved, efpecially in the *Pifcivorous*) where it is moiften'd and mollified by proper Juices, from the *Glandules* there diftilled in, then transferred from thence into the *Gizzard.*

Their *Lungs* adhere to the *Thorax,* and have little play; which is a good Provifion for their *fteady Flight.*

Wanting the *Diaphragm,* inftead of it they have diverfe *Bladders,* made of thin tranfparent *Membranes,* with pretty large Holes out of one into the other. Thefe *Membranes* contain *Air* in them, and are alfo Braces to the *Vifcera.* The *Lungs* have large Perforations, thro which the *Air* has a Paffage into the Belly. Doubtlefs the Body is hereby made more or lefs buoyant, and their *Afcent* or *Defcent* facilitated.

Their *Necks,* how proportioned unto the *Length* of their *Legs!* Indeed, they that muft fearch out their *Food* in the Waters, have them *longer* yet; and they have them fo long, that when their *Heads* are extend-
ed

ed in flight, they cause a due *Equipoise* and *Libration*
of the Body upon the *Wings.*

The Infpection of thefe Things would compel us
to confefs the glorious M A K E R of them all!

Indeed what *Steno* fays on a Defcription of a particular Subject, (the Myology of the *Eagle*) may be
more generally applied; *Non minus arida eft Legentibus,*
quam Inspectantibus jucunda. For which reafon I will
not offer the Readers too many Particularities.

The *Nidification* of *Birds*; a thing how full of Curiofity: They find out *fecure* Places, and very *proper*
ones; where their Young may lie fafe and warm, and
have their Growth promoted. But then, with what
an *artificial Elegancy* are fome of their *Nefts* prepared?
Human Skill could hardly imitate it. Among other
Curiofities of *Nidification*, I will mention one that is
obferved in *Pidgeons* of my own Country. They build
their *Nefts* with little Sticks laid athwart one another, at fuch diftances, that while they are fo near
together as to prevent the falling through of their
Eggs, they are yet fo far afunder, that the *cool Air* can
come at their *Eggs.* And the R E A S O N for this
Architecture of their *Nefts!* 'Tis this; their *Bodies* are
much *hotter* than thofe of other *Birds*; and their *Eggs*
would be perfectly addled by the *Heat* of their Bodies
in the Incubation, if the *Nefts* were not fo built, that
the *cool Air* might come at them to temper it.

We have feen the *Neft* of an *Indian Bird* compofed
of the *Fibres* of certain *Roots*, which were fo curioufly
interwoven, that it could not be beheld without Aftonifhment! Thefe *Nefts* they hang on the Ends of the
Twigs of the Trees, over the Water, to fecure their
Eggs and *Young* from the Ravage of *Apes*, and other
Beafts, that elfe would prey upon them. They are
juftly enough called *fubtle Jacks.*

And what fhall we fay of the *Flamingo's?* They
build their *Nefts* in fhallow *Ponds*, where there is
much *Mud*; which they ferape together into little
Hillocks,

Hillocks, like *Iſlands*, appearing out of the Water about a Foot and a half high from the Bottom. They make the Foundation of theſe Hillocks broad, bringing them up tapering to the Top, where they leave a ſmall hollow Pit, which they lay their *Eggs* in; and when they either lay or hatch their *Eggs*, they ſtand all the while, not *on* the *Hillock*, but cloſe *by* it, with their *Legs* on the ground, and in the Water, reſting themſelves on the Hillock, and covering the hollow *Neſt* upon it with their Bodies. Their *Legs* are very long, and building as they do upon the ground, they could neither draw their *Legs* conveniently into their *Neſts*, nor *ſit* down upon them otherwiſe than by reſting their whole Bodies to the prejudice of their *Eggs* or Young, were it not for this rare Contrivance. [Pſal. lxxxiv. 3.]

The *Incubation*, for which this Tribe of *Animals* is remarkable, opens a *new Scene* of Wonders unto us. The *Egg* with its cruſty Coat is admirably fitted for it. Here we find one part provided for the *Formation* of the Body before 'tis grown to any conſiderable Dimenſions, another for its *Nouriſhment* afterwards, till the *Bird* be able to ſhift for itſelf.

Willoughby confirms that Obſervation of *Pliny*, *Ipſum Animal ex albo Liquore Ovi corporatur : Cibus ejus in Luteo eſt.*

But then the accurate *bracing* of theſe parts, by which they are kept in their due place, Mr. *Derham* obſerves, muſt be a *deſign'd*, as well as it is a *curious* piece of Workmanſhip. They are ſeparated by *Membranes*. The *Chalazæ*, (which becauſe formerly thought the *Sperm* of the *Cock*, were called the *Treddles*,) are, as *Harvey* ſays, *As it were the Poles of this Microcoſm*, *and the Connexions of the Membranes*. But as Mr. *Derham* obſerves, they ſerve only to keep one and the ſame part of the *Yolk* always uppermoſt, let the *Egg* be turned which way it will. The *Chalazæ*, it ſeems, are ſpecifically *lighter* than the *Whites* in which they

ſwim;

swim; and being braced unto the Membrane of the *Yolk*, not exactly in the *Axis* of the *Yolk*, but somewhat out of it, it causes one side of the *Yolk* to be heavier than the other: so that the *Yolk* being by the *Chalazæ* made buoyant, and kept swimming in the midst of the two *Whites*, is by its own heavy side kept with the same side always uppermost, and probably this *uppermost side* is that on which lies the *Cicatricula.*

It is affirmed, that our *Hens* once in every day of their Incubation *turn* their *Eggs*, without ever turning of one more than once, or leaving any one unturn'd. This is for a Service which they understand not themselves.

The Conveyance of what *Colours* we please to the Fowl that is hatching, by our painting of the *Eggs*, is a Curiosity.

That *Birds* must lay *Eggs*, is a sensible Argument of a *Divine Providence*, designing to preserve them, and secure them, that there might be a greater plenty of them, and that the *Destroyers* might not straiten their Generations. Had they been *viviparous*, if they had brought forth a *great number* at a time, the burden of their Womb would have rendred them so heavy, their *Wings* could not well have served them: or if they had brought forth but *one or two* at a time, they would have been troubled all the Year long with bearing or feeding their Young. The Conveniency consulted in *oviparous* Animals, is one of Dr. *More*'s Triumphs over *Atheism*. Of these *Eggs* he makes an *Antidote* against that hellish Poison!

Dr. *Cheyne* will more particularly assure us, *We know* that the *Eggs* of *Animals* are only an *Uterus* for a little *Animal*, furnished with proper *Food*, and fenced from external Injuries: and *we know* likewise that all the Effects of *Incubation* are only to supply a proper degree of *Heat*, which may make the congealed *Fluids* to flow, and more easily pass into the nourishing Channels of the

the included *Animalcule.* On this occaſion he goes on, *We are ſure* that all the *Transformations* of *Inſects* and other *Animals*, are nothing but the *Expanſion* of their Parts, and the breaking of the *Membranes* that folded them up by the Augmentation of theſe Parts; and all the ſeveral *Figures* they put on, are owing to the ſeveral *Membranes* in which they are involved. His Concluſion is what I was wiſhing for: *It is impoſſible duly to conſider theſe things, without being wrapt into Admiration of the infinite Wiſdom of the Divine Architect, and contemning the arrogant Pretences of the World-wrights, and much more the Production of Chance and juſtling Atoms.*

As Mr. *Derham* obſerves, what a *prodigious Inſtinct* is it, that *Birds,* and only *they,* ſhould betake themſelves to *this way* of *Generation!* How ſhould they be aware that their *Eggs* contain their *Young,* and that they have in their power the *Production* of them? What ſhould move them to betake themſelves to their *Neſts,* and there with *Delight* and *Patience* abide the *due number* of Days? And when their *Chickens* are hatched, how ſurprizing is their *Art,* and *Care,* and *Paſſion,* in bringing them on *until,* and only *until,* they are able to ſhift for themſelves.

A Remark of our valuable *Ray* is worthy to be introduced here. It would be on many accounts inconvenient for *Birds* to *give ſuck* ; and yet no leſs inconvenient, if not altogether deſtructive unto the *Chicken,* upon Excluſion all of a ſudden, to make ſo great a change in its *Diet,* as to paſs from a *Liquid* unto a *harder Food,* before the *Stomach* be conſolidated, and by uſe habituated unto the concocting of it, and its tender and pappy Fleſh fitted to be nouriſhed by what ſhall be *ſtrong* and *ſolid* ; and before the *Bird* be by little and little accuſtomed to the uſing of his *Bill* in the gathering of it up, to which it comes not very readily : therefore there is a large *Yolk* provided in every *Egg,* a great part whereof remains after the *Chicken* is hatched, and is incloſed in its Belly, and

by

by a *Channel* made on purpose, receiv'd by degrees into the *Guts*, and serves inftead of *Milk*, to nourifh the *Chicken* for a confiderable time; which neverthelefs in the mean time feeds itfelf by the *Mouth*, a little at a time, and gradually more and more, as it gets a more perfect Ability.

I will add a Curiofity relating to the *Pidgeons*, which annually vifit my own Country in their *Seafons*, in fuch incredible numbers, that they have commonly been fold for *Two-pence* a dozen; yea, one Man has at one time furprized no lefs than *two hundred dozen* in his Barn, into which they have come for Food, and by fhutting the door, he has had them all. Among thefe *Pidgeons*, the *Cocks* take care of the *young* ones for one part of the day, and the *Hens* for the other. When they are taken, we generally take but *one Sex* at a time. In the Crops of the *Cocks*, we find about the quantity of half a Gill of a Subftance like a tender *Cheefe-Curd*: the *Hens* have it not. This *Curd* flows naturally into their *Crops*, as *Milk* does into the *Dugs* of other Creatures. The *Hens* could not keep their *young* ones alive when firft hatched; but the *Cocks* do fetch up this *thickned Milk*, and throw it into the Bills of their *young* ones, which are fo nourifhed with it, that they grow fafter, and fly fooner than any other Bird among us. None but the *Cocks* which have young ones to care for, have this *Curd* found in their *Crops*. Kill one of thofe *Cocks*, and all the young ones pine away to death in the *Neft*, nowithftanding all that their *Dams* can do for them. See Sirs, and be inftructed!

> *Mafculus ipfe fovet Fœtus, atque incubat Ovis;*
> *Conjugii fervat fœdera cafta fui.*

All Birds lay a *certain number* of *Eggs*, or near that number, and then betake themfelves to their *Incubation*: but if their *Eggs* be withdrawn, they will
then

then lay more. When they have laid ſuch a number
of *Eggs*, as they can conveniently cover, and brood,
and hatch, they give over, and begin to *ſit*. This is
not becauſe they are neceſſarily *determined* to ſuch a
number: For *Hens*, for example, if you let their *Eggs*
alone, when they have laid *fourteen* or *fifteen*, they
will give over, and begin to *ſit*; whereas if you daily
take away their *Eggs*, they will go on to lay five
times that number! This holds not only in *domeſtick*
Birds; and ſo, as Mr. *Ray* obſerves, it can't be thought
the effect of *Cicuration* and *Inſtitution*: But the like
was by Dr. *Liſter* obſerved in *Swallows* too.

But altho almoſt the whole Tribe of *Birds*, do produce their Young by *Incubation*, there is a marvellous
Deviation from it in ſome few Families which do it in
a more *novercal way*, and without any trouble at all,
only by laying their *Eggs* in the *Sand*, expoſed unto
the *Heat* of the Sun. This Inſtinct of the *Oſtrich* particularly, *who leaveth her Eggs in the Earth, and warm-
eth them in the Duſt*, is aſcribed unto G O D, who
ſupplies the want of Concern in the *Parent-Animal*
another way.

It is a ſurprizing thing, which the obſerving *Ray*
has mentioned. Such *oviparous* Creatures as are long-
lived, have *Eggs* enough at firſt conceived in them, to
ſerve them for many years laying; probably for as
many as they are to live: allowing ſuch a proportion
for every year, as will ſerve one or two *Incubations*.
But *Inſects* which are to breed but once, lay all their
Eggs at once, have they ever ſo many. He ſays moſt
juſtly, *Chance cannot govern it.*

The Scarcity of the *voracious* and *pernicious* Birds,
and the Plenty of the *manſuete*, and *uſeful*, and more
deſirable, is to go among the Matters of our Wonderment!

And ſo muſt the *ſwift Motion* of ſuch whoſe Food is
to be ſought in diſtant Places, and in different Seaſons;
the *ſlow Motion* and ſhort Flight of others more *dome·*

O

ſtick;

stick; and the Awkwardness of some to *Flight*, whose *Food* is to be got near at hand, and without much *flying* for it.

It is amazing, *Who feeds the young Ravens when they cry!* —— That *Birds* which feed their Young in the *Nest*, tho probably they cannot *count the Number* of them, and tho they bring but *one Morsel* of Meat at a time, and tho they have not fewer it may be than seven or eight *young* in a *Nest* together, which at the return of their Dams do *all at once*, and with equal greediness, hold up their Heads and gape, yet they forget not one of them, they feed them all. Our good *Ray* notes well, *'Tis beyond the possibility of a meer Machine to perform such a thing as this!*

With what an impetuous desire of *sitting* are the *Birds* inspired, while it is called for! After the Young are *hatch'd*, for some time they do almost constantly *brood* them under their Wings, lest they should suffer by any Inclemency of the Season; all this while how hard they labour to get them *Food!* *sparing* it out of their own Bellies, almost *pining* themselves to death rather than that their Young should want any thing! With what *Courage* are they inspired in this time, to venture their very Lives in defence of them, and even fly in the Face of a *Man* that shall molest their *Young*, (as a *Hen* or a *Goose* will do) which they would never do in their own defence! These things are contrary to the Instinct of *Self-preservation*, and are eminent Pieces of *Self-denial*. Our good *Ray* says well, *They must needs be the Works of Providence for the upholding of the World!* These *Pains* are bestowed upon a thing which takes *no notice* of it, makes *no amends* for it, never acknowledges it with 'Thankfulness; and when the *young* one is grown *old* enough to shift for itself, the ευγη is gone! The *old* one takes no further care of it, will beat it indifferently with such as it is not at all related to! The words of Mr. *Robinson* on this Occasion are agreeable: 'She does she *knows not what*, but 'yet

' yet it is what *ought to be done* by the most *exquisite*
' *Knowledge*; hence it is conclusive, that something
' else has *Knowledge* for her, even the *Creator* and *Con-*
' *triver* of all things, who is the omniscient and omni-
' potent God.' At the same time how remarkable to
see, that *Poultry* and *Partridge*, and other Birds, at the
first sight know the *Birds of Prey*, and make a *Sign* of it
with a peculiar *Note* to their *young* ones, who thereon
hide themselves.

We celebrate the *Dove* of *Archytas*, whereof *Gellius*
tells us, *Simulachrum Columbæ è ligno ab Archyta, ratione*
quadam, disciplinâque mechanica factam, volasse; the
same whom we find celebrated by *Horace* for a noble
Geometrician. This *Dove* surely had more Geometry
in it than the πλαταγὴ, or *Childrens Rattle*, for which
Aristotle celebrates him, as the Inventor of it. We
are surprized at what *Ramus* tells us of the *Wooden-*
Eagle and the *Iron-Fly*, made by *Regiomontanus;* the
former of which flew forth of the City, met the Emperor a good way off, saluted him, and returned with
him; the latter, at a Feast, whereto he invited his
Friends, flew out of his Hand, fetch'd a round, and
flew back to him again before the astonish'd Beholders.
Du Bartas employ'd his *Poetry* on these Curiosities.

But what! No *Honours*, no *Praises* due to that infinite G O D, who hath with so much Art contrived
all the Variety of *Birds*, and accommodated every part
of them within and without after so rare a manner,
that there is not so much as a *Feather* misplaced, redundant, or defective! *Austin* says well, *Deus non solum*
Angelum & Hominem, sed nec exigui & contemptibilis ani-
mantis viscera, nec Avis pennulam, nec Herbæ flosculum, sine
suarum partium convenientia dereliquit.

In the xivth of *Deuteronomy* there is a *Bird* called
Racham, which signifies *Mercy.* The *Talmudists* have
a Saying, That when this *Bird* appears, the *Mercy* of
God and His *Messiah* is then coming to the World.
Verily, in every *Bird* that flies into our World, there

is

is a display of the Divine *Goodness*, as well as *Power* and *Wisdom*. I wish that, in the reigning Dispositions of *Benignity* and *Compassion* among Mankind, *Racham* were making her Appearance!

Our excellent *Cosmologer* makes his religious Remark upon it, 'That the *Birds* (and so the *Beasts*) which are *domestick*, or the most *useful*, are the most *prolifick*; there are more *Hens* than *Kites*, more *Geese* than *Swans*. A *Crane*, which is but scurvy Meat, hatches no more than *two Eggs* in a Year; several *Sea-Fowls* but one. The *Pheasant* and *Partridge*, excellent Meat, and easily come at, hatch fifteen or twenty. The more valuable, which lay *fewer* at a time, sit the *oftner*, as the *Dove*. Thus, if it were not out of place to observe it here, there are more *Dogs* than *Foxes*; more *Cats* than *Lions*. The *Sheep* feeds and breeds in all Countries much alike.

Of *Wild-Fowl*, those which are the most *useful*, fly not singly, but are *gregarious*, which renders them the more *visible* and *audible* to us, and the more *plentiful* Game. And for our more quiet possession of things that are most *useful*, they are *naturally marked*, when there is occasion for it. *Wild-fowl*, and *Fishes*, and other Creatures, which are not fitted by Nature to be any Man's *Propriety*, have only such distinguishing Marks as belong to the whole *Species*; but of the *domestick*, as *Poultry*, *Horses*, *Dogs* and *Cats*, not only the *Species*, but the *Individuals* have their Marks. The *Sheep*, which are *proprietary*, if not so *marked*, it is compensated in this, that they do not *straggle*.

¶. 'My Great Saviour has given me this Direction, 'Matth. vi. 26. *Consider the Fowls of the Air.*'

'But is it possible to *consider* them without continual *Wonders* at the Divine *Workmanship* appearing 'in them! *Wonders* to be articulated and modulated 'into endless *Praises* of their Glorious Creator! Methinks the *sweet Notes* uttered by many *Tribes* of 'them invite me into a *Consort* with them.'

'I

' I know not what well to make of a Relation pub-
' lifhed a few Years ago, but fo well attefted, that
' a pious and worthy Man wrote a large Treatife up-
' on it, entitled, *Vox Corvi!* which affirms, 'That a
' *Raven* perching on the top of a Steeple, and thence
' turning towards a quarrelfome Neighbourhood, was
' heard very audibly and articulately to utter thefe
' Words, *Look into the third of the* Coloffians, *and the*
' *fixteenth:* But this I know, *Ask the Fowls of the Air,*
' *and they fhall tell thee.* There needs no *Genius* to take
' a poffeffion of our *Birds,* that we may hear from
' them the Admonitions of *Piety,* and Exhortations
' *to believe and adore an infinite* GOD intelligibly
' enough proceeding from them.'

' It was a celebrated Speech of the Philofopher, *Si*
' *Lufcinia effem, ut Lufcinia canerem;* I can *fly* much
' *higher* than they, and if I praife their Glorious Cre-
' ator, I fhall *fing* much *better* than they; *Homo fum,*
' *atque ut Homo canam colamque.*'

' The *Providence* of the Glorious GOD, in the
' Propagation and Suftentation of the *Fowls,* 'tis ad-
' mirable; it extends to *Ravens,* to *Sparrows;* and fhall
' I imagine *myfelf* excluded from the Care of that *Pro-*
' *vidence!* Holy Mr. *Dod* ventur'd upon the Difficulties
' and Contingences of a *married Life,* when he faw the
' *Hen* with her *Chickens* provided for. O *Unbelief,* I
' command an *eternal Silence* to thee! Shall the *Birds*
' *of Seafon* bring with them a Condemnation of my *In-*
' *advertency,* to my fitteft *Opportunities* for the doing
' and the getting of Good!'

' There are the *Images* of many *Virtues* in *Birds,*
' (which have been called *Simulachra Virtutum*) of
' which I would endeavour an Imitation, and therein
' glorify the God that fpeaks to me by them; among
' thefe I would efpecially pitch upon two. Teach
' me, O *Stork,* how *gratefully* to treat my *Parent;* fhew
' me, O *Dove,* how *lovingly* to treat my *Confort.*'

Of

Of fuch Reflections a famous Philofopher fays truly, *Rectis animis non poterunt non effe grata, licet perverfis ridicula videantur.*

The Man who learns all the Good which the *Birds* may mind him of, and then lives to the G O D, whofe *Work* and whofe *Voice* he difcerns in the *Birds*, this *Man* fhall be a *Phœnix*, and the Traditions of the Antients no longer a *Fable.*

ESSAY XXXI. *Of the* FOUR-FOOTED.

WE proceed to the *Animals* that are perfect, hairy, and *walking upon four.*

Thefe Quadrupeds are either *hoofed* or *clawed.*

Of the *hoofed* or *ungulate;* fome are *whole-hoofed,* whereof 'tis obferv'd that none have Horns, nor have the Males any appearance of Breafts: there are four forts of thefe.

Others are *cloven-footed;* of thefe there are two Divifions.

There is the *Bifulcate* Kind, which is alfo fubdivided.

There are the *Ruminant.*

Some of thefe have *perpetual Horns.*

Whereof there are fix of the *Bull-kind,* five of the *Sheep-kind,* eleven of the *Goat-kind.*

Others have *deciduous Horns;* thefe are the *Deer-kind,* whereof eight forts have been reckon'd up.

Of thofe who do not *chew the Cud,* there is only the *Swine-kind,* whereof there are five forts reckon'd up.

And then there is the Kind whofe *Hoof* is cloven into *four Divifions;* we know five of thefe, but we know no *Rumination* in any of them.

Of the *clawed* or *digitate;* there is one fort whofe Claws adhere to one another, cover'd with one common Skin, but with obtufe Nails, that ftick out round the margin of the Foot; this is the *Elephant,* who muft pafs for *anomalous.*

There

There is another fort, which has only two Claws; namely, the *Camels*, which, tho they have no *Horns*, do ruminate, and have the *four Stomachs* of the *horned Ruminants.*

A third fort includes thofe which the *Greeks* call Ἀνθρωπόμορφα, whofe Foot is divided into *many Claws*, with broad Nails on them: this is the *Ape-kind*, whereof there is a great variety; nine or ten Kinds have been defcribed by the Naturalifts.

A fourth fort is of thofe which have *many Claws*, yet they are not cover'd at the end with broad flat Nails, but have them rather like *Talons*, crooked and pointed; thefe had beft be diftinguifh'd by their *Teeth.*

Some of thefe have many *cutting Teeth* in each of their Jaws; of thefe there is a *greater* fort, which either have a *fhort round Head*, as the *Cat-kind*, whereof there are *feven* forts; and I hope the *Lion* will not be offended if *he* be reckon'd among them: or they have a *long Snout*, as the *Dog-kind*, whereof there are thirteen or fourteen forts; and among thefe there are Varieties of *Mungrels*, and hebricious Breeds: and there is alfo a *leffer* fort, which have a long and flender Body, with *fhort Legs*; thefe are the *Weafel-kind*, and there are about eight forts of them.

Others of thefe have only *two* large remarkable *Teeth* in each of their Jaws; thefe are the *Hare-kind*, which live mainly on *Plants* and *Fruits*; and there are about half a fcore forts of them.

To thefe Kinds of *Quadrupeds* there muft be added feveral that are *anomalous.*

Some have a *long Snout*, with Feet which are divided into *many Claws*, and are furnifh'd *with Teeth*; there are eight or nine forts of thefe, whereof the *Hedge-hog* is in the Van.

Others of thefe are deftitute of *Teeth*, and there are two forts of thefe.

There are *Quadrupeds* that are *Flyers* too, as the *Bat-kind*, whereof there are different Forms.

There

There is one very odd Anomale, which has but three Claws on each of his *four Feet*, and has a Name-ſake too often among them that go *not upon four*; 'tis the *Ignavus*, a *Sloth* we call it: he takes eight or nine Minutes to move one of his Feet three or four Inches; and when he has grown fat and plump with eating all the Leaves on a Tree, he will be Skin and Bone before he reach another, which will be five or ſix Days, tho' it may be very near the former.

There are alſo viviparous and ſanguineous Quadrupeds, breathing with Lungs, but having only one Ventricle in their Hearts; to theſe we may add the *Tortoiſe*, whereof there are many Species, tho they be rather *oviparous*.

But then there are ſome *oviparous* Quadrupeds, which have a long Tail, horizontally ſtretched out; theſe are the *Lizard-kind*, and there be fourteen ſeveral ſorts of them.

The *French* Gentleman who writes *A Demonſtration of the Exiſtence of G O D from the Knowledge of Nature*, makes this Remark: 'All the Animals owe their 'Birth to a certain Male and Female of their Species. 'All thoſe different Species are preſerved much the 'ſame in all Ages. We do not find that for three 'thouſand Years paſt any one has periſhed or ceaſed; 'neither do we find that any one multiplies to ſuch 'an Exceſs, as to be a Nuſance or Inconvenience to 'the reſt.'

And now ſince we are upon the *four-footed*, the Remarkables in their *Legs* and *Feet* may be thoſe which we may agreeably enough *begin* upon.

The *prone Poſture of the Body* in the *Quadrupeds* is not only moſt beneficial to themſelves, but alſo moſt advantageous to *Man*; they perform their own Actions the better for that Poſture, and they ſerve Man the better, both for *Carriage* and for *Tillage*.

But then it's obſervable how exactly their *Legs* are made conformable to this Poſture.

It

It invites yet more Obfervation, how admirably their *Legs* and *Feet* fuit the Exercifes of every Animal.

The *Elephant*, a Creature of prodigious Weight, has *Legs*, as *Pliny* notes, like *Pillars* rather than *Legs*.

The *Deer*, and the *Hare*, and other Creatures of a fingular *Swiftnefs*, have their *Legs* accordingly flender ; but they have therewithal an incredible *Strength* adapted to their *Swiftnefs*.

Some have their *Feet* made only for *walking* and *running*, but fome have them for *swimming* too.

The *Toes* on the Feet of the *Otter* are all conjoined with *Membranes*, and in *fwimming*, when the *Foot* goes forward in the Water, the *Toes* are clofe ; but when backward, they are fpread out ; whereby they more forcibly ftrike the Water, and are driven forward. The *French Academifts* are furprized at the extraordinary Structure in the *Feet* of the *Bever :* their *hindmoft* Feet, like thofe of a *Goofe*, are more proper to *fwim* than to *walk* with ; but their *foremoft* are like *Hands* rather than *Feet*, and wondroufly fuit their Occafions.

Some, as the *Moles*, have their *Feet* for *walking*, and for *digging*.

Some, as the *Bats*, for *walking*, and for *flying* too.

In fome the *Feet* are more lax and weak, for the plainer Lands ; but others have them ftiff, and lefs flexible ; their Joints hardly difcernible, as the *Elks*, and the *Goats*, which are to traverfe the Ice, or to pafs over the dangerous Precipices of the Mountains.

In fome the *Feet* are fhod with tough and hard *Hoofs*, (either whole or cleft, as there is moft occafion) in others they have only a *callous Skin.*

And here 'tis admirable to fee how their *Toes* are fupplied, according to their feveral Conveniences.

The Structure of the *Bones* in *Quadrupeds* would be a mighty large Field for Curiofity and Admiration.

Galen remark'd a fingular Provifion of Nature for the *Strength* of the *Lion*, that his *Bones* are much more *folid* than thofe of other Animals.

Mr.

Mr. *Ray* enquiring how so many Animals do to bear up against the extremest Rigor of the *Cold*, he notes, that the Extremities of their *Toes* are fenced with *Hoofs*, which in a good measure secure them : he adds, the main thing is, that the *Cold* is its own Antidote; for the Air being fully charged and sated with nitrous, or some other sort of Particles, (which are the great Efficients of *Cold*, and no less also the Pabulum for *Fire*) when it is inspired it causes a great Accension in the Blood (as we see the *Fire* burns fiercely in such Weather) as enables it to a vigorous resistance of the *Cold.*

The *defensive Armour* given to some Creatures, with the Skill to use it, how admirable! The *Hedge-hog*, filled with sharp and strong Prickles, has also a Muscle given him on purpose, which enables him to contract himself into a *globular Figure*, and so inclose himself in his Thicket, that his rapacious Enemies cannot lay hold upon him. *Olaus Borrichius* is amazed at the wondrous Fabrick of that Muscle. The *Armadilla*, described by *Marcgrave*, is covered with a strong, hard, scaly Crust or Shell, of a boney Substance, with four transverse Commissures in the middle of the Body, connected by tough Membranes. By a *peculiar Muscle* he brings his Tail to his Head, and so gathers himself into a round Ball, that there is nothing to be seen but his *Armature :* had such a Muscle been given to any Animal covered with soft Hair or Fur, there might have been a pretence to fancy that this was accidental and undesigned ; but seeing there is not one Instance of this kind, Mr. *Ray* very justly says, *It must be great Stupidity to believe it, and Impudence to assert it.*

Let us pass to the *Head.* The Head of *Man* is of one singular Form. In the *Four-footed* the Form of the *Head* is almost as various as the Species, in some square and large, suitable to their Food, Motion, and Abode; in others more small, more sharp, and more slender, still to suit those purposes. How surprizingly

zingly is the *Head* and the *Neck* of the *Swine* adapted
for his rooting in the *Earth!* How the Neck, Nose,
Eyes and Ears of the *Mole*, adapted in the nicest manner to its way of subterraneous living! The strong
Snout of the *Swine*, such that he may sufficiently thrust
it into the Ground, where his Living lies, without
hurting his Eyes; and of so sagacious a Scent, that
we employ them to hunt for us; and even his *wallow-
ing in the Mire,* is a wise Contrivance for the Suffocation
of troublesome Insects! The *Mole* so shaped, that our
Doctor *More* makes this Creature a notable Ingredient
in the Composition of his *Antidote against Atheism*; even
his want of a *Tail* is a considerable Contrivance for his
advantage.

The *Brain* of *Quadrupeds* obliges us to employ *ours*
in a particular Contemplation of it; it is larger in *us*
than in *them*, no doubt for the Accommodation of a
nobler Guest, which we entertain in ours: but an exact Anatomist of that Part, the famous Dr. *Willis*, has
led us more particularly to contemplate the Situation
of it. In *Man*, to whom God has given a *lofty Coun-
tenance*, with a Capacity to think on *heavenly things*, the
Brain is placed above the *Cerebellum*, and all the Sen-
sories; in *Brutes*, whose *Brain* is incapable of Speculation, the *Cerebellum*, whose Business it is to minister
to the Actions and Functions of the *Præcordia* (the
principal Office in those Creatures) is above the
Brain, and the Eyes and Ears are placed at least equal
to it: moreover, in the Head of *Man* the *Base* of the
Brain and *Cerebell* is parallel to the *Horizon*, by which
means there is less danger of their jogging or slipping
out of their place; but in *Brutes*, whose Head hangs
down, the *Base* of the Skull makes a *right Angle* with
the Horizon; and yet lest the *Cerebell* should be un-
steady, and the frequent Concussions thereof should
cause disorderly motions of the Spirits about the *Præcordia*, there is a sufficient provision made by the Artifice of Nature, by the *Dura Meninx* closely encom-
passing

paſſing of it; beſides which, it has alſo in ſome a ſtrong boney *Fence* about it.

The *carotid Arteries* paſſing thro the Skull of *Quadrupeds*, and their branching into the *Rete mirabile*, and ſome other ſuch things, are particular Accommodations to their Circumſtances, to prevent a too rapid Incurſion of *Blood* into the *Brains* of Creatures that hang down ſo much.

At the great Aperture of the Shell in a *Tortoiſe*, there is at the top a raiſed Border, to grant a liberty to the *Neck* and Head, for the lifting of himſelf upwards; and this Inflection of the *Neck* is of great uſe to him, for without it he would be unable to turn himſelf when thrown upon his Back. The *French Academiſts* look'd upon the Contrivance as a ſurprizing one!

The Varieties in the inner and outer *Ear* of *Animals* entertained Dr. *Grew* with obſervable Curioſities. In an *Owl*, that perches *above*, and hearkens after her Prey *below*, it is produced *further* out above than it is below, that ſo the leaſt Sound from that Quarter may be the more eaſily received; but in a *Fox* that ſcouts *underneath*, it is for the ſame reaſon produced further out *below*. In a *Polecat*, which hearkens directly forward, it is produced *behind*, for the taking of a forward Sound; but an *Hare*, which is very quick of hearing, and thinks of nothing but being purſued, has a *boney Tube*, a natural *Otacouſtick*, ſo directed *backward*, as to receive the ſmalleſt and fartheſt Sound that comes behind it; and in an *Horſe*, which receives the Sound of the Driver behind, the Paſſage into the Ear is like that of the *Hare*.

It is remarkable that in *Quadrupeds* the *Necks* are commenſurate to the *Legs*; the equality in the length of their *Necks* and their *Legs* is moſt remarkably ſeen in Beaſts that feed conſtantly upon *Graſs*. But that which is yet more ſurprizing, is, that in that ſort of Creatures which muſt needs hold their *Heads* down in

an

an *inclining Poſture* for a conſiderable while together, which would be very painful to the *Muſcles*, on each ſide the Ridge of the Vertebres of the *Neck*, Nature hath placed an ἀτονεύρωσις, or *nervous Ligament*, very thick and ſtrong, and apt to ſtretch, and ſhrink again, as need requires, and void of Senſe, extending from the *Head* (to which and the next Vertebres of the *Neck* it is faſtned at the end) to the middle Vertebres of the *Back* (to which it is knit at the other end) for the aſſiſting of them to ſupport the Head in that poſture; it is by the Vulgar called *the Whitleather.*

Indeed this Proportion is not kept in the *Elephant,* he has a *ſhort Neck,* the exceſſive Weight of his Head and his 'Teeth to a *long Neck* would have been unſupportable; but then his *Proboſcis!* *Tully* takes notice, *Manus data Elephantis, quia propter Magnitudinem Corporis, difficiles aditus habebant ad Paſtum.* He is provided with a *Trunk,* wherewith, as with an *Hand,* he takes up his Food, and his Drink, and brings it to his *Mouth;* a Member ſo admirably contrived, that Mr. *Derham* has juſt occaſion to ſay, *'tis a manifeſt Inſtance of the Creator's Workmanſhip.*

Galen obſerving the *Necks* of Animals, how accommodated to their feeding, is not able to forbear his Acclamations of an *Opus Artificis Utilitatis memoris!* He goes on with his Contemplation, and adds, as we cannot but alſo do, *Quo pacto non id etiam eſt admirandum!*

On the mention of the *Elephant,* we will introduce a particular Curioſity relating to him; he has no *Epiglottis,* becauſe there is no danger of any thing falling into his Lungs from eating or drinking, ſeeing there is in him no Communication between the *Oeſophagus* and the Paſſage into the *Lungs;* the Paſſage to the Ventricle is thro the Tongue, an Hole near the Root of it is the beginning of the *Oeſophagus,* and the Paſſage of the Air into the Mouth is quite ſtopped up; however, he is not ſufficiently ſecured from ſmall Ani-

mals

mals that may creep in and murder him; a *Mouſe*
creeping up his *Proboſcis*, might get into his *Lungs*,
and ſo ſtifle him: gueſs now the reaſon why an *Elephant* is ſo afraid of a *Mouſe!* To avoid this danger,
when he ſleeps he keeps his *Proboſcis* cloſe to the
ground, that nothing but *Air* could get in.　Mr. *Ray*
celebrates this as a rare Sagacity!

The *Stomach* of *Quadrupeds!* How adapted to the
various Food intended for it! One kind of *Stomach* in
the *Carnivorous*, another in the *Herbaceous!*

The peculiar Contrivance on the *Stomach* of the
Camel deſerves our Pauſe upon it; the words of the
Pariſian Anatomiſts upon it, are, *At the top of the ſecond
of the four Ventricles there are ſeveral ſquare Holes, which
were the Orifices of about twenty Cavities, made like Sacks,
placed between two Membranes, which do compoſe the Subſtance of this Ventricle; the view of theſe Sacks made us
think that they might well be the Reſervatories, where* Pliny
*ſaith that Camels do a long time keep the Water, which they
drink in great abundance, to ſupply the want thereof in the
dry Deſarts.*

In ſome of the *Quadrupeds* the *Stomach* is fitted for a
Digeſtion upon bare *Maſtication*; but in others there is
a whole Set of *Stomachs*, to digeſt with the help of *Rumination.* Mr. *Derham* is very ſenſibly affected with
the curious Artifice of Nature here; but for the
whole Buſineſs of *Rumination*, the learned *Peyerus* will
give you a very affecting Entertainment in his *Meryco-
logia, ſeu, de Ruminantibus & Ruminatione Commenta-
rius.*

Dr. *Grew* obſerves, all *carnivorous Animals* have the
ſmalleſt Ventricles, *Fleſh* going fartheſt; thoſe that
feed on *Fruits* and *Roots* have them of a middle ſize;
Sheep and *Oxen*, which feed on *Graſs*, have the *greateſt*;
yet the *Horſe*, tho graminivorous, has comparatively
but a little one, for that he is made for *Labour*: the
ſame is to be ſaid of the *Hare*, which is made for *Motion*, for which the moſt eaſy *Reſpiration* and the moſt
free

free play of the *Diaphragm* is requisite, and that could not be if the *Stomach* were very big and cumbersome upon it.

There are *domestick Animals* which look up to me for their *Food*, sometimes for the *Crumbs* that fall from my *Table*; I will consider myself as doing the part of a *Steward* for the Glorious G O D in feeding them; it shall be done with an *holy Delight*, and with such an Inference drawn from it as this: *And will not the Glorious G O D graciously and readily grant the Mercy which I look up to Him to bestow upon me!*

The Food of the *Castor* is generally of *dry things*, and such as are hard of digestion; and now there is a wonderful provision made in the *Stomach* of that Creature, by a *digestive Juice*, lodg'd in the curious little Cells of it; the admirable Structure and Order thereof is described by *Blasius* out of *Wepfer*, and then he adds, *Nimirum quià Castoris alimentum ex succum & coctu difficilimum est, sapientissimus & summè admirandus in suis Operibus rerum Conditor, D. O. M. ipsi pulcherrimâ istâ & affabrefactâ Structurâ benignissimè prospexit, ut nunquam deesset Fermentum, quod ad solvendum & comminuendum alimentum durum & asperum par foret.*

There is in the *Eye* of *Brutes* a *Periopthalmium*, or nictating Membrane, which the *Eye* of *Man* is a stranger to; the *Royal Academy* at *Paris* have been very curious and punctual in the description of it: their Opinion of it is, that this *Membrane* serves to clean the *Cornea*, and to hinder, that by *drying* it grow not less transparent. *Man* and the *Ape*, which are the only Animals wherein this Membrane is not found, have not wanted this provision for the cleansing of their Eyes, because they have Hands, with which they may, by rubbing their *Eyelids*, express the Humidity contain'd in them, which they let out thro the *Ductus Lachrymalis*; as is known by Experience, when the *Light* is darkned, or when the *Eyes* are pained, or itching,

itching, these Accidents do cease upon the *rubbing of the Eyes.*

In the *Heart* of *Quadrupeds* there is an excellent provision for the living of those Creatures.

The *Foramen Ovale* in some (that which in a *Fœtus* makes the *Anastomosis,* by the means whereof the *Blood* goes from the *Cava* into the *Aorta,* without passing thro the Lungs) is an Accession to the Wonders.

This Passage between the *Arteria Venosa* and the *Vena Cava* is kept open in *Amphibious Quadrupeds;* this maintains a degree of Heat and Motion in the Blood, which may be sufficient for them while they are under Water.

The *Epiglottis* in such Creatures is also larger and stiffer than it is in others, that so when they are feeding under Water, the Water may not break in upon their Lungs.

I confess Mr. *Cheselden* is of the Opinion, that it is not the *Foramen Ovale,* but the *Ostium Venarum Coronoriarum,* which being very near it, may easily be mistaken for it, that the Anatomists have made their curious Remark upon; however the provision is admirable!

The *Heart* in *Beasts* is near the *middle* of the whole Body, in *Man* it is nearer the *Head;* this *Aristotle* observes: but Mr. *Lower,* who has been a most curious Anatomist of this Part, gives us a reason for it; the Trajection and the Distribution of the *Blood* wholly depending on the *Systole* of the *Heart,* and so either the *Heart* must have been stronger in Man, or the *Head* would have wanted its due Proportion of *Blood,* if it had not been so near to the *Heart;* whereas in *Beasts,* whose *Heads* hang down, the *Blood* goes a plainer way, and often a steep one.

There are also peculiar *Nerves* reaching to the Heart of *Beasts,* besides the *sixth Pair,* as in *Man,* a Relief provided by Nature, lest their *prone Heads* might fail of imparting Animal Spirits copiously to it.

The

The *Cone* of the *Pericardium* in *Quadrupeds* is loose from the *Diaphragm*, whereas in *Man* it is faftned to it; thus the motion of the *Midriff*, in the neceffary Act of *Refpiration*, is notably affifted in the pofture of both. Dr. *Tyfon*'s Remark upon it is, *This muft needs be the Effect of Wifdom and Defign*, and it is plain was intended in *Man* to walk upright, and not upon all four, like the *Quadrupeds*.

In the *Four-footed* there is not that Communication between the *Head* and the *Heart* which there is in a *Man*, efpecially by the Branches of the *intercoftal Pair* of *Nerves*, which are fent from the *cervical Plexus* to the *Heart*, and the *Præcordia*, a thing which Mr. *Derham* cannot behold without calling it *a prodigious Care of Nature*; thus the *Head* and *Heart* of Man have a more *intimate Concern* with each other, and a greater and quicker Correfpondence, than what is in other Creatures: *Brutes* are more fimple Machines; but in *Man*, by the Commerce of the *cervical Plexus*, the Conceptions of the *Brain* prefently affect the *Heart*, and agitate its Veffels, and the whole Appendage thereof, together with the *Diaphragm*; whence the Alteration in the motion of the Blood, the Pulfe, and Refpiration: and when any thing affects or alters the *Heart*, the Impreffions are not only retorted by the fame Duct of the *Nerves*, but alfo the *Blood* itfelf, with a changed Courfe, flies to the *Brain*, and there agitating the Animal Spirits with diverfe Impulfes, produces various Conceptions in the Mind. This is Dr. *Willis*'s Obfervation; who adds, that the Antients therefore made the *Heart* the Seat of *Wifdom*; and certainly the Works of *Wifdom* and *Virtue* do very much depend upon the Commerce which is between the *Heart* and the *Brain*. This eminent Perfon diffecting a *Fool*, found, befides the Smallnefs of his *Brain*, the principal difference between him and a Man of Senfe to be, that the *Nervi Intercoftalis Plexus, in hoc Stulto valde exilis, & minorum Nervorum Satellitio fti-*

patus

patus fuerit. The want of the *intercostal Commerce* with the *Heart* in Brutes, is truly an admirable thing! MAN, ponder upon this, and say, *Where is God my Maker, who teaches us more than the Beasts of the Earth!*

I cannot here forbear to introduce a good Obſervation of a Gentleman who writes *Chriſtian Religious Appeal,* which he thus expreſſes ; ' That God ſhould ' endow us with *Reaſon,* and make us differ from the ' *Brutes,* only that we may rule *them,* and not our- ' *ſelves,* and put a *golden Mattock* in our Hands, only ' to dig *Dunghills;* has not the leaſt Congruity with ' the *Decorum* obſerved by Him in all His Works, ' which are framed in Weight, Number, and Order.'

Lactantius, do thou paſs a Cenſure on the *Men like the Brutes that periſh,* who do not from the *Beaſts* learn the Being and the Glory of a GOD! *Illos qui nullum omnino Deum eſſe dixerunt, non modo non Philoſophos, ſed ne Homines quidem fuiſſe dixerim; qui mutis ſimillimi, ex ſolo Corpore conſtiterunt, nihil videntes animo.* [lib. 7. c. 9.]

Galen gives us a notable Relation of a *Kid,* which he took alive out of the Belly of the Dam, and brought it up; the *Embrio* preſently fell to walking, as if he had *heard,* ſays *Galen,* that *Legs* were given him for that purpoſe; then he ſmelt into all the things that were ſet in the Room, and refuſing them all, only ſupped up the *Milk*: after two Months the tender Sprouts of *Shrubs* and *Plants* appeared, and then re- fuſing the reſt, he kept to thoſe which are the pecu- liar Food of *Goats.* But that which to *Galen* appeared moſt admirable of all, was, that a while after it began to *chew the Cud;* whereupon ſays he, Θεασάμενοι πάντες ἀνεβόησαν ἐκπλαγέντες ἐπὶ ταῖς τῶν ζώων δυνάμεσι, *All that ſaw cried out with Admiration, being aſtoniſhed at the na- tural Faculties of Animals.* He complains thereupon that many neglect ſuch *Works of Nature,* and admire none but Μόνα τὰ ξένα θεάματα, *unuſual Spectacles.* Mr. *Ray* notes, *One may fill a Volume with Comments on this pleaſant Story.*

The

The *Sagacity* of some *Quadrupeds*, tho so far short of *Man's*, yet is a matter of Astonishment to *Man*; and *Man's* will be short of *theirs*, if it see not the glorious GOD of Nature operating in it.

Indeed there was Humour enough in *Rorarius,* who upon hearing a learned Man prefer such a Wretch as *Frederick Barberossa*, before that great Emperor *Charles* V. was thereby so provoked, that he wrote his two Books to prove *that Beasts often have more Use of Reason than Men.* The Consequence of the *absurd Reasoning* he found among *Men* was this with him, *Itaque in Mentem mihi venit Animalia Bruta sæpe Ratione uti melius Homine.* But the Consequence of his own *absurd Reasoning* will soon be found such as will carry thousands of *Terrors* with it.

It is enough that what of *Reason* appears in the *Brutal Tribes,* is an immediate Effect of the Providence exerted by the all-wise Creator, and applied for the *Preservation* of His Creatures. *O Lord, thou preservest not only Man, but Beast also!*

The Words of the excellent Sir *Richard Blackmore,* in his Essay on *the Immortality of the Soul,* are worthy to be transcribed and pondered on this Occasion. ' I
' must acknowledge that I look upon the *Souls of Brute*
' Creatures as *immaterial,* for I cannot conceive how
' an internal Principle of *sensitive Perception* and *local*
' *Motion* can be framed of *Matter,* tho ever so subtile
' and refin'd, and modified with the most artful Con-
' trivance ; ——— yet they are plainly of a base and
' low Nature, and destitute of those *intellectual Fa-*
' *culties* and that *free Choice* that should make them
' Subjects of *Moral Government,* enable them to discern
' the Obligation of *Laws,* and the Distinction of *Vir-*
' *tue* and *Vice,* and understand the Notion of being an
' *accountable Creature,* and receiving *Rewards* and *Pu-*
' *nishments.* ——— Whether the *Animal Souls* in a State
' of Separation remain *stupid* and *asleep,* or whether
' they are *dispersed* thro the Creation, and employ'd to

' animate

' animate *other Beings*, or return to *one common Element*,
' whence they were at firſt deriv'd, is unrevealed;
' but this is certain, the *Souls* of *Brutes* are not de-
' ſign'd by the Great Creator for ſuch a Life of *Plea-*
' *ſure* and *Happineſs*, as that of *Human Souls* in a State
' of *Immortality* and *Perfeϵtion*, for the Enjoyment of
' which they have no Diſpoſitions and Capacities.'

The Opinion of *Deſcartes*, and *Gaſſendus*, and *Willis*,
and others, That the *Soul* of Brutes is *material*, and
the whole Animal a meer *Machine*, is clogg'd with in-
ſuperable Difficulties.

Our excellent *Ray* beſpeaks a *lower degree of Reaſon*
for them, and his Argument is fetch'd from ſome of
their Aϵtions, which, without allowing ſome *Argumentation* in *them*, can hardly be accounted for; he ſingles
out the *Dog*, the *Dog* running before his Maſter, will
ſtop at a divarication of the way, till he ſee which
way his *Maſter* will take. Again, when the *Dog* has
got a *Prey*, which he fears his Maſter will take from
him, he runs away to hide it, and afterwards returns
to it. Once more, if a *Dog* be to leap upon a Table
which he ſees too high for him to reach at once, let
there be a *Stool* or *Chair* near it, he will firſt mount
that, and ſo the *Table*, yea, tho the *Stool* ſtand ſo that
the Creature takes not a *direϵt Leap* towards the place
finally intended; if he were a meer Piece of *Clockwork*,
and this Motion cauſed by the ſtriking of a *Spring*,
there can be no reaſon imagin'd why the Spring being
ſet on work, ſhould not carry the Machine in a *direϵt
Line* towards the Objeϵt that put it in motion, as well
when 'tis on an *high* Table as when 'tis on a *low*.

They that have written *de Canum Fidelitate & Saga-
citate*, have entertained us with Stories full of Wonders. The Obſervers have thought themſelves obliged
ſometimes to ſuſpeϵt that the *Dogs* might have a *Spirit
of Python* in them. *Camerarius* in his *Horæ Subceſivæ* has
colleϵted ſurprizing, but credible Relations, of ſuch
as we may call *reaſonable Dogs*.

A

A well-known King, who dealt much in them, at a famous *Act* in one of our Univerfities, very publickly determin'd it, *that they could make Syllogisms*, and fo 'tis no longer to be difputed. The Authority is as great as that of *Jacobus Micyllus*, who wrote an *Elogium Canis*, which is thought a very elegant Epigram.

There is a furprizing thing related of the *Sea-Tortoifes*, both *Ariftotle* and *Pliny* have remark'd it; That when *Tortoifes* have been a long time upon the Water, during a Calm, their Shells will be fo dried with the *Sun*, that they are eafily taken by the Fifhermen, becaufe being become too light, they cannot plunge into the Water nimbly enough. The *French Academifts* do not refer this eafinefs to be now taken, merely to the *Lightnefs* of the Creature's Body, for he could eafily let *Air* enough out of the Lungs to render his Body heavier than the Water, upon which he would fink immediately, but to a *Sagacity* of the cautious Animal, which is truly marvellous. The *Tortoife* is always careful to keep himfelf in his *Equilibrium*, and therefore he dares not let the Air out of his Lungs, to acquire a Weight which would make him to fink immediately; for he fears left the wetting of his Shell fhould render it fo heavy, that being funk to the bottom of the Water, he might never afterwards have the power of re-afcending. What *Forefight* here! What a degree of *Argumentation* too!

They that have written *de Solertia Animalium* (as many befides *Plutarch* have done) have reported fuch Effays and Shadows of *Reafon* in many of them as are diverting.

The *Fox* is often catch'd in Tricks, which afford as pleafant Stories as any in that old Volume, *The delectable Hiftory of Reynard*. His way to get rid of his *Fleas* is notorious.

What notable *Architects* are our *Bevers*! They lay their *Logs*, and build their *Dams*, and form their *Chambers*, with a marvellous Artifice. A Nation of *Indians*

do

do ſometimes in ſcarce any thing but their Speech *out-man* a Nation of *Bevers.*

Elephants, what *reaſonable,* but what *prodigious* things have been related of them! Things that almoſt have *Religion* in them. The Story of *Hanno* is an amazing one, *Pierius* is our Author for it. Well may I *write* of them that have themſelves been ſo ſuſceptible of *Diſcipline* as to *write* whole Sentences; 'tis affirm'd that *Elephants* have done ſo. *Alſted* ſpends two whole Pages together, in his conciſe way, enumerating but the Heads of the *ſtrange things* which this *tractable,* and almoſt *rational* Quadruped arrives to!

What a notable, docible, tractable Animal the *Horſe!* The *Horſe,* of whom the admirable *Buchanan* ſings,

—— *Equus ad cunctos ſe accommodat uſus.*

Read *Solinus,* and ſee what Approaches the *Horſe* makes to *Reaſon!* One would queſtion which had moſt, *Caligula* or *Incitatus.* Dr. *Grew* admires him, as being *ſwift* and *ſtrong,* above moſt other Animals, and yet ſtrangely *obedient;* both comely and clean; he breeds no *Vermin* of any ſort; his Breath, his Foam, his Excrements and Sweat, all ſweet and uſeful; fitted every way for Service or Pleaſure, for the meaneſt or the greateſt Maſter. There are antient Examples of other *Horſes* beſides *Bucephalus* and *Lethargus,* that have been honour'd with ſtately *Funerals* and *Sepulchres* at their *Deaths,* as well as their Maſters; yea, tho the Epitaph of *Adrian* be loſt, his *Horſe's* is preſerved to this day. The *Riders* of *Horſes,* who in their *Lives* will ſubmit to no *Bridles,* nor do any *Service* for Him that made them, deſerve at their *Deaths* to paſs away no better eſteem'd than their *Horſes,* but will have a worſe Fate than they. The Gentleman, who going home with his Head full of the *ſickly Fumes* from the *Healths* of the Evening's Debauch, could not compel his *Horſe* to drink an *Health* which at the next Brook

he

he propoſed to him, had ſo much *Reaſon* left him (and a very little might ſerve) as to make that Reflection, *That the Man in the Saddle was the greater Beaſt of the two.*

How innumerable are the *Appearances* of Nature, which are above the Powers of *Mechaniſm?* 'Tis religiouſly and moſt reaſonably obſerved by Dr. *Cheyne,* that all theſe are ſo many undeniable Proofs for the Being of a G O D; there muſt be a *Power ſuperior* to thoſe of *Mechaniſm,* and this muſt lead us to Him, *who alone does great and marvellous things.*

How often have I heard this, and how plainly ſeen it; this Power belongeth to God!

After all, do we ſee ſomething in theſe, and other, and all *Creatures,* that appears *defective* to us? A wiſe Remark made by the Marquis of *Pianezza* ſhall be introduced upon it; his remarkable words are theſe:

' The *limited Perfections,* and the ſeeming *Irregula-*
' *rities* of the World, rather afford us occaſion to ac-
' knowledge and glorify the *Providence* of G O D,
' which not only declares, that all the Creatures are
' too *imperfect* to deſerve to be *worſhipped* as *Deities,*
' but alſo amidſt their *Imperfections* obliges them to
' confeſs, as it were with their own Mouths, *one in-*
' *finitely perfect Deity;* a *Deity* that would not have
' *Man* fix on *them* as the Objects of his Love and Ad-
' miration, but that from them he ſhould paſs on to
' the Love and Eſteem of his only true G O D.'

'There is one very ſurprizing thing, and without acknowledging a Superintendency of a *Divine Provi-dence* there can be no accounting for it. The *Manſuete Creatures* bring forth no more than one or two at a time, the *Beaſts of Prey* bring forth as often, and ſeven, or nine, or eleven at a Litter; and yet! what inex-preſſible Multitudes of the *Manſuete* have we to ſerve us! What vaſt Herds of *Beeves!* What vaſt Flocks of *Sheep!* Whereas they that live upon *Prey* appear in very little Numbers. How rarely is a *Wolf* met withal,

tho

tho a Price be set upon his Head! What Rarities are *Lions,* and *Tygers,* and *Ounces!* To be caged in the *Tower* for *Spectacles!*

And then the Liberty given us to *butcher* our useful Creatures at our pleasure; 'tis observed by Mr. *Robinson,* that this will be found a *Kindness,* rather than a *Cruelty* to the Creatures; if we kill them for our *Food,* their Dispatch is quick, and much less dolorous, than that they should be torn to pieces by such cruel Masters as the *Lion,* and the *Tyger,* and *Bear,* who would not give them time to *die,* but even eat their Flesh from their Bones *alive*; and if they should live to the tedious Condition and Melancholy of *Old Age,* it would, after many Tortures, kill them, and leave their Carcases rotting, stinking, and useless upon the ground.

The *short Life* of a *Beast,* compared with the *Life of Man,* deserves to have some Remark made upon it; this at least: *Man,* do not *lead* the *Life of a Beast,* if thou wouldst not be condemned and confined to the *short Life* of a *Beast,* nor come under the Execution of that Sentence, *The Days of the Wicked shall be shortned.* There is a way of *living,* by some called *living apace*; it is indeed not *living* at all, but rather *dying apace*; a *beastly* Life ought to be a *shortned* one.

What useful *Instructions* would the Properties of the several *Animals* yield to the *Christian Philosopher,* would he be duly and wisely attentive to them! *Franzius,* and *Simpson,* and others, have cultivated this Theme, not unusefully; 'tis capable of a much more vast Cultivation: *Christian,* hearken to the Voice of the many *Preachers* thou hast about thee, lest thou *mourn at the last,* and say, *I have not obeyed the Voice of my Teachers, nor inclined mine Ear to them that instructed me!*

I remember one Observation of *Seneca,* which a little exemplifies a *moral Remark* on the Properties of some *Four-footed*; *Omnia quæ Naturâ fera ac rabida sunt, consternantur ad Vana. Idem inquietis & stolidis Ingeniis evenit,*

evenit, rerum ſuſpicione feriuntur. ——— I thought this worth mentioning, but not becauſe I do not think a *Chriſtian* of a *good Underſtanding* might eaſily produce ten thouſand more.

The Account which honeſt *Leguat* gives of the *ſo-litary Bird*, which he and his Companions obſerved on the Iſle of *Rodrigo*, is as admirable as unqueſtionable; the *Bird* has *Wings*, but ſo ſmall that it cannot fly with them, they ſerve to flutter with a mighty noiſe when they call one another; they never lay but *one Egg*, which is bigger than that of a *Gooſe*; the *Male* and *Female* ſit upon it in their turns, and all the while they are hatching it, or bringing it to provide for i.ſelf, (which is divers Months) they will not ſuffer any other Bird of their own Species to come within two hundred Yards round of the place: but this is very ſingular, the *Males* will never drive away the ap-proaching *Females*, but call for their own *Females* to do it; the *Female* does the like, and upon the Approach of any other *Males*, call their own *Males* to chaſe them away. After theſe *Birds* have raiſed their *young one*, and left it to itſelf, ' we have often obſerved (ſays my ' ingenious Traveller) that ſome days after the *young* ' *one* leaves the *Neſt*, a Company of thirty or forty ' brings another *young one* to it, and the new-fledg'd ' Bird, with its Father and Mother joining with the ' Band, march to ſome by-place; we frequently fol-' lowed them, and found that afterwards the old ones ' went each their way alone, or in couples, and left ' the two *young ones* together, which we call'd a *Mar-*' *riage.*' My religious Traveller does give all poſſible Aſſurance for the Truth of this Relation, and adds, *I could not forbear to entertain my Mind with ſeveral Re-flections on this Occaſion. I ſent Mankind to learn of the Beaſts.*

It is an Obſervation made by one of the moſt refin'd Philoſophers by whom our Age has been illuminated; ' Moſt Creatures have ſome *Quality*, whereby they
' admoniſh

' admonifh us of what is BEST. Of *Neatnefs*, all
' *Birds* which love to be perpetually pruning of them-
' felves; and *Cats*, which commonly cover their Ex-
' crements, and wipe their *Mouths* after Dinner. Foul
' Water will breed the Pip in *Hens*, and Naftinefs
' Lice and Scabs in *Kine*; and all Creatures, even
' *Swine* themfelves, which love Dirt, yet thrive beft
' when kept clean. Of *Forecaft*, the *Sitta* and the *Ant*,
' which lay up Nuts and other Seeds in their Grana-
' ries, that ferve them in the Winter. Of *Modefty*,
' the *Elephants*, the *Dromedaries*, and the *Deer*, which
' always conceal their Venereal Acts. Of *mature*
' *Marriage*, all Animals which beget their beft Breed
' at their full Growth. Of *Conjugal Chaftity*, the *Doves*
' and *Partridges*, which keep to one Husband and
' Wife. Of *Conjugal Love*, the *Rook*, the Male help-
' ing the Female to make her Neft, feeding her while
' fhe fits, and often fitting in his turn. Of *Maternal*
' *Love*, the domeftick *Hen*, gentle by Nature, and un-
' armed, yet, in defence of her Chickens, bold and
' fierce; and the *Tyger* herfelf, the fierceft of Beafts,
' yet is infinitely fond of her Whelps.'

The fame excellent *Fellow of the* ROYAL SOCIETY
carries on his Obfervation; 'The moft odious or nox-
' ious things do ferve for Food or Phyfick, or fome
' Manufacture, or other good ufe; neither are they
' of lefs ufe to *amend our Minds*, by teaching us *Care*,
' and *Diligence*, and more *Wit :* and fo much the more,
' the worfe the things are, we fee and fhould avoid.
' *Weafels*, and *Kites*, and other mifchievous Animals,
' induce us to Watchfulnefs; *Thiftles* and *Moles* to
' good Husbandry; *Lice* oblige us to *Cleanlinefs* in our
' Bodies, *Spiders* in our Houfes, and the *Moth* in our
' *Clothes :* the Deformity and Filthinefs of *Swine* makes
' them the *Beauty-fpot* of the Animal Creation, and
' the Emblem of all *Vice*; and the *Obfcenity* of *Dogs*
' fhews how much more beaftly it is in *Men :* the *Fox*
' teaches us to beware of the *Thief*, and the *Vipers* and
' *Scorpions*

' *Scorpions* thofe more noxious Creatures, which carry
' their Venom in their *Tongues* or their *Tails*.'

I will profecute this Obfervation of my Brother,
with only obferving fo much further upon it ; that no
little part of the *Homage* we owe to the glorious *Creator* of all thefe things, is to learn thofe *Virtues,* and
thofe *decent* and *honeft* things, whereof, if the Faculties
of our Minds be awake, we fhall eafily perceive His
Creatures to be the *Monitors.*

In writing thefe things I cannot but call to mind
the expreffive Words of *Theodorus Gaza,* in his Preface
to *Ariftotle's* Books *de Animalibus* ; *In contemplandis Animalium Moribus, Exempla fuppetunt omnium Officiorum,
& Effigies offeruntur Virtutum fumma cum Authoritate
Naturæ, omnium Parentis, non fimulatæ, non inconftantes,
fed verè ingenuæ atque perpetuæ.* He goes on to fhew
how powerfully the Kindnefs of the Brutes to thofe of
their own Kind, rebukes the *unbrotherly Carriage* too
often found in Mankind ; and adds a variety of Admonitions, which, *my Reader,* thou art not unable to
difcover by thy own Ingenuity.

¶. ' One of the moft valuable Writers that ever was
' in the World, brings from the glorious Creator of
' the *Beafts* this Voice to Man ; *Sic utere illis, ut Ex-
' empla Virtutum quæ in illis apparent, obferves, & om-
' nibus Viribus coneris illa longo intervallo fuperare, ut ne
' Beftialem Animam reperiam in tuo Corpore Humano.*'

' It would not be a *Fancy* deftitute of *Judgment,* if
' I fhould fet before me the *Tabella Hieroglyphica,*
' wherewith *Alfted* has obliged us.'

' But of all the Tribes that graze in the Field,
' there is none that I would more chufe for an *Em-
' blem* than the *Sheep* ; the clean, patient, innocent
' Creature, which has nothing belonging to it but
' what is of a celebrated *Ufefulnefs. O thou moft honou-
' rable Creature, what a Dignity has the Son of God Him-
' felf put upon thee !*'

I

'I see so much of G O D in the Circumstances of
' the *Brutal Tribes*, as obliges me to *look upwards* in a
' way too high for them.'

' At the same time, tho I would by no means fall
' into *Pythagorean* and *Mahometan* Superstitions, yet I
' would abhor to treat any of the *Brutes* with bar-
' barous Cruelties, *Immanities* and *Inhumanities*; *cruelly*
' to delight in their *Miseries*, or to be *unmerciful* to
' them, is an Offence to God, and what a *righteous*
' *Man* would not be guilty of; *unknown Punishments*
' may be reserved for it.'

' *Great* G O D, *if I do not acknowledge Thee, I am con-*
' *demned by the Ox, which knows his Owner, and by the*
' *Ass, which knows his Master's Crib!*'

Luther seeing the *Cattel* go in the Fields, used this
Expression; *Behold, there go our Preachers, our Milk-*
bearers, and Wool-bearers, which daily preach to us Faith
towards G O D, *that we trust in Him as our loving Father,*
who will maintain and nourish us.

It is very certain our *Dominion* over the Creatures
is very much impair'd by our Fall from God. Those
Creatures do now either *fly from* us, or *fly at* us, which,
if we had been faithful to our God, would not have
done so. Honest *Egardus* propounds two *Admonitions*
of *Piety* on these Occasions; the one, *Fuga Animalium*
à te, moneat te de tua fuga à Deo per peccatum. The
other, *Animalium in te ad lædendum impetus hostilis, mo-*
neat te de Odio & Furore Diaboli, & Mundi, adversus te
immani.

I conclude with an Observation of Dr. *Grew's*;
' As the *Essence* of every thing, and its relation, in be-
' ing fitted, beyond any Emendation, for its *Actions*
' and *Uses*, evidently proceeds from a Mind of the
' *highest Understanding*, so the nature of these *Actions*
' and *Uses*, in as much as they are not any way de-
' structive or troublesome; no, but each thing tends
' apart, and all conspire together to conserve, cherish,
' and gratify: this is an Evidence of their proceeding
' from

' from the *greatest Goodness.* There are many who are
' very *cunning* and *subtile* in the Invention of *Evil*, and
' *Engines* have been fitted, with much Contrivance, for
' the tormenting of Men; how eafy had it been for
' the Creator of the Univerfe to have ftock'd it with
' Creatures that fhould never have moved fo much as
' one Limb without *Pain*, or have had the leaft Senfa-
' tion without a mixture of horrible *Torment*, or have
' entertain'd the leaft Imagination, but what fhould
' have had *Horror* in it? But behold, our good God
' has ordered it, that whatever is *natural* is *delightful*,
' and has a tendency to Good; He has employ'd His
' tranfcendent *Wifdom* and *Power*, that He might
' make way for His *Benignity*.'

Great *G O D, Thou art Good, and Thou doft Good; Oh
teach me Thy Statutes!* So fings the Poet:

> *O Deus, O Mundi folus qui flectis habenas,
> Ut tua nunc Bonitas oculis eft obvia cunctis!*

ESSAY XXXII. *Of* M A N.

A N D now let the *Lord of this lower World* be introduced, M A N, who is to do the Part of a
Prieft for the reft of the Creation, and offer up to God
the *Praifes* which are owing from and for them all.

In Libro Creaturarum continetur Homo (as one of the
School-Divines happens to exprefs it well) *& eft prin-
cipalior Litera ipfius Libri.*

It was moft reafonably done of thee, Father *Auftin*,
to tax the Folly of them who admired the *Wonders* in
the other Parts of the Creation abroad, *& relinquunt
feipfos, nec mirantur*, but fee nothing in *themfelves* to be
wondred at. It is not for nothing that *Mankind* is in
the *Gofpel* called *every Creature*; he that beholds *Man*,
may therein behold what is moft wonderful in *every
Creature.*

Ic

It is well exprefs'd in a Treatife entitled, *Schola &*
Scala Naturæ! 'Nature doth not lead thee towards
' GOD by a far-fetch'd and winding Compafs, but
' in a fhort and ftrait Line. The *Sun* waits upon the
' *Rain*, the *Rain* upon the *Grafs*, the *Grafs* ferves the
' *Cattel*, the *Cattel* ferve *thee*, and if *thou* ferve GOD,
' then thou makeft good the higheft Link in that *gol-*
' *den Chain*, whereby *Heaven* is joined to *Earth*; then
' thou ftandeft where thou oughteft to ftand, in the
' *uppermoft Round* of the *Divine Ladder*, next to the
' moft High; then thou approveft thyfelf to be indeed
' what thou wert defigned by God to be, *the High-*
' *Prieft and Orator of the Univerfe*; becaufe thou alone,
' amongft all the Creatures here below, art endued
' with Underftanding to know Him, and Speech to
' exprefs thy Knowledge of Him, in thy Praifes and
' Prayers to Him.'
I may now fay with honeft *Stigelius,*

Jam vocat ad pulchros nos Fabrica Corporis Artus,
Quæ mira Authorem monftrat in Arte Deum.

The BODY of MAN being *moft obvious* to our view,
is that which *we will firft* begin with; a *Machine* of a
moft aftonifhing Workmanfhip and Contrivance! *My*
God, I will praife Thee, for I am ftrangely and wonderfully
made!
' But is it poffible for me to confider this BODY as
' any other than a Temple of GOD! A *Vitruvius*
' will teach us that the moft exquifite and accurate
' Figure for a *Temple* will be found in a Conformity to
' an *Human Body*; indeed an *Human Body* ought for
' ever to be beheld and employed, as defigned for an
' *holy Temple*; for me to apply any Part of fuch a *Body*
' to any Action forbidden by God, would be a very
' *criminal Proftitution.*'
' By *ufing* my *Body* in and for the Service of God,
' and by *praifing* the Glorious-One, who has formed
' every

' every Part of my Body, *and clothed me with Skin and*
' *Flesh, and fenced me with Bones and Sinews,* I defire to
' affure my fhare in an happy *Refurrection* of this *Body*
' from the *Grave,* into which it is falling : for *tho a*
' *Man die, he is to live again;* an *appointed Time* will
' come, when *Thou, O my God, wilt call, and I fhall an-*
' *fwer thee, and thou wilt have a defire to fee the Work of*
' *thine Hands* revived and reftored.'

The *erect Pofture* of Man, the *Os fublime,* how commodious for a *rational Creature,* who muft have *Domi-*
nion over thofe which are not fo, and muft invent and
practife things ufeful and curious! *Tully* admires the
Providence of Nature, as he calls it, adding the reafon
for it ; *Sunt enim è Terra Homines, non ut Incolæ atque*
Habitatores, fed quafi Spectatores fuperarum rerum, atque
Cœleftium, quarum Spectaculum ad nullum aliud Genus
Animantium pertinet.   By this pofture Man has the ufe
of his *Hands,* which, as *Galen* obferves, are, *Organa fa-*
pienti Animali convenientia ; and his *Eyes,* which as they
have the glorious *Hemifphere* of the Heavens above
him, fo they have the *Horizon* of three Miles on a perfect Globe about them, when they are fix Foot high,
and by the Refractions of the *Atmofphere* they have
much more than fo : his *Head* is alfo fuftained, which
is heavy, and how painful to be carried in another
Pofture!

The provifion made for this Pofture is very furprizing ; what *Ligaments?* efpecially that of the *Peri-*
cardium to the *Diaphragm,* which, as *Vefalius* and *Blan-*
cardius note, is peculiar to *Man?* The *Bones,* how artificially placed and braced? Moft remarkably the
Vertebræ of the Back-bone? The *Feet,* how exquifitely
accommodated! For the rare Mechanifm whereof, a
Chefelden may be confulted ; yea, every Writer of *Ana-*
tomy will offer enough to *trample Atheifm under foot.*
To all add the Miniftry of the *Mufcles,* which anfwer
all Motions, and yet with eafy and ready Touches,
keeping the *Line of Innixion* and the *Center of Gravity*
where

where it ought to be! Yea, all the Parts of the Body
so disposed as to *poise* it! All in a nice *Equipoise*!
With a prodigious variety of *Muscles* placed throughout the Body for the Service! *Borelli* observes, ''tis
' worthy of Admiration, that in so great a variety of
' *Motions* Nature's Law of *Equilibration* should always
' be observed ; so that if it be transgressed or neglect-
' ed, the Body necessarily and immediately tumbles
' down.'

Every thing does conspire to assure us, that the
Maker of Man intended Man for such a *Posture*.

The most indigent Condition wherein *Man* is born
into the World, but the plentiful Provision which he
finds made by a gracious and merciful God for him in
the World, this invites *Man* to return to God, and to
taste His *Love*, in all the Creatures that accommodate
him, and rely upon His *Care* for ever, for the Supply
of all his Wants. And, as Mr. *Arndt* expresses it,
*Homo Dei Amorem in omnibus rebus eo intimius degustaret,
in caducis Creaturis Deum immortalem inveniens disceret,
quod immortalis Deus melius possit exhilarare, consolari,
corroborare, ac conservare hominem, quam omnes omnino
Creaturæ fluxæ & cito perituræ.*

A Comparison between the *Macrocosm* and the *Mi-
crocosm* would afford a very edifying and acceptable
Entertainment to a contemplative Mind ; the excellent
Alsted will therewith entertain the Gentlemen that
will visit his *Theologia Naturalis.*

Indeed he that speaks to MAN, speaks to *every Creature* ; and *Man* is therefore the more *concerned*, as well
as *capable* to hear *every Creature* speaking to him.

'Tis what calls for a deep Consideration with us,
that in the *Body* of Man there is nothing deficient, nothing superfluous, an *End* and *Use* for every thing.
Natura non abundat in superfluis, nec deficit in necessariis.
There is no Part that we can well spare, nor any that
can say to the rest, *I have no need of you!* The *Belly* and
the *Members* cannot quarrel with one another. Even
the

the *Paps* in Men, beſides their adorning of the *Breaſt*, and their defending of the *Heart*, ſometimes contain *Milk*, as in a *Daniſh* Family mention'd by *Bartholinus*. A Man mention'd by *Beccone*, upon the Death of his Wife, ſuckled the Infant himſelf. He concludes, that ſince, according to *Malpighius* and others, the *Paps* of Men have the ſame Veſſels with thoſe of Women, 'tis intended that, if need requires, the *Young* ſhould be ſuckled at them, who, upon a little pulling, ſoon fetch *Milk* into them.

What ſhould we do with a *Bavarian Poke* under our Chins?

Our pious *Ray* makes this Remark, That if we conſider no more than the very *Nails* at our Fingers ends, we muſt *be very ſottiſh if we can conceive that any other than an infinitely good and wiſe God was our Author and Former.* And there was an honourable Perſon who long before him ſaid, *An non videmus in ſingulis ſummis Digitis, Artificium Dei? Eſtne unguis aliquis qui non reddat Teſtimonium Deum eſſe Opificem eximium?*

No ſign of *Chance* in the whole Structure of our Body. It is remarkable, in Bodies of different Animals there is an *Agreement of the Parts*, as far as their *Occaſions* and *Offices* agree; but a *difference* of thoſe where there is a *difference* of theſe. Dr. *Dowglaſs* will tell you what *Muſcles* are in a *Man* that are not in a *Dog*, what in a *Dog* that are not in a *Man*. The Matter, the Texture, the Figure, the Strength, with the neceſſary Accoutrements of every Part, how amazingly commodious! How often does the *Ars, Providentia, & Sapientia CONDITORIS*, appear to the Pagan *Galen* upon the Contemplation!

In the *Body* of Man the *Lodgment* of the Parts is as admirable as the *Parts* themſelves. Where could the *Eye*, the *Ear*, the *Tongue*, be ſo commodiouſly placed as in the *upper Apartments* aſſigned for them? *Tully* ſays truly, *Mirifice ad uſus neceſſarios collocati ſunt!* And for the other Parts, he notes, *Rectè in illis Corporum par-*

Q *tibus*

tibus collocata ſunt. Four of the *five Senſes*, how commodiouſly lodged, near the *Brain*, the common Senſory, and a place well guarded ; *Galen* celebrated this wondrouſly agreeable Situation ! And how could the *fifth Senſe*, that of the *Touch*, be more agreeably lodged, than with a Diſperſion into all Parts of the Body! Where ſhould the *Hand*, the *Feet*, the *Legs* be, but juſt where they are ! Where the *Heart*, the *Sol Microcoſmi*, which is to labour about the whole Maſs of Blood, but in the *Center* of the Body ? Where can the *Viſcera* diſcharge their Offices better, than in the place aſſigned to them ? Where could the *Bones* and the *Muſcles* be better diſpoſed of ? And what better *Covering* were it poſſible for the whole Body to have, than the *Skin* ; whereof the *Microſcopical Views* given by *Cowper* in his *Anatomy*, muſt give a vaſt Surprize to us !

What can be more *ornamental*, than that thoſe Members which are *Pairs*, do ſtand by one another in an *equal Altitude*.

The Proviſion made in the Body of Man to *ſtave off Evils*, is very admirable. The *Secretions* made by the *Glands*, whereof *Cockburn*, *Keil*, *Moreland*, and others, give us notable Accounts, are ſuch as cannot be conſidered without ſome Amazement. How many Parts of the Body ſtand ready to do what belongs to faithful *Centinels!* The principal and more eſſential Inſtruments of Life and Senſe, how well *barricado'd* are they ? Of how many Parts are we ſupplied with *Pairs*, to make up a Defect which may happen in any of them ? The *Pairs* of *Nerves*, and the Ramifications of the *Veins* and *Arteries* in the fleſhly Parts, what *Caſes of Diſaſter* are anſwered in them ? Mr. *Derham* here juſtly adores *the infinite Contriver!* Dr. *Sloane* juſtly admires the Contrivance of our *Blood*, which on ſome Occaſions, as ſoon as any thing deſtructive to the Conſtitution of it comes into it, immediately by an *inteſtine Commotion* endeavours to thruſt it forth, and ſo
'tis

'tis not only freed from the new Gueſt, but ſometimes what likewiſe might long have lain lurking there.

What *Emunctories* has the Body, and what ſurprizing *Paſſages*, to carry off Miſchiefs, which we fooliſhly bring upon our ſelves! And how aſtoniſhing the *Methods* and *Efforts* of *Nature* to ſet all things to rights. *Valſalva* diſcovered Paſſages into the Region of the *Ear-drum*, which are of mighty uſe to diſcharge morbifick Matter from the *Head*. *Hippocrates* in his Book *de Alimentis* makes his Remarks upon the *Sagacity of Nature*, to find out Paſſages for the diſcharging of things offenſive to the Body; and indeed they who confeſs no Wonders in it, are *Hippocraticis Vinculis alligandi*. Modern Stories of what Nature has done for this, occurring in the *German Ephemerides*, and elſewhere, would ſcarce be credible, were not the Fidelity of the Relators unreproachable. Dr. *Grew* beſtows his juſt Remarks upon it, that in moſt *Wounds*, if kept clean and from the *Air*, the *Fleſh* will glue together with a *native Balm* of its own; and that *broken Bones* are cemented with a *Callus*, which they themſelves help to make: yea, *Diſeaſes* themſelves are not uſeleſs, for the *Blood* in a *Fever*, if well govern'd, like Wine upon the *fret*, will diſcharge itſelf of all heterogeneous Mixtures. But the Philoſopher laſt quoted obſerves, *Nothing can be more admirable than the many ways Nature hath provided for preventing or curing of Fevers.* Yea, Mr. *Boyle* and others have entertained us with ſurprizing Relations, how the Senſes of *Seeing* and *Hearing* have been reſtored and ſtrangely quickned by *acute Fevers* befalling thoſe that wanted them.

The *Harmony* and *Sympathy* between the Members of the Body, made by the Commerce of the *Nerves*, and their moſt curious *Ramifications* thro the whole Body, is, as Mr. *Derham* obſerves, a moſt *admirable thing*, and ſuch as greatly ſets forth the Wiſdom and Benignity of the Great Creator; to ſee how *God hath ſo tempered the Body together, that the Members ſhould have*

the

the same care one for another, and if one Member suffer, all the Members suffer with it !

One Instance is by Mr. *Derham* singled out ; there is one *Conjugation of the Nerves,* which is branched into the *Ball,* and the *Muscles,* and the *Glands* of the *Eye* ; to the *Ear,* to the *Jaws,* and the *Gums,* and the *Teeth* ; to the *Muscles* of the *Lips,* to the *Tonsils,* the *Palate,* the *Tongue,* and the Parts of the *Mouth* ; to the *Præcordia* too ; and lastly, to the *Muscles* of the *Face,* and very particularly those of the *Cheeks.* Hence 'tis that a *gustable* thing, seen or smelt, excites the *Appetite,* and affects the *Glands* and Parts of the *Mouth.* A *shameful* thing seen or heard affects the *Cheeks.* If the *Fancy* be pleased, the *Præcordia* are affected, and the Muscles of the *Mouth* and *Face* are put into the Motions of *Laughter.* When *Sadness* is caused, it exerts itself upon the *Præcordia,* and the *Glands* of the *Eyes* emit their *Tears;* wherein also, as was long since noted, *Fletus ærumnas levat,* and the Muscles of the *Face* put on a sorrowful Aspect. Hence also the *torvous Look,* produced by *Anger* and *Hatred;* and a *gay Countenance* accompanies *Love,* and *Hope,* and *Joy.* Finally, hence 'tis that, as *Pliny* notes, the *Face* in *Man* alone is the *Index of all the Passions.*

It is an inexplicable Sympathy which there is between the Diseases of the *Belly* and those of the *Skin;* whence very stubborn *Diarrhæa's* cured by *Diaphoreticks.*

What a Sympathy between the *Feet* and the *Bowels!* The Priests walking *barefoot* on the Pavement of the Temple, were often afflicted, as the *Talmuds* tell us, with Diseases in their *Bowels.* The Physician of the *Temple* was called a *Bowel-Doctor. Belly-achs* occasion'd by walking on a cold Floor, are cured by applying *hot Bricks* to the Soles of the *Feet.*

A glorious Providence of God is to be seen in three *remarkable Dissimilitudes* between *Men* and Men, *Faces, Voices,* and *Writings.*

First,

Firſt, Such is the variety of Lineaments in the *Faces* of Men, that tho *Valerius Maximus*, and ſome others, gives us Examples of Men that have been very *like* one another, yet there are no *two Faces* in all things alike. Had Nature been a blind Architect (as our curious *Ray* well obſerves) the *Faces* of ſeveral Men might have been as like as *Eggs* laid by the ſame Hen, or *Bullets* caſt in one Mould. It was one of *Pliny*'s Wonders, *In Facie Vultuque noſtro, cum ſint decem aut paulo plura membra, nullas duas in tot miliibus Hominum indiſcretas Effigies exiſtere.* Now, as my modern and better *Pliny* proceeds upon it, 'ſhould there be an in-'diſcernible Similitude between *divers Men*, what 'Confuſion and Diſturbance would neceſſarily follow? 'What *Uncertainty* in all Conveyances, Bargains and 'Contracts? What *Frauds* and *Cheats*, and ſuborning 'of *Witneſſes*? What a Subverſion of all *Trade* and 'Commerce? What Hazard in all *judicial Proceedings*? 'In Aſſaults and Batteries, in Murders and Aſſaſſi-'nations, in Thefts and Robberies, what *Security* 'would there be to Malefactors? How many other 'Inconveniences?'

Secondly, The *Voices* of Men differ too; not only divers Countries pronounce in ways peculiar to them-ſelves, but in the ſame Country how many Dialects? *Britain* as well as *Greece* exemplifies this variety; thus *Gileadites* can diſcover *Ephraimites*. *A-Lapide* tells us how the *Flemings* diſcover a *Frenchman*; and *Fuller*, what way they took in *England* long ſince to diſcover a *Dutchman*: yea, ſome have demonſtrated that *Voices* do diſtinguiſh *Individuals* as much as *Faces*, and in ſome Caſes more; for this way the Diſcovery is made in the *Dark*, and by the *Blind* alſo.

Thirdly, Dr. *Cockburn* ſhall ſupply us with one *Diſ-fimilitude* more: 'To no other Cauſe than the wiſe 'Providence of God can be referr'd the no leſs ſtrange 'variety of *Hand-writings*. Common Experience ſhews, 'that tho Hundreds and Thouſands were taught by

'one

'one Master, and one and the same Form of Writing,
'yet they all *write differently*; there is something *pe-*
'*culiar* in every one's *Writing*, which distinguishes it;
'some indeed can counterfeit another's Character and
'Subscription, but the Instances are rare, nor is it
'done without Pains and Trouble: nay, the most
'Expert and Skilful cannot *write much* so exactly like,
'that it cannot be known whether it be genuine or
'counterfeit; and if the Providence of God did not
'so order it, what Cheats and Forgeries too would
'be daily committed, which would run all into Con-
'fusion? The diversity of *Hand-writing* is of mighty
'great Use to the Peace of the World; and what is
'so very useful is not the Effect of any Human Con-
'cert; Men did not of themselves agree to it, they
'are only carried to it by the secret Providence of
'God.'

My God, let me never do any thing that may be to the
Damage of that which thou proclaimest thyself so very tender
of! HUMAN SOCIETY, *Mankind associated.*

The *Variety* of the *Parts* whereof the Body is composed cannot but oblige our Admiration, cannot but
compel our admiring Souls to acknowledge our glorious Maker!

The *Bones* in a Skeleton are two hundred and
forty-five, besides the *Ossa Sesamoidæa*, which are forty-eight.

The *Muscles* of the Body are four hundred and
forty-six.

The *Nerves* which come immediately out of the
Skull, from the *Medulla oblongata*, are ten Pair.

The *Nerves* which come out between the *Vertebræ*
are thirty Pair.

The *Scarf-skin* examin'd with a Microscope, appears made up of Lays of exceeding small *Scales*, which
cover one another more or less, according to the different Thickness of the *Scarf-skin* in the several Parts
of the Body; but in the Lips they only in a manner
touch

touch one another. *Leuenhoeck* reckons that in one *cuticular Scale* there may be five hundred *excretory Channels*, and that one Grain of *Sand* will cover two hundred and fifty Scales; wherefore one Grain of Sand will cover one hundred and twenty-five thousand *Orifices*, thro which we are *daily perspiring*. What a prodigious number of *Glands* must there now be on the Surface of the whole Body! Into every one of these *Glands* there enters an *Artery*, a *Vein*, and a *Nerve*. How many *Organs* now in all the Body!

Look upon thy *Skin*, O Man, and say, *Great God, how wondrously hast thou clothed me!*

Daily perspiring, I said. The Sum of all the Particles that are strained thro the *cuticular Glands,* is reckon'd by *Sanctorius* to amount to about *fifty Ounces* in a day; so that supposing a Man's Body to weigh *one hundred and sixty Pounds,* in *fifty one Days* a Quantity equal to the whole Body is perspired. The *Medicina Statica* will multiply the Calls to us to glorify the God who so upholds our *Souls in Life.*

But then the *multitude* of *Intentions* which our Creator has in the Formation of our several Parts, and the *Qualifications* they require to fit them for their various Uses, this also calls for our Wonders. **Dr.** *Wilkins* takes notice of it, that according to *Galen* there are in an Human Body above six hundred several *Muscles,* and there are no less than ten several Intentions to be observed in each of these; about the *Muscles* alone there are at least six thousand several Ends or Aims to be attended to. They reckon the *Bones* to be two hundred and eighty-four, the distinct Intentions of each of these are no fewer than forty; the whole Number of Scopes for the *Bones* arise to an hundred thousand: thus it is in proportion with all the other Parts, the *Skin, Ligaments, Vessels, Glandules, Humours,* but more peculiarly with the several Members of the Body, which do in regard of the *multitude* of Intentions or Qualifications required to

them,

them, very much exceed the *homogeneous* Parts; a failing in any one of these would cause an Irregularity in the Body, and in many of them, as the Doctor notes, it would be such as would be very notorious. *My Friend*, contemplate the Figures of *Spigelius*, and *Bidloe*, and *Lyferus*, if thou canst without Astonishment! Who can behold a Machine composed of so many Parts, to the right Form, and Order, and Motion whereof there are such an infinite number of Intentions required, without crying out, *Who can be compared to the Lord!*

The *variety of Offices* which sometimes *one Part* performs, will here come into Consideration. Thus the *Tongue*, it serves not only for *tasting*, but also for the *Mastication* and the *Deglutition* of our Food; and then for the Formation of our Words in *speaking*, the use of it is admirable! The *Diaphragm*, with the Muscles of the *Abdomen*, are of use, not only in *Respiration*, but also for the compression of the *Intestines*, that the *Chyle* may be forced into the *Lacteal* Veins, and out of them into the *Thoracick* Channel; and no doubt the comminution of the Meat in the *Stomach* is likewise hereby assisted. The *muscular Contraction* of the *Heart*, in the Pulse of it, serves not only for the *Circulation* of the *Blood*, but also for the more perfect *Mixture* of it, by which it is preserved in its due Crasis and Fluidity, and it incorporates the *Chyle* and other Juices it receives with it.

Even *Pain* itself, however afflictive it be, yet is of *Use* to us; it quickens us to seek for Help, and makes us careful to avoid what may be for our *Hurt*; it is, as Mr. *Ray* calls it, a πολύχρηστον in the Government of the World.

The mention of *Pain* leads one to think on *Sleep*; *Sleep*, a thing so necessary to repair the great Expence of Spirits we make in the day-time, thro the constant exercise of our *Senses* and motion of our *Muscles*. 'Tis a little surprizing, that tho we lie long on one side,

we

we have no fenfe of *Pain* during our *Sleep,* no, nor when we awake. One would think the whole Weight of the Body preffing the Side on which we lie, fhould be very burdenfome and uneafy, and create a grievous *Pain* to us; and if we lie *long awake* we really find it fo. Our ingenious *Ray* fuppofes that our Eafe in this cafe may be owing to an *Inflation of the Mufcles,* whereby they become foft, and yet renitent, like fo many Pillows, diffipating the force of the Preffure, and fo the feeling of the Pain. Hence when we reft in our *Clothes* we loofe our Garters, our Buckles, and other Ligatures, to give the Spirits a free Paffage, elfe thefe Parts will be *pained,* which when we are awake are not fo. The reafon of this Ἀναλγησία, during and after a long Sleep on one fide, is by Dr. *Lyfter* and by Dr. *Jones* attributed to the *Relaxation* of the *Nerves* and Mufcles in the time of Sleep; or *Pain* while we lie awake, is owing to the *Tenfion* of them.

O merciful God, thou makeft my Bed for me!

Let more particular Parts of our *Body* come into Confideration with us; 'tis impoffible for them to do fo without coming into Admiration too!

The *Head* ought certainly to be firft confidered. The *Head,* becaufe it muft contain a large *Brain,* is made of a moft capacious Figure, as near as may be to a *Spherical.*

What an infinite number of *Glands* in the *cortical* part, and of beginning *Nerves* in the *medullar* part; an hundred whereof exceed not one *fingle Hair.*

Upon the *Head* grows the *Hair,* which is of great ufe, not only to quench the Stroke of a Blow at the Skull, but alfo to cherifh the *Brain;* it ferves alfo to disburthen the *Brain* of a fuperfluous Moifture, wherewith it abounds. *Marchetti* finds that *Baldnefs* comes from the *Drynefs* of the *Brain,* and the fhrinking of it from the Skull; he found an *empty Space* between the *Brain* and the *Skull* in the Bald. The *Hair* is likewife a graceful Ornament, elfe, as Mr. *Ray* obferves, *the*

prefent

present Age would not beſtow ſo much Money upon Peri-
wigs.

How commodiouſly are the *Nerves,* wherewith four
of the *Senſes* are ſerved, as well as all the *ſuperiour
Parts,* all ſent out the ſhorteſt and ſafeſt ways, thro
proper Holes in the *Head.* And thoſe that ſerve the
Inferiour, carried down in a *Bony Channel.* And as
Dr. *Cheyne* remarks, it is very remarkable, that the
Veins do not paſs out at the ſame Holes the *Arteries*
enter; for if they did, then upon any violent Motion
of the Blood, or any greater Quantity thereof than
ordinary, lodged in the *Arteries,* their *Dilatation* and
Pulſation would compreſs the *Veins* againſt the *Bony*
Sides of their Paſſage, and ſo occaſion a *Stagnation* and
Extravaſation of the Blood in the *Brain,* to the Deſtruction of the whole *Machine,* which by theſe different *Entries* and *Exits* of theſe Veſſels is prevented.

The *Brain,* the *cortical* Parts thereof, ſerve to
make the *Animal Spirits;* that is, to ſeparate them
from the Blood: The *Medullary* Parts to receive
them, and convey them from thence into the *Nerves.*

The inner *Meninx,* by its *Conſtriction,* upon occaſion, cauſes a more vigorous Efflux of the Spirits, and
thereby the better Irradiation of the *Organs* of Motion and Senſe. By the frequent Repetition of this
Conſtriction all the day, being tired, as all other *Muſcles* are by continual Action, it is anon relaxed, or
ſuſpended from Action. Hereupon, the Efflux of the
Spirits into the ſaid *Organs,* being made more ſlowly,
we fall *aſleep.*

A great Philoſopher obſerves and affirms, that the
Clearneſs of our *Fancy* depends on the *regular Structure*
of the *Brain;* by which it is fitted for the receiving
and compounding of all Impreſſions with the more
Regularity. In *Fools* the *Brain* is deformed. The
Deformity is not eaſily noted in other People: But,
no doubt, a ſmaller Difference than can be imagined,

may

may alter the Symmetry of the Brain, and so the Perspicuity of the Fancy.

Gracious God ! how much ought I to adore the Goodness of thy superintending Providence, which gave my Brain that Conformation, that enables me now to see and write thy Praises.

The *Head* has wonderful things to show : But can any thing in the World be shown so curious and marvellous as the E Y E ! Our excellent *Ray* says truly, *Not the least Curiosity can be added to it.* What *Rhetorick* what *Poetry* can sufficiently celebrate the Glories of this admirable *Organ ! How perverted the Eye, which is not ever unto the Lord, the glorious Maker of it !* There was much Discourse all over *Europe* a while ago, concerning a Child, in whose *Right Eye* there were very apparent and legible, those *Latin* Capitals, *D E U S M E U S ;* and in whose Left Eye, those *Hebrew* Letters, אדני, *My Lord.* This we may justly say, No rational Beholder can look upon the *Eye*, without seeing Reason in the wondrous Workmanship thereof, to make this Confession, *The Maker of this Organ is for ever to be adored, as M Y God and M Y Lord.*

The Place of the *Eye*, even in the *Head*, how agreeable ! 'Tis here not only near to the *Brain*, but also advantaged for the *better View* of Objects, and better defended and secured. How unhappy were the People, if there were any such as *Pliny* tells of, *Oculis Pectori affixis*, and *Oculos in humeris habentes ;* from whom our famous Romancer *Mandeville*, doubtless, took hints for some of his Fables. *Galen* would satisfy us, if we wanted any Satisfaction, that the *Eye* in the *Hand* would have had many inconvenient Circumstances.

The *spherical Form* of the *Eye*, how commodious ! To lodge the Humours, and also take in the Objects, and likewise to befriend the Motions ! The Parts of the *Eye* being made convex, especially the *chrystaline,* which is of a lenticular Figure, convex on both sides ;

by

by the Refractions there made, there is a direction of many Rays coming from one point in the Object, namely, as many as the Pupil can receive, to one point answerable in the bottom of the Eye, without which the Sense would be obscure and confused. The difference between a Picture that is received on a *white Paper* in a *dark Room*, thro an open or empty Hole, and the same received thro an Hole furnished with an exactly polished lenticular Chryftal, is brought by Mr. *Ray* to illustrate this.

The *Membranes* and *Humours* of the *Eye* are all purely *transparent*, purely *pellucid*; thus none of the Rays let in are suffocated before they reach the bottom of the *Eye*, nor are they *sophisticated* with the Tincture of any *Colour*, by which that Colour might be refunded on the Object, and the Soul deceived.

The *uveous Coat* or *Iris* of the *Eye* has a musculous Power, and can contract or dilate the Pupil; the former is to preserve the *Eye* from Injury, by too lucid an Object that may be too near to it; the latter is to apprehend a remoter Object, or one placed in a fainter Light: all, as 'tis justly said by *Scheiner, Tam miro Artificio, quam munifica Naturæ largitate.* There are some Animals which can so close the *Pupil* as to admit of, one may say, one single Ray of *Light*, and by throwing all open again they can take in the faintest Rays; 'tis an incomparable provision for them who must watch for their *Prey* in the *Night*. These have also another astonishing provision for their business, which is a *Radiation of the Eyes*, from the shining of the *Retina* about the *Optick Nerve*. Man has not this provision, because he has no occasion; and yet there have been Instances of some whose *Iris* has had the Faculty so to dart out Rays of *Light*, that they could see in the Dark. *Willis* and *Briggs* mention divers Instances; and *Pliny* tells us, 'twas reported of *Tiberius Cæsar*, that *Expergefactus noctu paulisper, haud alio modo quam luce clara, contueretur omnia.*

The

The *uveous Coat* and the infide of the *Choroides* are wonderfully blackened; this is, that the Rays may be fuppreffed there, and not fo reflected backwards as to confound the Sight: if any be reflected by the *retiform Coat*, they are foon choak'd in the black infide of the *Uvea*; were they to and fro reflected, there could be no diftinct Vifion; as the *Light* admitted into a dark Room would obliterate the Species, which before were feen upon white Paper, by the Light let in thro an Orifice in the Wall; Dr. *Briggs* adds this reafon for it, *Quod Radii in Vifione fuperflui, qui ab Objectis lateralibus proveniunt, hoc ritu abforbeantur.*

Dr. *Grew* makes a juft Exclamation: What more wonderful than to fee *two Humours* of *equal Ufe* to true Vifion, bred fo near together as to be contained within one common Coat, and yet one of them as *clear* as Chryftal, the other as *black* as Ink!

Since the *Rays* from an Object nearer to us, or farther from us, don't meet juft in the fame diftance behind the *chryftalline Humour*, therefore the *ciliary Proceffes*, or the Ligaments obferved in the infide of the *fclerotick Tunicles* of the *Eye*, do ferve inftead of a Mufcle, by their contraction, to alter the Figure of the *Eye*, and make it broader; and confequently draw the *Retina* nearer to the *chryftalline Humour*, and by the relaxation thereof fuffer it to return to its natural diftance, according to the Exigency of the Object, in refpect of diftance more or lefs. Dr. *Grew* afcribes to the *Ligamentum Ciliare* a power of making the *Chryftalline* more convex, as well as of moving it either to or from the *Retina*; and indeed by the Laws of *Opticks* there muft be fomething of this neceffary to diftinct Vifion.

The *chryftalline Humour*, when dried, appears manifeftly to be made up of many very thin *fpherical Scales*, lying one upon another; *Leuenhoeck* reckons there may be two thoufand of them in one *Chryftalline*, from the outermoft to the Center: every one of thefe wonderful

ful Scales is made up of one fingle Fibre, or the fineſt Thread imaginable, wound in a ſtupendous manner this way and that way, ſo as to run ſeveral Courſes, and meet in as many Centers, and yet not in any one place to interfere ot croſs one another. Some ingenious Men have queſtion'd this, but Mr. *Derham* ſilences them with, *It is what I myſelf have ſeen, and can ſhew to any body with the help of a good Microſcope.*

Peter Herigon has obſerved a remarkable thing about the Inſertion of the *Optick Nerve* into the Bulb of the *Eye.* The Situation of it is not juſt *behind* the *Eye,* but on *one ſide,* leſt that part of the Image which falls upon the Hole of the *Optick Nerve* ſhould want its Picture. But Mr. *Ray* will rather have the reaſon to be, becauſe if the *Optick Axis* fall upon ſuch a Center, as it would were the *Nerve* ſeated juſt behind the *Eye,* this great Inconvenience would follow, that the middle point of every Object we view'd would be inviſible, or there would a dark Spot appear in the midſt of it. Behold, a Situation of a *Nerve,* which any one would at firſt have thought inconvenient, now evidently found to be aſſign'd by a moſt admirable Wiſdom!

And then, what a wiſe Contrivance, particularly about the motion of the *Eye,* in uniting into one that Pair which are called *the motory Nerves?* Each of theſe do ſend their Branches in each Muſcle of each *Eye;* this would cauſe a *Diſtortion* of the *Eyes:* but being united near their Inſertion, they cauſe *both Eyes* to have but *one motion;* when one Eye is moved this or that way, the other is turned the ſame way with it. But what ſhall we ſay concerning this? There is a decuſſation of the *Rays* in the *Pupil* of the *Eye,* the Image of the Object in the *Retina,* or bottom of the *Eye,* is *inverted;* whence does it come to paſs that it appears not ſo, but in its *natural Poſture?* Why the *viſual Rays* coming in ſtrait Lines by thoſe Points of the Senſory, or the *Retina,* which they touch, affect the common Senſe or Soul, according to their direction;

tion ; they ſignify to it, that the ſeveral Parts of
the Object, from whence they proceed, lie in ſtrait
Lines (Point for Point) drawn thro the *Pupil,* to the
ſeveral Points of the *Senſory,* where they terminate,
and which they preſs upon : Whereupon the Soul
muſt needs conceive the Object in its true Poſture.
The *Nerves* are naturally made, for to inform the
Soul, not only of the external Objects, which do preſs
thereupon, but alſo of their *Situation.* Hence the
Objects will appear double, if the *Eyes* be diſtorted.
This is *Des Cartes*'s way of accounting for this My-
ſtery : *Notitia illius ex nulla Imagine pendet, nec ex ulla
Actione ab objectis veniente, ſed ex ſolo ſitu exiguarum
partium cerebri, è quibus Nervi expullulant.* Mr. *Molyneux* contents himſelf with this Account : *The
Eye is only the Organ or Inſtrument, it is the Soul that ſees
by means of the* EYE. *To enquire how the Soul perceives
the Object erect, by an inverted Image, is to enquire into
the Soul's Faculties.*

Even the *aqueous Humour* is not an uſeleſs one : It
ſuſtains the *Uvea Tunica,* which elſe would fall flat
upon the *Chryſtalline.*

Becauſe the *outermoſt Coat* of the *Eye* might chance
to be wounded or pricked, and this fluid Humour
be let out, there is therefore a Proviſion made, ſpeedily to repair it, by the help of certain *Water-Pipes,* or
Lymphaducts, inſerted into the Bulb of the *Eye,* proceeding from *Glandules* deſigned by Nature to ſeparate this Water from the Blood for that Uſe. *Antonius Nuck* found, that if the *Eye* of an Animal be
pricked, and the *aqueous Humour* ſqueezed out, in the
ſpace of ten hours the Humour and Sight would be
reſtored unto the *Eye,* at leaſt if the Creature be kept
in the Dark. *Verzaſcha* gives divers Examples, both
antient and modern, of *Sight* ſtrangely recovered, by
the Reparation of the *aqueous Humour,* after it had
been let out at very dangerous Wounds.

It

It is remarkable, that the *horny Coat* of the *Eye* does not lie in the same Superficies with the White of the *Eye*; but it rises up, as it were on Hillock, above its Convexity, and is of an *Hyperbolical* or *Parabolical* Figure. Tho' the *Eye* seems to be perfectly round, in reality it is not so; but the *Iris* thereof is protuberant above the *White*: and the Reason is, because if the *Cornea Tunica*, or *Chryſtalline Humour*, had been concentrical to the *Sclerodes*, the *Eye* could not have admitted a whole Hemisphere at one View; and as by *Sheiner* noted upon it, *Sic Animalis Incolumitati in multis rebus minus cautum eſſet.*

Dr. *More* has now a Remark, That the Eye being thus perfect, the Reason of Man would easily have rested here, and admired the Contrivance. Being able to move himself every way, he might have thought himself every way sufficiently provided for. But, behold! An Addition to this Perfection! There are *Muſcles* also added unto the *Eyes!* For we have occasion, particularly in *reading*, to move our *Eyes*, without moving our *Head*. The *Organ* is therefore furnished with no less than *ſix Muſcles*, to move it upwards, downwards, to the right, to the left, obliquely, and round about.

And now, for the Security of this wonderful *Organ*, the *Eyes* are sunk in a convenient Valley, where, as *Tully* says, *Latent utiliter*; and they are encompassed round with Eminencies, as within a Rampart: *Excelſis undique partibus ſepiuntur.* This defends them from the Strokes of any flat or broad Bodies. Above stand the *Eye-brows*, to keep off any thing from running down upon them, says the same Orator, *Superiora Superciliis obducta, ſudorem à Capite & Fronte defluentem repellunt*; the *Eye-lids* then fence them from sudden and lesser Stripes: whereas the *Fiſhes*, who have no occasion for a Defensative against Dust and Motes, are destitute of *Eye-lids!* The *nictitating Membrane* is an abundant Provision for all their Occasions! These

Eye-lids,

Eye-lids, also round the Edges, are fortified with *Bristles*, like Palisadoes, to keep off the Incursions of troublesome Insects. 'Tis remarkable, that these Hairs grow to a *determinate*, but a most *commodious* Length, and need no *cutting*, as many other Hairs of the Body do; and that their Points do stand out of the way, bending *upwards* in the upper Lid, in the lower *downwards*. But then *Sleep* is necessary for us. This would be disturbed, if the *Windows* were always open to the Light. Here are *Curtains* then to be drawn, for the keeping of it out. Yet more: The outward Coat of the *Eye* must be kept *pellucid*. This would anon dry and shrink, and lose its *Diaphaneity*, if the Eyes were always open. The *Eye-lids* are therefore so contrived, as often to wink. Thus they varnish the *Eyes* with their *Moisture* over again: They have *Glandules*, on purpose to separate an Humour for that use, and withal wipe off whatever Dust or Filth may stick to them. And lest the Sight should be hinder'd, they do it, with what Celerity! *Cicero* adds, they are *Mollissimæ tactu, ne læderent Aciem:* And I will add, *Man*, who is a *sociable Creature*, and should exhibit *social Affections* by some *visible Tokens*, is here furnished with *Tears* for that purpose, beyond any other Animal.

My God, let me ever employ them, on the just Occasions for them.

It is a Passage which drops from the Pen of *a Person of Quality*, in a Treatise, entitled, *A View of the Soul*: 'It does not seem wonderful to behold a Dis-
' tillation from the Eyes, 'tis to be found in *Beast*, as
' well as in *Man*, upon an *offensive Touch* thereof: But
' when there is no such Cause to be alledged, to have
' the *Body*, as it were, *melted* on a sudden, send forth
' its Streams thro that unusual Channel, makes it seem
' to me no less than the quick and violent Agitation
' of some *Divine Flame*, thawing all the *vital Parts*,
' and drawing the Moisture thro the chief and clearest

R ' Organ

' Organ of the Body, the *Eye*, and not to be caufed
' by any thing, which is part of itfelf.'

This brings to my mind an antient **Problem**: *Cur
Deus Oculos fletus inftrumentum effe valuit.* And the
Anfwer to it, *Ut quò fordes peccatorum hauriuntur, eo-
dem per lachrymas diluantur.*

And then the *Ball* of the *Eye* has the exterior Coat
made fo thick, fo tough, fo ftrong, that it is a very
hard matter for to make a Rupture in it. But becaufe
the *Eye* muft be expofed at all Seafons, and in all Wea-
thers, there is provided for it an hot Bed of *Fat*,
which fills up the Interftices of the Mufcles ; nor is it
fo fenfible of Cold, as other Parts of our Body. 'Tis
a ftrange thing, which the *French* Academifts found
by Experience ! The *Aqueous Humour* of the *Eye* will
not *freeze*. Admirable ! It has the Fluidity and Per-
fpicuity of common Water, nothing fingular to be
difcovered in the Tafte or Smell of it. Of what *Ethereal Nature* muft we imagine it ?

Shall we, on this occafion, *look back* on the *Eyes* of
other *Animals*, and compare *ours* with *theirs*? The
Chryftalline Humour, in the *Eyes* of the *Fifhes*, is much
nearer to a *Sphere*, than that of *Land-Animals*. 'Tis
becaufe the Light has a different *Refraction* in the *Water*, from what it has in the *Air* : That *Convexity*,
which would unite the Rays of Light in the *Air*, will
not in the *Water*. In thofe *Animals*, that gather their
Food from the Ground, the *Pupil* is *Oval* or *Elliptical*,
the greater *Diameter* going *tranfverfely* from Side to
Side. In thofe that feek their Food on higher Places,
the greater *Diameter* is the *Perpendicular*. Thefe two
Figures are wonderfully fitted unto their different Neceffities. Thofe *Animals*, that have no Motion of
their *Neck*, have a Clufter of *Semifphærical Eye-balls*,
which fend in the Pictures of Objects all round about
them ; and they that feek their Food in the dark, have
a *Retina* coloured *white*, which reflects the Light, and
enables them to fee beft, when they have leaft of it.

An

An acute Philoſopher ſays juſtly, ' Theſe are won-
' derful and ſurprizing Inſtances of *Foreſight* and *Coun-*
' *ſel,* in the Being who framed thoſe *Organs.*'

But why don't we *ſee double* with our *two Eyes?*
Galen, and others after him, took this to be from a
Coalition, or Decuſſation of the *Optick Nerves.* I paſs
by the Aſſertion of the *Bartholines,* that they are
united, not by any Interſection, *ſed per totam Subſtan-*
tiæ Confuſionem. Dr. *Gibſon* ſays there is the cloſeſt
Conjunction, but no *Confuſion* of the Fibres. Others
apprehend only a *Sympathy* between the *Optick Nerves.*
Mr. *Briggs* thinks that the *Optick Nerves* of each Eye
conſiſt of *homologous Fibres,* and that theſe *Fibrillæ* have
the ſame Tenſion and other Circumſtances in both
Eyes ; and ſo when an Image is painted on the ſame
correſponding and ſympathizing Parts of the *Retina,*
the ſame Effects are produced, the ſame Notice or Information is carried to the *Thalamus Nervorum Optico-*
rum, and ſo imported and imparted to the Soul, that
is to judge of all. Our great Sir *Iſaac Newton* ſays,
Are not the Species of Objects ſeen with both Eyes, united
where the Optick Nerves meet, before they come into the
Brain, the Fibres on the right ſide of both Nerves uniting
there? Monſieur *Tauvry,* in his *Rational Anatomy,* thinks
this Anſwer to be enough : ' When we ſee the ſame
' Body with *two Organs,* we judge it to be one, be-
' cauſe we ſee it ſtill in *one place,* and refer it to *one*
' *place;* for every Point of the ſeen Object is directed
' upon *one place,* by the perpendicular Rays of each of
' the two Cones ; this is what we call *the Direction of*
' *the Optick Axis.* 'Tis a natural Conſequence from
' this Explication, that certain Diſtortions of the Eye
' will make the Object appear double, becauſe we
' then direct the ſame Point of the Object to two
' different places.'

We might go on and reſume our Enquiry, Why
Objects which are *inverted* in the bottom of the *Eye*
do not appear ſo, but in a direct Poſition? *Tauvry*

thinks

thinks it enough to fay, 'We do not judge of the Si-
' tuation of the Bodies by the *Part* which is affected
' in the *Eye*, but by the *Manner* in which it is affected;
' the Soul judges of the Object by the *Manner* in
' which the *Organ* is affected.'

To conclude our Observations of the *Eye*; Mr.
Derham very juftly fays, *None lefs than G O D could
contrive, order, and provide an Organ as magnificent and
curious as the Senfe is ufeful.* And *Sturmius* had reafon
enough to fay, he was fully perfuaded, that no Man
who furvey'd the *Eye* could abandon himfelf to any
fpeculative Atheifm. And *Cheyne* paffes a moft equal
Sentence, when he fays, *He certainly deferves not to enjoy the Bleffings of his Eyefight, whofe Mind is fo depraved
as not to acknowledge the Bounty and Wifdom of the Author
of his Nature, in the ravifhing and aftonifhing Structure of
this noble Organ!*

' *Good God!* How *unreafonable* am I, if the *Eyes*
' made by Him fhould not *be ever to the Lord!*

' An *envious Eye* is an *abufed* one; an *haughty Eye*
' is a *diftorted* one; an *unchafte Eye*, how ignominioufly
' mifapplied! It has *Dirt* thrown into it. *Gracious*
' *God*, let not my Eyes be *Port-holes of Wickednefs*. Let no
' *Death get into my Soul by thofe Windows.*'

' A *pitiful Eye* a *bountiful Eye*, and the *Eye* on the
' *Book* that will feed it well, how much to be wifh'd
' for! And an *Eye* upon a C H R I S T at His Table,
' *evidently fet forth as crucified* before it.'

' 'Tis an odd Queftion in *Tympius*, Why the *Eyes*
' are the *laft* things *quickned*, and the *firft* that are de-
' cayed? It is anfwered, *Ut quo magis eft ipforum Peri-
' culum, eo minus fit nocendi Spatium.*'

The E A R is what falls next under our Confideration; *double*, not only to provide againft the *Lofs* of
one, but alfo for the more commodious *hearing*.

'Tis aftonifhing to fee the Sagacity of fome *deaf*
Perfons, who come to underftand things that are fpo-
ken, only by *feeing* the motion of the Lips in the Spea-
ker;

ker; but the Inſtances of this are ſo rare, that they abate nothing of our Obligations to our glorious Maker for beſtowing the noble Senſe of *Hearing* upon us.

The Situation of the *Ear* is where it may give the moſt *ſpeedy Information*, and where it will *occaſion* and alſo *encounter* the leaſt Annoyance.

The *outward Ear* is moſt nicely adjuſted to the peculiar Circumſtances of every Animal. Dr. *Grew* celebrates the marvellous *Varieties* in the *Ears* of ſeveral Animals for the reception of Sound, according to their ſeveral Exigences. And Mr. *Derham* challenges our Confeſſion of a *notable Proſpect of the Handy-work of God even in ſo inconſiderable a Part as this.* In *Man* the *Form* of it is of all the moſt agreeable to the *erect Poſture* of his Body. 'Tis pity the moſt eminent of our modern *Anatomiſts* cannot yet agree whether it has any *Muſcles* belonging to it.

What a ſurprizing Spectacle the *Helix*, which in its tortuous Cavities collects the *ſonorous Undulations*, and gives them a gentle *Circulation*, with ſome *Refraction*, and conveys them to the *Concha*, that large and round Cell at the entrance of the *Ear!* Then to bridle the Evagation of the *Sound* when arrived thus far, but at the ſame time avoid any Confuſion thereof by *Repercuſſions*, what a curious proviſion is there made by thoſe little Protuberances called the *Tragus* and the *Antitragus* of the *outward Ear*, ſofter than the *Helix*, and blunting the Sound without repelling it! Monſieur *Dionis* obſerves, they that have this *Ear* cut off have *but a confuſed way of hearing.*

That the Subſtance of the *outward Ear* ſhould be *cartilaginous*; this is an admirable Contrivance of the moſt wiſe Creator. Dr. *Gibſon* obſerves, if it had been *Bone*, it would have been troubleſome, and might by many Accidents have been broken off; if it had been *Fleſh*, it would have been ſubject to Contuſion, yea, we may add, it would not then have remained ſo well expanded, nor have ſo kindly received *Sounds*, but

R 3 have

have abforbed them, and retarded them; whereas now the Sounds have their agreeable *Volutations*, as in well-built Arches, and the *Whifpering-places*, whereof the World has had many famous ones.

How artfully tunnell'd the *auditory Paffage!* But then, becaufe the Paffage muft be always open, therefore to prevent the invafion of *noxious things*, which love to retreat into every little Hole, behold, the Paffage fecured with a bitter and naufeous Excrement, afforded from *Glands* appointed for that purpofe! Where the *Meatus auditorius* is long enough to afford harbour to any Infects, there this *Ear-wax* is conftantly to be found; but *Birds*, whofe Ears are cover'd with Feathers, and where the *Tympanum* lies but a little way within the Skull, have none of it. *Schelhammer* confutes the old Anatomifts, who make this *Ear-wax* an Excrement of the *Brain*, and juftly fays, *Nil abfurdius!* Dr. *Drake* has given us an handfome Cut of the *Glandulæ Ceruminofæ. Pliny* afcribes a great medical Virtue to the *Ear-wax*, the *Sordes ex Auribus*, as curing the *Bites* of *Men*, (which he fays, *inter afperrimos numerantur*) and of *Scorpions* and *Serpents.* And Mr. *Derham* afferts he had found it a good *Balfam* in his own Experience.

The Notion of an *innate Air* in the *Ear*, is by *Schelhammer* found but a Fancy; the Paffage into the *inner Ear* from the *Throat* confutes it: but in this Paffage there is a wife provifion, as he notes, that no *Air* might pafs in thither but what fhall be changed and warmed, and fo rendred harmlefs: *Imo fortaffis non facile alius, nifi ex Pulmonibus.*

The Paffage from the *Ear* to the *Palate* (the *Tuba Euftachiana*) accurately defcribed by *Valfalva*; this is to give way to the *inner Air* upon every motion of the *Membrana Tympani*, the *Malleus*, the *Incus*, and the *Stapes*; and if this be fhut up, *Deafnefs* enfues.

And then the *Os Petrofum*, that *Bone* which contains the reft, this has a remarkable Texture and Hardnefs
above

above the other Bones of the Body, and fo it ferves
not only as a very fubftantial *Guard* to the Senfory,
but alfo, as Dr. *Vieuffens* obferves, to oppofe the Impulfes of the *æthereal Matter*, that there be no lofs of
Sound, and no confufion in it, but that the *auditory
Nerves* may have it regularly convey'd to them.

The *Membrana Tympani*, as long ago as *Hippocrates's*
Time, had fome notice taken of it, whether it has
any difengaged part, by which it is not faftned to the
boney Circle, in which it is enchafed, as Monfieur *Dionis*
affirms, is difputed.   Mr. *Derham* could not find it.
But then Dr. *Vieuffens* difcover'd a further inner Membrane, *Tenuiffimæ raræque admodum Texturæ*, whereof
the Ufes are to keep the Gate of the *Labyrinth*, left
the *thick Air* abroad hurt the *pure Air* within, and
that a due Heat may be preferved in the Bafis of the
Labyrinth.

But now the aftonifhing *four little Bones*, and *three
little Mufcles* about them, to move them, and adjuft
the whole Compages to the feveral Purpofes of *Hearing*, and for all manner of *Sounds!*

Thefe were wholly unknown to the antient Anatomifts.   *Jacobus Carpenfis* was he by whom the *Malleus* and the *Incus* were firft of all difcovered; the
Gentleman who was indeed the firft Reftorer of the
Anatomick Art, which *Vefalius* afterwards carried on.
The *Stapes* was found out by *Johannes ab Ingraffia*, a
learned *Sicilian*.   The fourth was what *Francis Syl-
vius* firft lit upon.

In *Man*, and in the *Four-footed*, they are *four*, curioufly inarticulated with one another, with an external
and internal Mufcle, to draw or work them in extending or in relaxing of the Drum.   In *Fowls* Dr. *Moulen*
could never find any more than *one Bone* and a *Cartilage*, making a Joint with it, that was eafily moveable.

It is a probable Thought of *Rohault*, That for us
to *give Attention*, is nothing elfe but for us, by ex-

tending

tending or relaxing the *Tympanum* of the *Ear*, to put it into that position, *in qua tremulum aeris externi motum excipere possit*, wherein it shall be most sensible of the motion of the *external Air*. The Benefit which *deaf* Persons receive by *loud Noises*, enabling to hear what shall be spoken to them in the midst thereof, helps to clear this Matter. Dr. *Willis* tells of one who hired a Servant who was a *Drummer*, on purpose that his *deaf Wife* might hear his Discourses, which, while the *Drum* was beating, she was able to do.

In *Birds* the *auditory Nerve* is affected from the impression made on the Membrane, only by the intermediation of the *Columella*; but in *Man* it is done by the intervention of the *four little Bones*, with the Muscles acting upon them, his *Hearing* being to be adjusted to all kinds of Sounds or Impressions made upon the *Membrana Tympani*; the Impressions are thus made upon the *auditory Nerve*, they first act upon the *Membrane* and the *Malleus*, the *Malleus* upon the *Incus*, the *Incus* upon the *Os orbiculare* and *Stapes*, and the *Stapes* upon the *auditory Nerve*, the Base of the *Stapes* not only covering the *Fenestra ovalis*, wherein the *auditory Nerve* lies, but also having a part of the *auditory Nerve* spread upon it. Our valuable *Derham*, upon a diligent Examination, found this to be the *Process of Hearing*.

How will the *Wonders* grow upon us, if we pass now to the *Labyrinth*! And there survey the wonderful Structure of the *Vestibulum* and the *Cochlea*, and yet more particularly the *semicircular Canals*! These last are three, and of three different Sizes. *Valsalva* thinks, that as a part of the *auditory Nerve* is lodg'd in these Canals, thus they are of *three Sizes*, the better to suit all the variety of Tones; and tho there be some difference as to the Length and Size of the Canals in different Persons, yet lest there should be *Discord* in the *auditory Organs* of one and the same Man, those *Canals* have always in the same Man a most exact Conformity to one another.

Shall

Shall we take notice of one Curioſity more! There is one of the *auditory Nerves*, whoſe Branches do ſpread partly to the Muſcles of the *Ear*, partly to the *Eye*, partly to the *Tongue* and Inſtruments of *Speech*, and inoſculated with the *Nerves*, to go to the *Heart* and *Breaſt*; by means hereof there is an uſeful and wondrous *Conſent* between theſe Parts of the Body. It is natural for moſt Animals, upon the hearing of any uncouth Sound, preſently to erect their *Ears*, and prepare them for the catching of every *Sound*, and therewithal open their *Eyes*, to ſtand as faithful Centinels upon the Watch, and be ready with the *Mouth* to call out, or utter, according to the Dictates of the preſent Occaſion; when ſurprized with any frightful Noiſe, they give a Shriek immediately.

Dr. *Willis* obſerves another great Uſe of this *nervous Commerce* between the *Ear* and the *Mouth*; *Uſum alium inſigniorem præſtat*: that is, that the *Voice* may correſpond with the *Hearing*, and be a kind of *Echo* to it; that what is *heard* with one of the two *Nerves*, may be readily expreſſed with the *Voice*, by the help of the other.

S O U N D is the Object of this admirable Senſe; the intricate nature of it has puzzled the beſt of Naturaliſts.

How many *ſounding Inſtruments* have yet been contrived by the Wit of Man, whereby *Sounds* have been augmented, and conveyed, and rendred ſerviceable!

The biggeſt Bell in *Europe* is reckon'd to be at *Erfurt* in *Germany*, which may be heard, they ſay, *four and twenty Miles*.

It is reported that *Alexander* the Great had a *Tube*, which might be heard an hundred *Stadia*, whereof the Figure is preſerved in the *Vatican*. It is a little ſtrange that no one ſhould hit upon the like Invention, till *Athanaſius Kircher*, in our Days, and ſoon after him Sir *Samuel Moreland*, whoſe *Tuba Stentorophonica* was publiſh'd in 1672.

Caves

Caves have out-done *Tubes* for bellowing. *Olaus Magnus* defcribes a *Cave* in *Finland*, into which if a Dog or any other Animal be caft, it fends forth fo dreadful a Sound as to knock down every one that is near it ; and they have therefore guarded it with high Walls to prevent fuch a Mifchief. *Peter Martyr* informs us of a *Cave* in *Hifpaniola*, which with a fmall Weight caft into it, will with its hideous noife at five Miles diftance endanger Deafnefs. *Kircher* in his *Phonurgia* finds a Pit in the *Cucumer Mountains* of *Switzerland*, that fends out a fearful *Noife*, and *Wind* accompanying of it ; and a Well in that Country, a noife in which is equal to that of a great Gun.

Olaus Magnus mentioning the vaft high Mountains of *Augermannia*, tells, that the Waves of the Sea ftriking at the bottom thereof, make fuch a terrible noife, as not only to *deafen* the Mariners, but alfo to *ficken* them, and even to fright them out of their Wits, if they dare approach them. *Habent Bafes illorum Montium in Fluctuum ingreffu & egreffu tortuofas rimas, five fciffuras, fatis ftupendo Naturæ Opificio fabricatas, in quibus longa Voragine formidabilis ille fonitus, quafi fubterraneum tonitru generatur.*

The prodigious *Cataract* of *Niagara*, whereof *Hennepin* has given fome relation, produces a *Noife* which perhaps nothing on Earth has equall'd ; a *Noife* which it might well nigh deafen one to think upon.

What is the Matter of *Sound* ? The *Atmofphere* in grofs ? Or the *ethereal part* of it ? Or fome foniferous *Je-ne-fçay-quoy* Particles of Bodies ?

That the *Air* is the Medium of *Sound*, is manifeft from Experiment. In an *unexhaufted Receiver* a fmall Bell may be heard at the diftance of feveral Paces ; but when it is exhaufted, it can fcarce be heard at the neareft diftance : if the *Air* be compreffed, a *Sound* will be louder, proportionably to the Compreffion, or the Quantity of *Air* crouded in ; the Experiment fucceeds, not only in *forced* Rarefactions and Condenfa-

tions

tions of the Air, but alſo in ſuch as are *natural.* The Story of the *Piſtols* diſcharged by *Frædlichius* on the *Carpathean* Mountains, related by *Varenius,* gives an Inſtance how the *Sound* was diminiſhed, by the rarity of the Air, at the great Aſcent up to the Atmoſphere; but how magnified by the *Polyphoniſms,* or the Repercuſſions of the Rocks and Caverns, and other *phonocaptick Objeɛts* in the Mount below!

The *Water* alſo is capable of tranſmitting a *Sound;* the *Sound* of a *Bell* ſtruck under Water is heard, tho as much more dull, and not ſo loud: Judges in *muſical Notes* pronounce it about a *fourth* deeper.

Divers at the bottom of the Sea can hear *Noiſes* made above, but confuſedly; thoſe above cannot hear the *Divers* below at all.

Dr. *Hearn* tells of Guns fired at *Stockholm,* which were heard an hundred and fourſcore *Engliſh* Miles. In the *Dutch* War, Guns were heard above two hundred Miles. If we go more Southward, Guns at *Florence* are heard at *Leghorn,* which is ſixty-five Miles. When the *French* bombarded *Genoa,* they were heard at *Leghorn,* which is ninety Miles. In the Inſurreɛtion at *Meſſina* they were heard at *Syracuſe,* which is an hundred Miles. This inclines Mr. *Derham* to think that *Sounds* fly near as far in the Southern as in the Northern Regions, tho the *Mercury* in the *Barometer* does riſe higher without the *Tropicks* than within the *Tropicks;* and the more Northerly, ſtill the higher, which may increaſe the *Sounds.*

Celebrated Authors differ about the Velocity of *Sounds.* Mr. *Derham* has by nice Experiments determined, that there is a ſmall difference in *Sounds* before the *Wind* and againſt it, and this a little abated or augmented, according to the Strength of the *Wind;* but nothing elſe in the World will affeɛt it: and there is one motion to all kinds of *Sounds,* whether loud or low; and they all fly *equal Spaces* in *equal Times;* and laſtly, the *Mean* of their Flight is at the rate of a

Mile

Mile in $9\frac{1}{4}$ half Seconds, or 1142 Feet in one *Second* of Time.

The Power of *muſical Sounds* over the *Spirits* of *Men*, yea, and over their *Bodies* too, is very ſurprizing. What could the famous *Timothy* the Muſician do upon *Alexander?* What another upon *Ericus?* *Athanaſius Kircher* in his *Phonurgia*, and *Iſaac Voſſius* writing *de Poematum Cantu & Rythmi Viribus*, report ſtrange things of the Power which *Muſick* has over the Affections.

The *German Ephemerides* mentions thoſe, who at ſome Notes of *Muſick* are unable to hold their *Water*. *Morhoff* tells us of thoſe who would break *Romer Glaſſes* with their *Voice*. Great Sea-Commanders have ob-ſerved, that their *wounded Men*, with broken Limbs, undergo much Pain at the Enemies Diſcharges. 'Tis well known that *Seats* will ſometimes tremble at the Sound of *Organs*.

The Force of *Muſick* on Perſons poiſoned with the *Tarantula*, is altogether aſtoniſhing!

Iſmenias the *Theban*, by playing on the *Flute* or *Harp*, cured the *Sciatica*. In the late *French* Hiſtory of the *Academy of Sciences*, there is a Man cured of a *Fever* and *Frenzy* by *proper Tunes* play'd to him.

But after all, who but a God infinitely wiſe could contrive ſuch a *fine Body*, ſo ſuſceptible of every Im-preſſion that the Senſe of *Hearing* has occaſion for; and thus empower Animals to expreſs their *Senſe of things* to one another?

Mr. *Derham* thus juſtly concludes his Diſcourſe on the Senſe of *Hearing*; 'Who can ſurvey all this admi-' rable Work, and not as readily own it to be the ' Work of an omnipotent and infinitely wiſe and good ' God, as the moſt *artful Melodies* we hear, are the ' Voice or Performances of a living Creature!'

Great God, let me ever uſe my Ear to learn what thou wouldſt have me to know, and ſhut my Ear upon thoſe things, wherewith to be unacquainted is a learned Ignorance!

' May I have the Happineſs of that Experience, ' *Faith comes by hearing.*'

I

I will add one Remark : Many have been born deſtitute of *Seeing*; many born deſtitute of *Hearing*; expoſed unto many Inconveniences by the want of the *Senſe* whereof they were deſtitute ; however capable of being provided for. I could never learn, that any Child of Man was born deſtitute of *both Senſes*; one deſtitute of both could not be in any Capacity of being provided for. *My God, I behold thy Compaſſion, and I adore it !*

What a Proviſion has our Glorious Creator made for our Smelling ? The Apertures of our *Noſtrils,* which are cartilaginous, and accommodated with proper and curious *Muſcles*, have, as our *Derham* notes, *all the Signatures of Accuracy.* And long before him, *Tully* ; *Nares, eò quod omnis odor ad ſuperiora fertur, recte ſurſum ſunt, & quod Cibi & Potionis Judicium magnum earum eſt, non ſinè cauſâ vicinitatem Oris ſecutæ ſunt.* Here the *olfactory Nerves* receive the odoriferous Effluvia of Bodies ; and becauſe the odorant Particles are drawn in by Breathing, the upper part of the Noſe is barricadoed with *Laminæ*, which fence out noxious Bodies from entering the breathing Paſſages ; (for which purpoſe the *Vibriſci*, or Hairs placed at the entrance of the Noſtrils, are a notable Contrivance) and they receive alſo the Divarications of the *olfactory Nerves*, which are here ſpread very thick, and thus meet the *Scents* which enter by the *Breath,* and ſtrike upon them. The more accurate the Senſe of *Smelling* is in any Animal, the longer theſe *Laminæ* are, and the more in Number, folded and crouded with the more nervous Filaments, to detain and fetter the *odorous Particles*. There are Animals, the *chief Acts* of whoſe Lives are performed by the Miniſtry of this *wonderful Senſe*, and theſe have certain *Points of Proviſion*, which are not in *Man* ; but, I will not ſay, are *wanting* in him : For he has enough ; and he has utterly loſt all *Sagacity*, if he be not ſenſible of *enough*, to oblige his Praiſes of the God that made him.

Our

Out *Tasting* is as well provided for.

For the Causes of *Tastes*, and their Diversities, Dr. *Grew* will give us a more accurate Account than *Theophrastus.*

Concerning the *Organ* of *Tasting*, we will not recite the various Opinions of *Bauhin*, and *Bartholin*, and *Laurentius*, and our *Wharton.* Our *Willis* determines, *Præcipuum & fere solum gustatus Organon est Lingua.* Our *Derham* inclines to that of *Malpighi*, that since the outward Covering of the *Tongue* is perforated, and under this there lie the *Papillary Parts*, whereof Mr. *Cowper* has given us Cuts full of Elegancy, the Taste probably lies in these: *Occurrunt Papillaria Corpora, probabilius est in his ultimò, ex subintrante sapido Humore, Titillationem & Mordicationem quandam fieri, quæ Gustum efficiat.*

There are *Nerves* curiously divaricated about the *Tongue* and *Mouth*, to receive the Impressions of every *Gust*, and these Nerves guarded with a firm and proper Tegument, which defends them from Harms, but so perforated in the *Papillary Eminences*, that the *Tastes* of all things are freely admitted there.

Admirable the Situation of the *Taste* with the *Smell*, for the Discharge of their Offices, at the first Entrance into the way to the grand Receptacle of our Nourishment : that they may therefore judge what is nourishing, and what unsavoury and pernicious.

The *Taste : Qui sentire eorum quibus vescimur genera debet* ; as *Tully* long since observed, *Habitat in ea parte Oris, qua esculentis, & poculeatis iter Natura patefecit.*

Our most wise Creator has established a great Consent between the *Eye*, and the *Nose*, and the *Tongue*, by ordering the Branches of the *same Nerves* to each of those three Parts. Hereby there is all the Guard that can be against Food that may hurt us ; it is to undergo the Scrutiny of *three Senses*, before it goes into the *Stomach.*

But if the other Senſes have their *peculiar Seats*, there is one, to wit, *Feeling*, that is diſperſed thro the whole Body, both without and within. *Every Part* needs to be *ſenſible* of what may be for its own Safety, and therefore our moſt wiſe Creator has admirably lodged the Senſe of *Feeling* in *every part.* It was *Tully's* Remark, *Toto Corpore æqualibiter fuſus eſt, ut omnes Ictus, omneſque nimios & Frigoris & Caloris appulſus ſentire poſſumus.* *Pliny* adds, *Tactus ſenſus omnibus eſt, etiam quibus nullus alius.*

The *Organ* of this wonderful Senſe, is the *Nerves*; which are, in a moſt curious, aſtoniſhing, incomparable manner, ſcattered throughout the whole Body.

Malpighi, upon many Obſervations, has determin'd, that as *Taſting* is performed by the *Papillæ* in the *Tongue*, ſo *Feeling* is performed by the like *Papillæ* under the *Skin.* That theſe *Papillæ Pyramidales*, thruſting their Heads up to terminate in the outer Skin, are thoſe by which we *feel*; he ſpeaks of an *Animus abunde certior redditus.* Our diligent *Cowper* has confirmed this, and given us elegant Cuts of theſe *Papillæ*, from the Informations of the Microſcope.

Dr. *Cheyne* obſerves, the apt proportioning of that Senſe, our *Feeling*, unto the Actions and Impulſes of the Bodies among which we live, is wonderful! Had the Senſe been ten times as exquiſite as it is, we ſhould have been in perpetual Torment. Had it been many times duller and more callous than it is, we ſhould have loſt many of our moſt agreeable Delights, and we ſhould have had our tendereſt Parts conſumed without Knowledge or Concern. This nice Adjuſtment!

We were but now pretty near the *Teeth*; of theſe the *Numbers* are *thirty two.* But, Oh! how many more the *Wonders* ! *Galen* obſerves, we commend the Skill and Senſe of him that ſhall well marſhal a Company of *thirty two* : and ſhall we not admire him who hath ſo admirably diſpoſed theſe *thirty two* ?

We

We will here single out eight or nine things, that are very remarkable : The *Teeth* continue to *grow* in their Length as long as we live, as appears by the unsightly Length of a *Tooth*, when the opposite happens to be pulled out. Thus Providence repairs the waste that is daily made of the *Teeth*, by the frequent Attrition in Mastication. That part of the *Teeth*, which is above the Gums, is not invested with the sensible Membrane, called *Periostium*, with which the other Bones are covered; but then the *Teeth* are of a *closer* and *harder* Substance than the rest of the Bones, that they may not be so soon worn down by grinding the Food. For the *nourishing* of these necessary Bones, the Glorious Creator has wonderously contrived an *unseen Cavity* in each side of the *Jaw-Bone*, in which are lodged an *Artery*, a *Vein*, and a *Nerve*, which thro lesser Gutters do send their Twigs to each particular Tooth. But because *Infants* are to feed a considerable while upon *Milk*, and lest their Teeth should hurt the tender Nipples of the *Nurse*, Nature defers the Production of them for many Months ; whereas divers Animals, which must *seek betimes* a Food that needs Mastication, are born with them. The different Figure of the *Teeth*, how surprizing ! The *Foreteeth*, called *Incisores*, broad, with a thin and sharp Edge, to cut off a Morsel from any solid Food. The *Eye-Teeth*, called *Canini*, stronger, deeper, and more able to tear the resisting sort of Aliments. The *Jaw-Teeth*, called *Molares*, flat, broad, uneven, accommodated with little Knobs, to hold, and grind, and mix the Aliments.

Because the Operations, to be performed by the *Teeth*, sometimes require a considerable Strength, what strong *Muscles* is the lower Jaw provided withal ! And every *Tooth* is placed in a strong, a close, a deep Socket ; and the *Teeth* are furnished with *Holdfasts*, that are suitable to the stress, which in their different Offices they may be put unto. The *Fore-teeth* and the

the *Eye-teeth* have usually but *one Root*, which, in the latter, is very long; but the *Grinders*, that must manage hard Bodies, have *three Roots*, and in the upper Jaw often *four*, because these are pendulous, and the Jaw something softer.   How convenient the Situation of the *Teeth!* The *Grinders*, nearest the Center of their Motion, because the greatest Force is required in them; the *Cutters*, where they may readily cut off what is to be transmitted to the *Grinders*.   Finally, the *Jaw*, that is furnished with *Grinders*, has an oblique or transverse Motion, which is necessary for the Comminution of the Meat : But this Motion is not in the Jaw of Animals, which have not such *Teeth* belonging to them.

' *Temperance* in *Feeding*, is one special Article of
' the Homage we owe to the Glorious One, who has,
' in our *Teeth*, so display'd his admirable Workman-
' ship!'

And we are now not far from the *Tongue*, the *Uses* whereof are, how various! how marvellous! and the *Texture* how much to be wonder'd at! You were in the right of it, *Vesalius*, when you told us, *That no Mortal had ever yet thorowly consider'd all the Wonders of it.*

This is the main Organ of *Tasting*; it helps also in the *Mastication*, and the *Deglutition* of the Food.

Here the *Spittle* has its Vent; which, tho commonly taken for an *Excrement*, is indeed an *Humour* wonderfully serviceable; because a great part of our Food is dry, there are provided several *Glandules*, to separate this Juice from the Blood, and no less than four pair of *Channels* to convey it into the Mouth, which are lately found out, and called the *Ductus Salivales*; and through which the *Saliva* continually distilling, serves to macerate our Food, and, by tempering of it, render it fit for chewing and swallowing. And hereby also the *Concoction* in the Stomach is not a little promoted.

S   But

But the grand *Glory* of the *Tongue*, is, that it is the main Inftrument of *fpeaking*; and *therewith we blefs God, even our Father!* This is a Faculty peculiar to *Man*: It was never known that a *Beaft* could attain to any thing of it. A *Bird* indeed has been taught now and then a few words, and with no little difficulty; but then he *underftands not* the meaning of his few words, nor does he ufe them for Signs of things conceived by him. The moft that can be pretended, is, that a *Parrot* being ufed unto fuch or fuch Enjoyments or Afflictions, at the Prolation of certain *words*, may exprefs his Paffions by the noife of thefe *words*. The *Jewifh* Rabbins were not fo very abfurd in defining a Man, *Animal loquens*, a Creature that fpeaks. By the way, ' you that are *Stammerers* ought
' exceedingly to humble yourfelves before the Holy
' God, under his Rebuke upon you, in an *Organ*,
' which, well employed, would be your *Glory*. Our
' Saviour, feeing a Man that had *an Impediment in his
' Speech*, he *fighed* upon it; no doubt it grieved him
' to fee a Man fo *marked* by the Difpleafure of God,
' in a moft fenfible Wound upon fo diftinguifhing a
' Faculty. *My Friends*, learn to *fpeak deliberately.*
' This Expedient alone would help you wonderful-
' ly: For in *Singing* there is no *Stammering.* Speak
' but *little*, don't affect a *Loquacity*; a Folly *your Tribe*
' are often fubject to! tho 'tis more burdenfome and
' ungrateful in *them*, than in other People. What *lit-*
' *tle* you fpeak, let it be very *wife*, very *good*; fuch as
' may befpeak fome refpectful Regard for what you
' fay. Then be not altogether difcouraged under
' your Calamity: A MOSES, a PAUL, and a
' BOYLE, will make a noble *Triumvirate* of Compa-
' nions for you, under your uneafy Infirmity.' I go
on: The neceffity of the *Tongue* for *Speech* will remain generally to be afferted, notwithftanding the Tricks of the *Ventriloqui*, taking advantage of the Duplicature of the *Mediaftinum*, to form various Voices; and
notwith-

notwithſtanding the rare Inſtance reported by *Roland,* in his *Agloſſoſtomagraphia, ſive Deſcriptio Oris ſine Lingua, quod perfectè loquitur, & reliquas ſuas functiones naturaliter exercet.*

What the Emperor *Juſtinian* himſelf aſſerts in his Reſcripts ; [*Vidimus venerabiles Viros, qui abſciſſis radicitus Linguis ;*] that he himſelf ſaw *venerable Men,* who when their *Tongues* were cut out, at the very Root, yet continued plainly ſpeaking the Truth of Chriſtianity againſt the *Arians* ; a Fact whereof many Witneſſes are ſubpœna'd by *Cujacius :* it looks miraculous !

My God, thou haſt made Man's Mouth ! Make thou the Speech of mine what it ought to be. A pure Language! I have ſaid, I will take heed, that I do not ſin with my Tongue. Aſſiſt me to keep ſuch a Reſolution, and abhor all rotten or faulty Communication. I reſolve my Mouth ſhall ſpeak the Praiſe of the Lord : Oh that my Tongue may be like choice Silver, for the good Uſe and Worth of what is thereby articulated, and as a Tree of Life, in all my Converſation !

If we paſs down from the *Mouth,* we are quickly entertained with a *Wind-Pipe,* which is all made up of *Wonder !* A continual *Reſpiration* is neceſſary for the Support of our Lives ; it is therefore made with *annulary Cartilages,* to keep it conſtantly open, and that the Sides of it may not flag and fall together. And leſt, when we ſwallow, our Meat or Drink ſhould fall in to do miſchief there, it hath a ſtrong Valve, an *Epiglottis,* to cover it when we ſwallow. For the more convenient bending of our Necks, it is not made of one *continued Cartilage,* but of many *annular* ones, which are joined by ſtrong Membranes ; and theſe Membranes are *muſcular,* compounded of ſtrait and circular Fibres, for the more effectual Contraction of the *Wind-pipe,* in any violent Breathing or Coughing. And that the *Aſperity* of the Cartilages may not hurt the *Gullet,* which is of a tender and ſkinny Subſtance,

or

or hinder our ſwallowing of our Food, theſe annulary Griſtles are not entire Circles ; but where the *Wind-pipe* touches the *Gullet*, there the Circles are fitted up with only a ſoft Membrane, which may eaſily give way to the Dilatation of the *Gullet*. But now to proclaim a plain Deſign in this Conformation, as ſoon as the *Wind-pipe* enters the *Lungs*, its *Cartilages* are no longer *deficient*, but perfect *Circles* ; it was no longer neceſſary they ſhould be deficient, it was more convenient they ſhould be *perfect*. And then, to finiſh the Collection which our excellent *Ray* has made (for I have him now before me) of theſe Curioſities ; for the various Modulation of the *Voice*, the upper end of the *Wind-pipe*, is endued with ſeveral *Cartilages* and *Muſcles*, to contract or dilate it, as we would have our *Voice* flat or ſharp ; and the whole is continually moiſtened, with a *glutinous Humour* iſſuing out of the ſmall *Glandules*, that are upon its inner Coat : ſo 'tis fenced, that neither the *Air* fetched in, nor the *Breath* going out, may hurt it ; yet it is of ſo quick a Senſe, that it is provoked eaſily to caſt out, by *coughing*, whatever may be offenſive to it.

Caſpar Bartholin has further obſerved, that where the *Gullet* perforates the *Midriff*, the carneous Fibres of that muſcular Part are inflected and arcuate, as a *Sphincter* embracing it, and cloſing it faſt ; which is a ſenſible Providence, leſt, in the perpetual Motion of the ſaid *Midriff*, the upper Orifice of the Stomach ſhould gape and caſt out the Food as faſt as it received it.

Dr. *Grew* obſerves, that the Variation of the *Wind-pipe* is obſervable in every Creature, according as it is neceſſary for that of the *Voice* ; and the *Rings* of the *Wind-pipe* are fitted for the Modulation of the *Voice*.

The Faculty of the *Glottis*, in ſo exquiſitely *contracting*, or *dilating* of itſelf, as to form all *Notes*, is, as Mr. *Derham* ſays, *prodigious !* For, as Dr. *Keil* notes, if you ſuppoſe the greateſt Diſtance of the two ſides

of

of the *Glottis*, to be one *tenth part* of an *Inch*, in founding *twelve Notes*, to which the Voice eafily reaches, the Line muft be divided into *twelve Parts*, each of which gives the Aperture that is requifite for fuch a *Note* with a certain Strength. But if we confider the *Subdivifion of Notes*, into which the *Voice* can run, the Motion of the Sides of the *Glottis* will be ftill vaftly nicer. A *Voice* can divide a *Note*, at leaft into an *hundred Parts*, which a *juft Ear* can perceive; but then it follows, that the different Apertures of the *Glottis* actually divide the *tenth Part* of an *Inch* into *twelve hundred Parts*, and a *good Ear* will be fenfible of the Alteration. But becaufe each fide of the *Glottis* moves juft equally, therefore the *Divifions* are double, the Sides of the *Glottis*, by their Motion, do actually divide one *tenth part* of an *Inch*, we muft fay, into *two thoufand and four hundred Parts*.

My God, I defire that never any evil Word may have my leave to go thro fo curious a Paffage, and that the Difpofitions of my Mind may not be fo vicious and odious, as to render fo elegant a Paffage, the vent of an open Sepulchre. ' 'Tis fit that nothing but *Confeffions* of ' *God*, and *Kindneffes* to *Men*, fhould have fuch an ' *exquifite Paffage* found for them.'

We cannot leave thefe Parts, without confidering *Refpiration*. A Faculty of fuch importance to *Life*, that in the facred Oracles, and indeed in our common Phrafe alfo, *Breath* and *Life* are fo concomitant, as to be equivalent : *Lord, thou takeft away their Breath, and they die.*

The Ufes of *Refpiration* were but indifferently affigned, until *Malpighi's* Difcoveries. *Willis*, and *Mayow*, and others, do mention Ufes thereof that are not contemptible ; but our *Thurfton* rejects the Opinion of their being the *principal*, and thinks, 'tis principally to move, or pafs the *Blood*, from the right to the left Ventricle of the Heart. Experiments made, by divers ingenious Men, on ftrangled Animals, have

demon-

demonstrated his Opinion : For which cause the learned *Etmuller* also espoused it, who having reckoned up no less than *thirteen* Uses of *Respiration*, which are of great consequence, but conduce rather to the *Well-being*, than the *Being* of the living Creature, he concludes with a *fourteenth*, as the chief of all, which is, *For the passing of the Blood thro the Lungs, that is thrown into them by the Heart.* Anon comes Dr. *Drake*, and he not only establishes this Notion of *Respiration*, but also carries it further, and makes it the true Cause of the *Diastole* of the Heart ; which neither *Borelli*, nor *Lower*, nor *Cowper*, much less any before those eminent Persons, have well accounted for. Dr. *Lower* has proved, that the *Heart* is a *Muscle*. The Motion of all *Muscles* does consist in *Constriction*. This accounts for the *Systole*: but the *Heart* has no *Antagonist Muscle*. What shall we now do for the *Diastole* ? Great Wits have been puzzled here. But now Dr. *Drake* makes the weight of the incumbent *Atmosphere* to be the true *Antagonist* for all the *Muscles* ; which serve both for the Constriction of the Heart, and for ordinary *Respiration*.

Dr. *Cheyne* adds yet one Use more for this great Faculty and Action ; that is, to form the *Elastick Globules*, of which the *Blood* does principally consist, and without which there would be a general Obstruction in all the *capillary Arteries*.

Dr. *Wainwright* observes, the *Air* can't remain in the *Lungs*, without being much heated, and thereby having the Spring of it unbent, and so become specifically lighter than the external *Air :* For which reason it will, by a known Principle in *Mechanicks*, give place to it, and rise to such an height, as till it meet with *Air* of its own Weight, and there it will remain. But then the Sides of the *Blood-Vessels*, which by the Inflation of the *Lungs* were drawn asunder, now, when the *Lungs* are crouded on an Heap, will be forced together, and so the *Blood* contained in them will be broken into innumerable Parts, exceeding

small,

small, and thereby rendered the fitter to pass the several *Strainers* of the Body.

Great God! thou hast in thy Hand my Breath and all my ways ; I resolve to serve thee as long as I breathe ; I resolve to look on thy Service as the end for which thou dost continue my Breath ; I resolve to employ my Breath in thy Service to the last : I will praise thee as well as I can to and in my last Breath ; and when I have no Breath, I shall do it better.

Behold now the *Lungs*, a most surprizing Piece of Workmanship ! Consult the Description of them given by *Malpighi*, who first of all discovered their *Vesiculæ* ; and by *Willis*, who, writing after him, has proceeded upon it yet more accurately, and by *Cowper* in his admirable Tables. Then stand and *admire the Work of God.* You can do no otherwise ! We will not meddle with the Controversy between *Etmuller* and *Willis*, whether the *Vesiculæ* of the *Lungs* have any muscular Fibres, or no. We will content ourselves with *Galen's* Conclusion upon the Parts ministring to *Respiration*, that *admirabilem Sapientiam testantur.*

While the *Fœtus* is yet in the *Womb* (as Dr. *Keil* observes) the Vesicles of the *Lungs* lying flat upon one another, compress all the *capillary Blood-Vessels*, which are spread upon them. As soon as we are born, the *Air*, by its Gravity and Elasticity, rushes into the empty Branches of the *Trachea Arteria*, and blows up the Vessels into Spheres : by which means the Compression being taken off from the *Blood-Vessels*, and they equally expanded with the *Lungs*, all the *Blood* has a free Passage thro the *Pulmonary Artery.* But when the *Air* is thrust out again, by a Contraction of the Cavity of the *Thorax*, it being a fluid Body, compresses the *Vesicles* and *Blood-Vessels* upon them, every where equally. By this Compression, the red Globules of the *Blood*, which thro their languid Motion, in the Veins, were grown too big to circulate in the fine *capillary Vessels*, are broken, and again divided in the

S 4 *Serum,*

Serum, and the *Blood* is made fit for Nutrition and Secretion. This Preſſure of the *Air* on the *Blood-Veſſels,* Dr. *Keil* ſays, is equal to an hundred pound weight. It is alſo probable, he thinks, that Particles of the *Air* muſt enter the *Blood-Veſſels,* and mix with the *Blood* in the *Lungs.*

The Divine Workmanſhip about the HEART, who, that has any *Heart,* can forbear admiring of it, with moſt ſenſible Acknowledgments! This is that admirable Bowel, which with its inceſſant Motion diſtributes the *Blood,* the Vehicle of Life, throughout the whole Body. From this *Fountain of Life* and *Heat,* there are *Conduit-Pipes* even to the leaſt, yea, and moſt remote Parts of the Body. 'Tis the Machine, which receives the *Blood* from the *Veins,* and forces it out by the *Arteries,* thro the whole Body. The force with which the *Heart* ſqueezes out the Blood into the *Arteries,* is, in *Borelli's* Reckoning, equal to the force of *three thouſand Pound weight.* For this important Uſe it is moſt exquiſitely contrived. Being a *muſcular* Part, the Sides of it are compoſed of two Orders of *Fibres,* running circularly or ſpirally from the Baſe to Tip, contrarily the one to the other; and ſo being drawn contrary ways, do violently conſtringe and ſtraiten the *Ventricles,* and ſtrongly force out the *Blood.* And then the Veſſels, we call *Arteries,* which carry from the *Heart* to the ſeveral Parts, have their *Valves,* which open *outwards* like Trap-doors, and give the *Blood* a free Paſſage out of the *Heart,* but will not ſuffer any Return of it thither; and the *Veins,* which bring it back from the ſeveral Members to the Heart, have their *Valves,* or Trap-doors, which open *inwards,* and give way for the running of the Blood into the *Heart,* but prevent its running that way back again. Moreover, the *Arteries* conſiſt of a *Quadruple Coat,* the third of which is made up of annular, or orbicular, carneous *Fibres,* to a good Thickneſs, and is of a *muſcular* Nature, (which was firſt obſerved by Dr.

Dr. *Willis*) and this, after every Pulſe of the *Heart*, ſerves to contract the Veſſel ſucceſſively with incredible Celerity, ſo by a kind of *periſtaltick Motion*, forcibly and very ſwiftly impelling the *Blood* onwards to the *capillary Extremities*, and thro the *Muſcles*; wherefore the Pulſe of the *Arteries* is not cauſed only by the Pulſation of the *Heart*, which drives the Blood thro them after the manner of a Wave, as many would have it, but alſo by the *Coats* of the *Arteries* themſelves, as it has been confirmed by the Experiments of many modern Phyſicians, yea, and of *Galen* alſo. We may add one thing more, that the *Heart* and the *Brain* do notably enable one another to work; for the *Brain* cannot live unleſs it receive continual Supplies of Blood from the *Heart*, much leſs can it perform its Functions of preparing and of diſpenſing the *Animal Spirits*; nor can the *Heart* afford a *Pulſe*, unleſs it receive Spirits or ſomething deſcending from the *Brain* by the *Nerves:* do but cut aſunder the *Nerves* that go from the *Brain* to the *Heart*, the *Motion* thereof ceaſeth immediately.

For the Motion of the *Heart*, Monſieur *Tauvry* flies to a *ſubtile Matter* managing the *Fibres* of it, but ſeems to acknowledge it a *Matter which no Mortal has traced yet to Satisfaction.* In fine, the *Heart* is a compound *Muſcle*, and each Ventricle of it will (as Dr. *Keil* obſerves) contain an *Ounce* of Blood. We may well ſuppoſe the *Heart* throws into the *Aorta* an *Ounce* of Blood every time it contracts; the *Heart* contracts four thouſand times in one Hour, ſometimes more, ſometimes leſs; hence there paſſes thro the *Heart* every Hour *four thouſand Ounces of Blood*, that is to ſay, three hundred and fifty Pound. Now the whole Maſs of Blood is no more than twenty-five Pound, ſo that a Quantity of Blood equal to the whole Maſs paſſes thro the *Heart* *fourteen times in one Hour*, which is about once in every four Minutes; not the *whole Maſs* itſelf: we don't ſuppoſe that the *Blood* which goes to the Extremities,

can

can return to the *Heart* as soon as the *Blood* which goes only to the *Kidneys* or the *Liver.*

'Without making any fanciful Excursions upon
'*Metaphors* drawn from the *Figure* and *Office* of the
'*Heart*, I am sure 'tis infinitely reasonable that I
'should behold this *Bowel* with a most hearty and
'lively Sense of my Obligations *to give thee my Heart,*
'*O my God, and love thee with all my Heart!*'

The *Stomach* has in it how many things that are truly admirable! The greatest Philosophers have cried out, 'How great a Comprehension of Nature did it
'require to make a *Menstruum* that should corrode all
'sorts of *Flesh* coming into the *Stomach*, and yet not
'the *Stomach* itself, which is also *Flesh!*' 'Tis *membranous*, and capable of being *dilated* or *contracted*, according to the Quantity of Meat contained in it; the Situation of it under the *Liver*, accommodates with an *Heat*, that carries on the *Concoction*; when it has gone thro with the *Concoction*, it can shrink itself, and cast out the Food. But, *Concoction*, how performed? Inform us, Dr. *Drake!* —— There is in Bodies a *Principle of Dissolution*, which upon the Extinction of their vital and vegetative Faculty, begins to exert itself towards the *Destruction* of the Subject. This *Principle of Corruption* is, perhaps, the same that in a State of *Circulation* and *Vegetation* was the *Principle of Life*, but now being denied that Passage which it had before, it makes its way *irregularly*, and so destroys the Continuity of the *Solids*, in which it is included, and introduces that Change in the whole Mass which is called *Corruption*. This *active Principle* is a sort of Air, which is mixed in a considerable Quantity with all sorts of *Fluids*; this (tho its natural and essential Motion be expansive or *quaquaverfum*) when it is introduced into Bodies, has two kinds of motion, one *expansive*, by which it communicates that *intestine Motion* which all Juices have, and by which the containing Parts are gradually extended, and have their
Growth;

The Christian Philosopher. 267

Growth; but the other *progreſſive*, and indeed *circu-
latory*, which is occaſioned by the Renitency of ſolid
Parts, and obliges its taking that Courſe which is
moſt open and free. This *Motion* being ſtopt, the *expanſive* ſtill remains, and continues to act, till by degrees it hath ſo far overcome the Reſiſtance of the including Bodies, as to bring itſelf into an equal degree of *Expanſion* with the *external Air*, which cannot
be done without a *Deſtruction* on the Texture and
Continuity, or ſpecifick degree of Coheſion of the
Solids; and this is called *a State of Corruption.* This
deſtructive Quality of the *Air* in Bodies may be promoted, either by *weakening* the Tone of them, and the
Coheſion of the Parts, and ſo facilitating the Work of
the *Air*, as it is done when *Fruit* is bruiſed; or by in-
tending the *expanſive Force* of the *Air* itſelf with *Heat*,
or other co-operating Circumſtances. The former is
done in *Maſtications*, the latter is done by the *Heat* of
the *Stomach*, which forcibly rarefying the *Air*, enables
it to rend the including Bodies to pieces the ſooner,
and ſo to let looſe the Fluids, and perhaps likewiſe
produce a Comminution upon ſeveral parts of the *Solids*,ſo as to make them ſuſtainable in the *Liquor;* which
latter is the Operation that compleats the *Digeſtion in
the Stomach.* In *ſtewing*, tho the *Heat* be unſpeakably
ſhort of what is in *roaſting* and in *boiling*, the Operation is of all the quickeſt, becauſe it is performed in a
pretty cloſe Veſſel, and full, by which means the *Succuſſions* are more often repeated, and more ſtrongly re-
verberated. The Operation of the *Stomach* is mightily reſembled by the *Digeſtor* of Monſieur *Papin*; in
this the *Meat* is put, together with ſo much *Water* as
exactly fills the *Engine*, the Lid is then ſkrewed on ſo
cloſe as to admit of no external *Air*, and with two or
three lighted *Charcoal*, or the *Flame* of a *Lamp*, it is
reduced into a perfect *Pulp*, or indeed a *Liquor*, in a
very few Minutes, in ſix, or eight, or ten, or twelve,
or ſixteen, according to the Toughneſs of the Matter
to

to be digested, or the Augmentation of this little Fire;
this way even the *hardeſt Bones* are preſently diſſolved.
Thus the *Stomach* naturally cloſes on the Aliments,
which deſcend to it; it ſtrictly embraces them when
it is full; by keeping out extraneous *Air*, it fortifies
and invigorates the *Succuſſions* of that which is contained in the Aliments, and this is enabled hereby to
break and reſolve the Bodies which included it, into
Particles that may be ſmall enough to enter the *Lacteals.* When all the *Chyme* and *Chyle* is preſſed out,
the *Stomach,* which follows the motion of its Contents,
is again by means of its *muſcular Coat* reduced into a
State of Contraction, and the inner is brought thereby to lie in Folds, and by means of the *Periſtaltick Motion* rubbing lightly upon one another, produce that
Senſe of a *Vellication* which we call *Hunger :* this being
felt firſt in the upper Orifice, which is firſt evacuated,
begins firſt therefore to prompt us to repleniſhing;
but as by degrees the remainder of the Contents are
expelled, this Friction of the Membranes upon each
other, ſpreads gradually over the whole *Stomach,* and
renders our *Hunger* more impatient.

*Great God, I bleſs thee for all my Food. My gracious
Feeder, I bleſs thee that I have not known the terrible Fa-
mine. I will take no Food without looking up to thee for thy
Bleſſing, by which alone I live !*

The *Inteſtines;* theſe receive the *Chyle* from the *Py-
lorus;* theſe further digeſt it, prepare it, ſeparate it:
theſe by their periſtaltick Motion drive it into the
Lacteals; but the excrementitious Parts they ſend off
elſewhere, from whence there is no regreſs, unleſs
upon a Relaxation or Laceration befalling the Valve
of the *Colon.* Can you behold the Structure of the *Inteſtines,* as reported by *Kerkringius,* by *Gliſſon,* by *Willis,* and *Peyer,* and others, without Aſtoniſhment !

The *Inteſtines,* 'tis wonderful, they are ſix times as
long as the *Body* to which they appertain; and now
that they ſhould keep their *Tone,* and their *Site,* and
hold

hold on doing their *Office,* and give an undisturb'd Passage to what every day passes thro them, and this for some Scores of Years together, 'tis impossible for me to consider it without falling down before the glorious God, and making that Acclamation, *What hast thou done in me, O thou Preserver of Men! How much do I depend upon thee for my Preservation from grievous Diseases!*

The *Liver* does admirable things, in continually separating the *Choler* from the Blood, and emptying it into the *Intestines,* where it is useful, not only to provoke Dejection, but also to attenuate the *Chyle,* and render it so subtile and fluid, that it may enter at the Orifices of the *Lacteals.*

The *Bladder* is an admirable Vessel! The Substance is *membranous,* and extremely dilateable, for the receiving and containing of the *Urine,* till a convenient opportunity of emptying it; it hath also Shuts for the Ends of the *Ureters,* which are so artificially and marvellously contrived, as to give the *Urine* a free entrance, but stop all passage backward: the *Wind* itself cannot be transmitted thro the Shuts, tho never so strongly forced upon them!

In the *Kidneys,* how admirable the innumerable *Siphons,* the little and curious *Tubes,* conveying the urinous Particles into the *Ureters!* discovered first by *Bellini,* afterwards illustrated by *Malpighi.*

Leuenhoeck has discovered Vessels in an Human Body, the *Diameters* whereof are more than *seventy-nine thousand* times less than an *Inch;* and, as Dr. *Wainright* observes, at least so small must be the Diameters of the *Lacteals. My God, how exquisite, how curious are thy Works! But then how much do I depend upon thee to keep all the Vessels of my Body, doing their Office in their order!*

—— That so fine an Engine is not ruin'd a thousand times in *a day,* but holds on in its motion for *twenty-five thousand five hundred and sixty-seven* Days!

All

All the *Glands* of the Body, each of them an admirable *Congeries* of many Veſſels, in a ſtupendous Variety, curled, complicated, circumgyrated, and marvellouſly woven into one another; theſe give the *Blood* an opportunity to ſtop a little, and ſeparate thro the Pores of the *capillary* Veſſels into the *ſecretory* ones, which after all exonerate into one common *Ductus.* Read *Wharton,* and *Bartholin,* and *Bilſius,* and others; but prepare always for a Field of *Wonders,* equal to any *in the Field of Zoan!* —— But then conſider too the Variety of *Humours* that are ſeparated by the *Glands;* all different in Colour, in Taſte, in Smell, and in other Qualities.

The *Bones,* how admirable in their Circumſtances! The *Back-bone* is contrived with an Artifice truly aſtoniſhing! It is divided into many *Vertebres,* for the commodious *bending;* one entire and rigid *Bone* of that length would have been often in danger of ſnapping; it is *tapering,* in the form of a *Pillar,* the lower *Vertebres* being the broadeſt and largeſt, the ſuperior in order leſſer and leſſer, that ſo the Trunk of the Body may have the greater Stability: but the ſeveral *Vertebres* are ſo elegantly compacted and united, that they are as firm and ſtrong as if they were but one ſingle Bone; they are all perforated in the middle, with a large Hole for the *Spinal Marrow* (that wondrous *Pith!*) to paſs along, and each of them hath an Hole on each of their ſides, to tranſmit the *Nerves* to the *Muſcles* of the Body, and thereby convey both Senſe and Motion. By the cloſe Connection of the *Vertebres,* the *Back-bone* is formed ſo as to admit of no great Flexure and Receſs from a right Line; it alſo admits no *angular,* nor any but a moderate *circular* bending, left the *Spinal Marrow* ſhould be compreſſed, and ſo the Paſſage of the Spirits to and fro meet with ſome Obſtruction.

Dr. *Grew* obſerves, that in *Trees* there is a new Ring added every Year out of the Bark to the Wood; ſo
too

too in *Animals*, while they grow, there is a new *Peri-oſtium* added from time to time out of the *muſcular Membranes* to the Bones: *The ſweet Harmony with the vaſt Variety in the Works of God!*

Admirable the Proviſion that is made for the more eaſy and expedite Motions of the *Bones* in their Articulations: a twofold *Liquor* is prepared, by the Inunction whereof their *Heads* or *Ends* enjoy ſome Lubrification; firſt, there is an *oily* one, furniſh'd by the *Marrow*; and then there is a *mucilaginous* one, furniſhed by certain *Glandules*, that are ſeated in their Articulations; both of theſe together make up the moſt *proper Mixture* for this purpoſe that can poſſibly be thought upon; both of the Ingredients are *lubricating.* But more than this, from their Compoſition they mutually improve one another; the *Mucilage* adds to the ſmoothing Efficacy of the *Oil*, and the *Oil* preſerves the *Mucilage* from Inſpiſſation, and from contracting the Conſiſtency of a Jelly. Hereby the *Motion* of the *Bones* is facilitated; for if they were dry, they would not readily obey the Pulls of the *motory Muſcles*, which we find in the Wheels of our Clocks; the ends of the *Bones* are hereby alſo kept from an inconvenient *Incaleſcency*, which, if they were dry, being ſo hard, a ſwift and long Motion would neceſſarily give to them; and thus the Wheels of our Coaches muſt be beſmeared with a Mixture of *Greaſe* and *Tar* (an Imitation of *ours!*) that they may not be ſet on fire. What a *ſlothful World* muſt we have had, and how confined to Deliberation, if this Care had not been taken of our *Bones!* And finally, a great Miſchief is now prevented, the *Ends* of our *Bones* are not *worn down*, by a grievous Attrition in their motion rubbing againſt one another; 'tis indeed a ſtrange thing that this proves a ſufficient Preſervative to prevent the Conſumption of the *Bones*, when we ſee the tops of *Teeth*, which are harder, worn off by *Maſtication*, and brought ſo low, that the very *Nerve* lies bare, and for meer Pain they

can

can be ufed no more. The ingenious Mr. *Havers,* who makes thefe Remarks in his *Ofteology,* makes this Conclufion : *Here we cannot avoid the notice of the vifible Footfteps of an infinite Reafon, and we can never fufficiently admire the Wifdom and Providence of our great Creator !*

We may add, wonderful the *Conftruction* of the *Bones,* that are to fupport the Body, or bear heavy Burdens, or be employed in difficult Exercifes ; they are made *hollow,* this wonderfully accommodates them for both *Lightnefs* and *Stiffnefs ;* an *hollow* Body is more inflexible than a *folid* one, of the fame Subftance and Weight : but the *Ribs,* which do not carry *Loads,* nor do any thing wherein fo much Strength is required, but are only to fence the Breaft, thefe have no *Cavity* in them, and thefe, towards the fore part of them, are broad and thin, fo that they may give way, without much danger of any Fracture ; and when they are bent, they do by their *elaftick Property* again return to their Figure : and yet the *Hollow* of the *Bones* is not ufelefs, but it contains the *Marrow,* which fupplies an *Oil,* for the Maintaining and Inunction of the *Bones,* and of the *Ligaments,* and facilitating their Motion, and to fecure them from Difruption, to which they would by any fudden Contortions be otherwife obnoxious. The mention of the *Ribs* will bring on one Obfervation more ; That altho the *Breaft* is encompaffed with *Ribs,* the *Belly* is left free ; this is, that it may give way to the motion of the *Midriff* in *Refpiration,* and to the neceffary reception of our Food, and to the convenient bending of our Body. The *Females* alfo find the Benefit of it in the time of their Pregnancy. *Great God, all my Bones muft fay, who is like to thee ! I blefs thee for that thou doft not chaften the multitude of my Bones with ftrong Pain !*

It cannot be without Admiration looked upon, that all the *Bones,* and all the *Mufcles,* and all the *Veffels* of the Body, fhould be fo contrived, fo adapted and compacted, for their feveral Motions and Ufes ! All according

cording to the strictest Rules of the *Mathematicks!* If
you attempt an Innovation or Alteration, you *mar* all
instead of *mending* any thing. In the *Muscles* alone
there is more *Geometry* than in all the artificial Engines
in the World; the greatest Mathematicians have not
found a nobler Subject for their Disquisitions and
Contemplations than *de Motu Animalium.* The Essays
of *Croon,* and *Steno,* and *Borelli,* on that Subject, have
been very curious.

Dr. *Grew* observes, that no less than forty or fifty
Muscles, besides many other subservient Parts, go to
execute that one *Act of Laughing;* certainly then *laughing for nothing* may be indicted for an *Act of Folly!* He
goes on with his Observation, That in some Cases we
cannot execute *one single Thought* without such a Retinue. Suppose one sitting in a Room has a *Thought*
of looking at something out of a Window, that one
Thought has immediately seventy or eighty *Muscles* put
into motion to wait upon it; *so that,* says the Doctor,
*there is not a Monarch upon Earth served with such Maje-
sty as every Man is within the Territory of his own Body:*
But then how *reasonable* is it, O Man, for thee to serve
the *Maker* of all these! *Glorious God, I will do it with all
my Muscles, with all my Powers!*

Dr. *Grew* has a further Observation; What can be
more admirable, than for the Principles of the *Fibres* of
a *Tendon* to be so mixed as to make it a soft Body; fit
both to receive and impart the Species of *Sense,* and to
be easily nourished and moved, and yet with such a
Softness to have the *Strength* of *Iron!*

Those *Muscles* which appear as contemptible as any
of the Body, even the *Muscles of the Belly,* tho *Galen,*
and other Anatomists after him, have contented themselves with reckoning four or five *Uses* of them, they
are indeed more than can be reckoned. Dr. *Grew* has
employed almost a large Page in the Enumeration.

'Tis admirable that under our *Skin* there should be
such an unknown *variety of Parts,* and so very variously

T   mingled,

mingled, all so pack'd that there is no *unnecessary Vacuity* in the whole Body, yet so far from clashing with and hindring of one another, that they do all in the most friendly manner *conspire* to assist one another, and concur in the general Design, which is the Preservation of the whole. Behold, *Arguments* (as our pious *Ray* well notes hereupon) *of infinite Wisdom and Counsel!* *He must be worse than mad, that can find in his Heart to imagine all not provided by a most wise and intelligent Cause!*

Every Part is clothed, joined, corroborated by *Membranes,* which are capable of a prodigious Extension; those of the *Peritonæum* are a particular Instance of *that,* out of which alone, in *hydropical Persons,* there have been drawn forty Gallons of Water, by a *Paracentesis.* The undoubted Authorities of *Tulpius,* and *Blasius,* and other Physicians, oblige us to believe surprizing things of this Importance.

It is notable, that all our Organs are involved in *Coats,* one or more, consisting of tough or muscular Fibres, intended not only to *protect* them, as has been commonly thought, but also by a due Constriction to assist them in *straining* off their several Contents.

These Parts which at first appear to be of no more use than to fill up empty Spaces, will upon Examination be found exceeding serviceable. The *Fat* serves to cherish the Body, and keep it warm; yea, will maintain it for some time, when *Food* is wanting, and be as a sulphurous *Pabulum,* to preserve the *Heat* of the *Blood.* By what Vessels the *Fat* comes to be separated from the *Blood,* is a Point of curious Enquiry; the collection of it more on some certain Parts (as the *Caul* and the *Reins*) than on others, appears to be for the cherishing of those Parts with *Warmth;* the *Caul* is like an Apron of *Woollen Cloth* to the lower Belly. The *Gladiator,* whose *Caul* was cut out by *Galen,* felt so much *Cold,* that he was forced constantly to keep his Belly covered with *Wooll.* The *Intestines* containing
much

much Food, there to undergo its laſt Concoction, and
Veſſels of Blood not flowing thither, need ſuch a *Co-
vering* to defend them; doubtleſs a conſtant *Heat* is re-
quired about the *Reins*, for the Separation of the *Urine*
from the Blood: for we ſee if the Blood be chilled, the
Secretion of the *Urine* will be ſenſibly ſtopt, and the
Serum caſt upon the *Glandules* of the Mouth and
Throat.

Monſieur *Bernoulli*, in a curious Meditation about
muſcular Motion, has obſerved another thing, that muſt
not be pretermitted; that in *muſcular Motion* the Expence of *Animal Spirits* is not in proportion to the Labour which the Animal is at: and ſo a Man reduc'd
to hard Labour, is not reduc'd to the neceſſity of having twice or four times as much Victuals as one that
is under no ſuch neceſſity of working. Now the *Spirits* are the moſt precious things in all the *Animal Body*,
we live by them; ſo needful and uſeful a Subſtance
was to be ſaved by all the Means that were poſſible.
And behold, as Dr. *Cheyne* expreſſes it, *we ſee the wiſe
Author of Nature has taken wonderful Care that no Expen-
ces ſhould be made that could be avoided.*

It has been obſerved by ſome, that to provide Matter for the generation of *Spirits* in *Man*, a vaſt Quantity of *Blood* is prepared, far exceeding what is found in
other Animals. The *Blood* for the Body of *Man* bears
the Proportion to his Weight, of *one* to *ten*; in other
Animals 'tis but *one* to *twenty*. And for the fetching of
Spirits out of this Matter, there is the *Laboratory* of the
Brain, which in a *Man* is twice as much as in a *Beaſt*
four times as big.

It is Dr. *Cheyne*'s Propoſition; That the *Strength of
Animals* is in a *triplicate* Proportion to the Quantity of
Blood running in the Veſſels.

The *Lympha* of the Blood is a marvellous thing;
a Liquor ſeparated in the *Membranes* and *Glandules,*
which is the Medium whereby the *ſerous* and *fibrous*
Parts of the *Blood* are united, and the *Bones* and *mem-*

branous Parts of the Body are nouriſhed. But how marvellous the *Lymphatick Veſſels,* which convey this *exquiſite Liquor*! They diſappear when the *Animal* dies; their number is unaccountable: they were firſt of all diſcovered by *Thomas Bartholin* and *Olaus Rudbeck,* in the Years 1650 and 1651. *Pecker* made a progreſs in the diſcovery of them; and their Valves were demonſtrated by *Frederick Ruyſch,* which permit this tranſparent Liquor to paſs thro them towards the *Heart,* but are like ſhut *Floodgates* upon the returning; they riſe in all Parts of the Body. The *Glands* that ſeparate the *Lympha* are of the ſmalleſt kind, and ſcarce viſible by the fineſt *Microſcopes;* but the *Lymphaducts* unite with one another, and grow larger as they approach the *Heart;* and yet they do not, like the *Veins,* open into one common Channel. —— The whole Contrivance of theſe *fine Veſſels,* who can behold without Amazement!

About the *Blood,* this is admirable; the Branches which go off at any ſmall diſtance from the Trunk of an *Artery,* unite their Channels into one Trunk again, whoſe Branches likewiſe communicate with one another, and with others; whence it comes to paſs (as Dr. *Keil* obſerves) that when any ſmall *Artery* is obſtructed, the Blood is brought by the communicating Branches to the Parts below the Obſtruction, which muſt otherwiſe have been deprived of their Nouriſhment. And in the *Veins* there is the like Proviſion, that ſo juſtly ſurprizes us in the *Arteries.*

The *Viſcidity* of the *Blood* is increaſed by the *Heat* in a *Fever;* if we apply a much leſs degree of *Heat* than will boil Water, it will turn the *Serum* into a Jelly; the *Heat* of the Skin, where the Pulſe will beat ſixty Strokes in a Minute, is to the *Heat* of *boiling Water* as 16 to 52; *boiling Water* is but little more than three times as *hot* as the *Blood* of an healthy Man. If the *Heat* of the *Blood* increaſe in proportion to the Beat of the Pulſe (as it muſt, if it beat with the ſame

Strength it did) a Man whofe Pulfe beats 195 Strokes in a Minute, would be as hot as *boiling Water*; now 120 Strokes is common. Behold whence the *Sizinefs* of the Blood in inflammatory Diftempers!

' Why fhould I finfully *over-heat* my *Blood*? But ' fince my Life depends on the good Conftitution of ' this *red Liquor*, which is yet fo eafily depraved, fo ' eafily difturbed, fo eafily overturned; *O God of my* ' *Life, I wonder that I live! I defire to live as a dying* ' *Man! But I live, becaufe thou art the God of my Life!*'

But at laft the *Inftrument* all this while employed in writing thefe things, that *Ὄργανον Ὀργάνων,* demands of me that it be not forgotten; the HAND, the HAND, whereof I need no *Cicero* to be my Monitor, *Quam aptas, quamque multarum Artium Miniftras, MANUS, Natura homini dedit!* It is divided into four Fingers, bending *forwards*, and one ftronger than any of them that bends *backwards*, to join with them; 'tis fitted thus to *lay hold* on Objects of any fhape, or fize, or quantity; and fometimes *one Finger* alone can difcharge many Offices: the *Fingers* are ftrengthned with feveral *Bones*, jointed for motion, furnifhed with *Mufcles* and *Tendons*, to bend them circularly forwards; how convenient this for the holding and griping of any Object! The *Fingers* alfo have their *Mufcles*, to extend and open the *Hand*, and move them to the right and left; and thus the *whole Hand* may be employed, as all of a piece.

But then how notable is it, how wonderful! That the *Tendons* bending the *middle Joint* of the Fingers are fo *perforated*, as to give paffage to the *Tendons* of the *Mufcles* which draw the uppermoft Joints, and all bound clofe down to the *Bone* with ftrong *Fillets*, like fo many Bow-ftrings, left they fhould ftart up, and hinder the Hand in its Operations: finally, the *Ends* of the *Fingers* are fortified with *Nails*, which indeed *adorn* them as well as *defend* them; yea, and have their further Ufes too, if what *Camillus* writes in his Trea-

T 3

tife

tife upon the forming of *Judicia Medica* from the Infpection of the *Nails,* may be relied upon : and how
thin the *Skin,* and how exquifite the *Senfe* at our *Fin-
gers-ends,* by which we may judge of what we have
there to be handled ! We know who confidered this
Queftion, and how long ago ; *Num eam omnino Confti-
tutionem habeat* Manus, *qua meliorem aliam habere non
potuit ?*

The *Ufes* of this *aftonifhing Inftrument* cannot be reckoned up ; a whole *Book* written by *it,* might be eafily
filled with an Enumeration of its *Ufes. Ariftotle* fays
well, They *do ill* who complain that Man is *worfe* dealt
with than other Creatures, who are born with *natural
Weapons* to defend themfelves, and offend their Enemies ; an *Hand,* with *Reafon* to ufe it, abundantly
fupplies the Ufes of all thofe *natural Weapons* ; 'tis an
Horn, an *Hoof,* a *Claw,* a *Tufh,* and all ! Dr. *Grew* fays
very truly, *Never was there made an Inftrument fo curious !* The fixteen feveral general *Motions* of it are the
Elements of Operation, as the *Letters* are of *Speech* ; how
infinitely to be diverfified ! What fhall we call this
but *the Handy-work of our God !*

Galen having defcribed the Parts of the Fingers, and
their Motion, cries out, *Confidera hic mirabilem C R E-
A T O R I S Sapientiam !*

' When I apply *my Hand* to *any Action* which could
' not be done without it, I have *my Mind* invited to
' fuch a Thought upon it ; *Great God, I blefs thee for*
' *arming me with fo curious and fo adapted an Inftrument !*
' *May I never ungratefully put forth my Hand to an evil*
' *Action.*'

' Such a Thought often rolling in my *Mind,* and
' ruling of my *Hand,* would be a better *Token for Good*
' to me, than the moft promifing *Lines* of any filly
' *Chiromancy.*'

Voluntary Motion fhould not be left unconfidered ;
whereof Dr. *Cheyne* obferves, the only Conception we
can form, is, that the *Mind,* like a fkilful Mufician,

ftrikes

ſtrikes on that *Nerve* which conveys *Animal Spirits* to the *Muſcle* that is to be contracted, and adds a greater force than the *natural* to the *nervous Juice,* whereby it opens its paſſage into the Veſicles, of which the *muſcular Fibres* conſiſt; but this Action of the *Mind* or *Will* on theſe *Animal Spirits,* is altogether *unaccountable* from the Laws of Motion. *My God, in thee I move! The aſtoniſhing Power of ſpontaneous Motion is what thou haſt given me! Oh! may I never employ it in any Acts of Rebellion againſt Him that gave it.*

Certainly Men may do well alſo to conſider, whether the very *Configurations* of ſeveral Parts, may not afford good and great Admonitions of *Morality* to them. I need not explain my ſelf, when I offer an Hint I have ſomewhere met withal: *Ponder, O Man, what Parts of thy Body have Bridles of Nature upon them!*

Some Conſideration is alſo due to the aſtoniſhing *Strength* with which the *Bones* of Men have been ſometimes endued. The *Strength* for which a *Samſon* has been ſo famous, was indeed owing to a Poſſeſſion and Aſſiſtance of *a Spirit* entring into him from above; but the *ordinary Strength* of our *Nerves,* exerted in *moving* and *lifting,* is truly admirable; the Force of the *nervous Fluid!* And the Ability of the *little Fibres,* to ſuſtain what it puts them on! And there are now and then, ſince the Days of *Milo* the *Ox-carrier,* Examples of *Strength,* which will yet more *ſtrongly* call for our growing Admiration; it would ſwell my Eſſay ſo big, that it would require a Man of ſuch *Strength* to carry it, if on this and other Occaſions I ſhould inſert all that has occurred to our purpoſe, in *Valerius Maximus,* in *Cælius Rhodiginus,* in *Zuinger,* in *Camerarius,* in *Hakewell,* in *Wanly,* and in other Collectors; however, a touch or two may not be unacceptable.

The Tyrant *Maximus* would with his Hands draw loaden *Carts* and *Wains,* break the Bones of *Horſes,* and cleave *Trees* aſunder. *Marius,* who of a *Cutler* became an *Emperor,* could with his fourth Finger ſtop a *Cart*

T 4 that

that was drawn with Horfes, and force it backwards; and a *Fillip* of his Finger (which they alfo report of *Tiberius*) would knock a Man down like a Blow of an *Hammer*. One *Salvius*, mentioned by *Pliny*, having an *hundred-Pounds* weight at his *Feet*, and as many in his *Hands*, with twice as much on his *Shoulders*, could go up a pair of Stairs. *George Caftriot* with his maffy *Scimeter* did amazing Executions, he cut the *Turks* to pieces, *Barletius* affirms, three thoufand of them with his own Hands, and fcorn'd ever to throw away more than *one Blow* upon an Object; he could cleave *Helmet* and *Harnefs*, as if they were but Straw before him. *Cardan* faw one dancing with two in his Arms, two on his Shoulders, and one hanging about his Neck. A Baron of *Mindelheim* would with his middle Finger do things that furpafs Imagination; he would fhove a *Cannon* where he pleafed; he would break *Horfe-fhoes* with his Hands like Potfherds; (which is a Circumftance they alfo relate of *Pocova*, a *Polifh* Gentleman.) Little *Venetianello* would with his Hands wreath great Pins of *Iron*, as if they were foftned with the Fire, and carry on his Shoulders an erect *Beam* of twenty foot long and a foot thick, and fhift it without the ufe of *Hands* from one Shoulder to another. A Provoft at *Mifna* would make nothing with his bare *Hands* to fetch a Pipe of Wine out of a Cellar, and lay it on a Cart. *Mayolus* affirms he faw a Man who took a Pillar of Marble three foot long, and one foot in diameter, which he caft up very high into the Air, and received it again in his Arms, and play'd with it as a little Ball; and another who would break a *Cable* as big as a Man's Arm, as eafily as if it were a Thread of *Twine*. *Froifard*, a faithful Hiftorian, tells of a Man who would make nothing to carry a great *Afs*, with all his *Load*, upon his Back. The Stories we have of the mighty Burdens carried by fome of our *Cornifh* Men, related by Mr. *Carew*, and others, are truly wonderful,

Can

Can we now do any other than fall down before the glorious G O D, who has given ſuch *Strength* to the Children of Men, as if their *Strength* were *the Strength of Stones,* or *their Fleſh were Braſs;* (and yet, when God pleaſes, *cruſh'd before the Moth!*) with the antient Adoration, *O Lord God of Hoſts, who is a ſtrong God like to thee!*

I conclude with the pathetical Words of an outlandiſh Doctor of Philoſophy; *O Deus, ſi totius Corporis mei Membra verterentur in Linguas, Nominis tui magnificentiam enarrare non poſſem.*

But in M A N, muſt that have the *laſt* Conſideration, the *State* whereof, alas, is that which too commonly is the *laſt* conſidered! The S O U L, which has muſtered the many *Thoughts* wherewith our *Chriſtian Philoſopher* has fill'd his Pages, muſt now be thought upon. But oh! How much is *the Father of Spirits* to be herewith acknowledged and glorified! Even the Pagan Orator ſhall be our Monitor; *Jam vero Animum ipſum, Mentemque Hominis, Rationem, Conſilium, Prudentiam, qui non Divina Cura perfecta eſſe perſpicit, is his ipſis Rebus mihi videtur carere.*

'Tis high time for us now to take the S O U L of Man into our Contemplation. The S O U L, whereof *Juvenal,*

Senſum à cœleſti demiſſum traximus arce,
Cujus egent prona,, & terram ſpectantia. ——

The S O U L, whereof *Claudian,*

—— *Hæc ſola manet, buſtoque ſuperſtes*
Evolat. ——

And if our *Philoſophy* terminate in *Theology,* the ſurprizing Words of a Pagan Phyſician will be proper to be introduced on the Occaſion : *O Galen,* we Profeſſors of *Chriſtianity* will be thy ſurprized Hearers, while
thou

thou ſpeakeſt at this rate to us: *Si quis nulli Sectæ ad-
dictus, ſed libera ſententia rerum Conſiderationem inierit,
conſpicatus in tantâ Carnium & Succorum colluvie tantam
Mentem habitare, —— (omnia enim declarant Opificis Sapientiam,) —— perfectiſſimæ Theologiæ verum principium con-
ſtituet; quæ Theologia multo eſt major atque præſtantior to-
ta Medicina.* [De uſu Part. lib. 17. c. 1.] Wonderful
Words from a *Pagan Phyſician!*

The ſtupendous Faculties of the Soul!

The *Wiſdom*, with which a Soul may perform
wonderful things. 'Tis the *Wiſdom* that *God puts into
the Heart* of a *Solomon.*

The Performances of that reaching *Philoſophy*,
which we have ſeen ſagacious Minds endued withal,
they have been amazing ones!

The Performances of the *Politician*, have ſometimes
been as amazing as thoſe of the *Philoſopher.*

Men of a *Great Soul*, what aſtoniſhing things have
they arrived unto!

And yet, I will venture to ſay, the *Love of GOD*
in the Soul, or a *Principle of Grace* infuſed into it, is a
Divine Workmanſhip, that is more *noble* than all its o-
ther Faculties, and will unſpeakably *enoble* them all.

I have read, in the *Aſceticks*, of a Servant of God, a
Paſſage of this Importance: ' I am not unable to write
' in *ſeven Languages*; I feaſt myſelf with the Sweets
' of all the *Sciences*, which the more polite part of
' Mankind ordinarily pretend unto. I am entertained
' with all kinds of *Hiſtories*, antient and modern. I
' am no Stranger to the *Curioſities*, which by all ſorts
' of Learning are brought to the Curious. Never-
' theleſs, it appears unto me more valuable than all of
' this, it appears more delectable, it is a thing of a
' ſuperiour Character, with a true *Spirit of Charity*,
' to relieve a poor, mean, miſerable Neighbour;
' much more to do any extenſive Service for the Re-
' dreſs of thoſe *Epidemical Miſeries*, under which *Man-
' kind*

' *kind* in general is languishing, and to advance the
' *Kingdom of God* in the World.'

REASON, what is it, but a *Faculty* formed by
GOD, in the Mind of Man, enabling him to discern
certain *Maxims of Truth*, which God himself has established, and to make true *Inferences* from them! In all
the Dictates of *Reason*, there is *the Voice of God*. Whenever any *reasonable thing* is offered, I have GOD speaking to me. Behold a Method in which a *Man*, (who
will *shew himself a Man*, and *hearken to Reason*) may
fill his Life with *Acts of Obedience* to GOD! Whatever
I see to be *Reason*, I will comply with it, from this
Consideration, *'tis what GOD calls me to! Reason*
extends to Points of *Morality*, with as much Evidence
as to those of *Mathematicks*. 'Tis as evident, *that*
GOD, *my Maker, is to be glorified*; and, *that I am to
do as I would be done unto*; as it is, *that three and four
makes seven*; or, *that a Square is double to a Triangle, of
equal Base and Height*. May the *Fear of GOD* for
ever preserve me from doing any thing, whereof I
may say, *it seems to me unreasonable*.

The prodigious *Learning*, wherewith some great
Literators have been enriched! *Ideas*, like the *Sands
on the Sea-shore*, for the vast *variety* of them! There
have been Men of so extensive a *Genius*, that they
have been worthy to have a Celebration of their Ob-
sequies, in as many Languages as were those of *Pei-
reskius*: A Collection whereof, entitled *Panglossia*, had
in it no fewer than *forty Languages*.

We see sometimes a much richer Soul than that of
Tostatus; of whom yet *Bellarmine* says,

Hic stupor est mundi, qui scibile discutit omne.

What a Character could *Vives* give of his *Budæus?*
Casaubon reports of *Joseph Scaliger*, *There is nothing that
any Man could desire to learn, but that he was able to
teach*: *He had read nothing*, (*and yet what had he not
read?*)

read?) but what he did readily remember. *Salmaſius*
gives a Report, little ſhort of this, concerning *Caſau-*
bon. *Voetius* and *Voſſius,* how do they celebrate the vaſt
Erudition of our *Uſher!* Others will or may do as
much for theirs. *Bochart* is rarely mentioned without
the Epithet of *the incomparable.* *Grotius* was no *little*
Man, *Selden* was not much ſmaller than he, both con-
cluding their Lives with Teſtimonies to the Preference
of *real Piety,* before all their Skill in *Languages* and
Sciences.

My dear *Witſius,* lately dead, muſt for ever *live* in
the Catalogue of *wonderful Men;* and Mr. *Baxter* too!

Of theſe two, and of ſome others, what *Ambera-*
chius writes of *Zuinger,* may be the conſummate Elogy;
Cujus magna fuit Doctrina, ſed exigua, ſi cum Pietate con-
feratur. Such was *he,* of whom I am going to repeat
what I have heretofore aſſerted ; had I Learning
enough to manage a Cauſe of that nature, I ſhould be
ready to maintain, that there never was known under
the Cope of Heaven a more learned Man than the incomparable *A L S T E D I U S;* he has written on every one of the Subjects in the whole *Circle of Learning* as
accurately and as exquiſitely as thoſe Men who have
ſpent all their Lives in cultivating but any one of the
Subjects. The reaſon why many of his Compoſures
are no more eſteemed, is the *Pleonaſm* of their Worth,
and their deſerving ſo much Eſteem. To hear ſome
ſilly and flaſhy Men, with a ſcornful Sneer, talk as if
they had ſufficiently done his Buſineſs, by a fooliſh
Pun, of *All's-tedious,* is to ſee the ungrateful and exalted Folly of the World ; for *Conciſeneſs* is one of his
peculiar Excellencies : they might more juſtly call him
any thing than *tedious.*

The early Attainments and Atchievements of ſome,
have been the juſt Admiration of the World. Mr.
Baillet has drawn up a curious Liſt of *illuſtrious Youths.*

When

When I see such *Men*, and their *Works*, I must for ever *look off*, and *look up* to the glorious God, and acknowledge, *Great God, thou art the Father of these Lights! These had nothing but what they received from thee! And if such Perfections may be found in frail and weak Men, what, Oh! what are the Excellencies of the infinite God, before whom all these Men are but as the Drop of the Bucket, and the light Dust of the Balance!* But when I consider how far the sinful Children of Men may come to have the *Chambers of their Souls* filled with *precious things*, it leads me to think, *What is that M A N, who is more than a meer M A N! That M A N who is the Son of God! O God, the Heavens do praise thy Wonder!* B O O K S which have in them vast Amazements of most *valuable Treasures*, cannot well be laid out of our Hands without such Thoughts as these.

But what shall we say when we see the vast *Performances* and *Capacities* of some S O U L S, from which the want of *Bodily Senses* would have prohibited all our Expectations of any thing that should be considerable. *My God, I know that thou canst do every thing; all Souls are thine, and thou canst make them do what thou pleasest!*

The *Jews* tell us of a Professor in their Academy of *Sora*, who was called *Sagi Nahor*, or *Joseph of great Light*; he was *blind*, but it seems he had a Soul full of Knowledge.

We have had eminent *Preachers* who were *blind* Men, and educated for and serviceable in the Evangelical Ministry; Mr. *Cheesman* of *East-garston* was one, who lost his Eyes by the Small-Pox before he was four Years old: thus Mr. *Francis Tailor*, and Mr. *Homer Jackson*.

But then that they should prove *Writers* too, learned, acute, polite *Writers!*

The

The Books of Mr. *John Troughton* are valuable things; his *Lutherus Redivivus* could be writ by none but a *Seer*, and an Eagle-ey'd one.

But if *many blind Men* have done learnedly, thou, Mr. *William Jameson*, haft *excelled them all!* That miraculous Man, a Profeſſor of Hiſtory in the famous Univerſity of *Glaſgow*, tho blind from his Nativity, has publiſhed a variety of Books, and theſe in the *Latin* as well as the *Engliſh* Tongue, and full of *Quotation*, full of *Criticiſm*, full of accurate and exquiſite Explanations on the niceſt Controverſies: when I read ſuch things, I cannot but ſee, and ſay, *the Finger of God!*

That one Faculty of the Soul, the M E M O R Y, how amazing the Powers of it, how ſtupendous the Performances! The Account *Seneca* gives of himſelf, if half of it be true! —— *Nam & duo millia Nominum recitata, quo ordine erant dicta, reddebam.* Of his *very dear Companion*, as he calls *Latro Porcius*, he affirms, that he retained in his *Memory* all the Declamations he had ever ſpoken, and never had his *Memory* failing him ſo much as in one ſingle word. *Pliny* will give us more Examples of what the *Memory* of Man has done; a *Cyrus*, who could call all the Soldiers in his Army by Name; a *Mithridates*, who could ſpeak to twenty-two ſeveral Nations in their own Languages; a *Carneades*, who *Quæ quis exegerat in Volumina in Bibliothecis, Legentis modo repreſentavit.* Such was the *Memory* of Dr. *John Rainolds*, that he was called *a living Library*, and *a third Univerſity*. *Lipſius* had all *Tacitus* exactly in his Memory, and *Suarez* had all *Auſtin*. *Homer's Iliads* have thirty-one thouſand ſix hundred and ſeventy Verſes, his *Odyſſes* no leſs; and yet the younger *Scaliger* committed all *Homer* to his *Memory* in one and twenty Days. The *Memory* of our famous *Jewel* would perform Wonders, he would readily and exactly repeat any thing he had written, after once reading of it, and would have done it if the Auditors had been ſhouting, or fighting, and given him the greateſt Occaſions of

Con-

Confusions; even Scores of barbarous Words, after once reading, he would repeat forwards and backwards, without hesitation. *Zuinger* mentions many strange Examples of a strong Memory, among which that of *Christopher Longolius* is very memorable; scarce any Length of Time was able to dislodge any thing he had once lodged in his *Memory!* But then how unaccountable the Instances of a *Læsa Memoria,* reported by *Zuinger,* and *Forestus,* and *Schenkius,* and others, especially when an *Apoplexy* has left a Man *Memory* enough to *write* Volumes, but unable to *read* a Syllable! The various *Inclinations* of the S O U L are a most admirably wise Provision of our good God, that the *Business of the World* may be all transacted, and with Satisfaction:

Diversis gaudet Natura ministris.

We find *Homer* sometimes admiring this Variety; and *Horace* entertains us with a *Sunt quos Curriculo,*——which might have been extended to a Volume; for as one says, ‘ there may be found a *Sunt quos* for every ‘ thing under the Sun.

Tho *Solomon* declares truly, *that much Study is a Weariness to the Flesh,* yet with what Assiduity do many apply themselves to it, and how delightfully! There have been other *hard Students* besides *Cato,* of whom *Tully* says, *Erat in eo inexhausta aviditas legendi, nec satiari poterat.*

The *Jews* have done well to place this among their *Beracoth* ; *Deus facit ut unicuique suum Opificium placeat.* The *blessed* God is to be acknowledged in it. There is an Instance which Dr. *Edwards* has pitch'd upon: Would a *Gentleman* brought up a *Scholar,* and one very nice, neat, and curious, visit sick Persons whenever they call him, and leave his own Bed that he may give his Visits to them in theirs, and enter into Rooms that are filled with the most ungrateful Steam and Stench,

Stench, and all his Days converse with Excrements, continue situated *inter Stercus & Urinam?* One would think this were a Degradation to the *Velvet Cap* and *Scarlet Robe*; to go in Silk and Plush to the most squalid and nasty Chambers, looks a little strange; to suck in the Air of a Room which the Breath of the Diseased has infected, for this to be done by Persons of an honourable Character, and for them to undergo patiently and cheerfully more servile things than what are undergone in the basest and most servile Callings! But, ——

'Behold, *I have created the Smith, who blows the Coals
' in the Fire!* so saith our God: and he is to be seen
' in the disposition to *profess every honest Trade for ne-
' cessary Uses!* When I behold any Man cheerfully fol-
' lowing the Business of his *Calling*, I would upon the
' Invitation say, *Glorious God, it is well that thou hast so
' disposed the Mind of this my Neighbour!*'

They who have written *de Morbis Artificum*, have mentioned no Case more deplorable than this, *for a Man to be sick of his Calling.*

Our Great G O D is to be seen, confessed, adored, in that admirable *Variety* of Matters which the *Invention of Man* has reach'd to! And the admirable *Sagacity* that prosecutes them! When such inventive Wits as *Helmont* and *Wallis* have taught the *Deaf* and the *Dumb* to *read* and *speak*, methoughts I have seen that *Sagacity* notably exemplified.

'Glorious G O D, my Soul with all possible Pro-
' stration before thee receives thy *faithful Sayings*,
' wherein thou hast instructed me: *Every good Gift
' comes down from the Father of Lights!* And *the Lord
' giveth Wisdom!* Not only of the *four Children* that
' had it, but of all that have ever had any thing of it,
' it must be own'd *God gave them Knowledge and Skill
' in all Learning and Wisdom:* If a *Bazaleel* have it, *O
' Spirit of God,* thou art He who givest him *Knowledge
' in all manner of Workmanship.*'

But

But then there is another thing wherein the Super-intendence of the Glorious Creator and Governor of the World is moſt conſpicuous; and that is, the *Pro-greſs* which the *Invention* of Man has made: things of *greater* uſe were *ſooner* invented, things of a *leſſer* uſe *later*, every thing in the *Time* wherein our Great God has had his excellent Purpoſes to be ſerved with it; things *equally plain* with ſuch as have been formerly diſcovered, and as much deſired, have been lock'd up from Human Underſtanding, till the God, *in whoſe hand are our Times*, is pleaſed wiſely to make them underſtood by the Children of Men. 'Tis not from your *fortuitous Concourſe of Atoms*, ye fooliſh *Epicureans!* Why muſt *Printing* be with-held from the Service of Mankind till the Year 1430, when the *Firſt-born of printed Books* was by the Hand of *Laurence Koſter* mid-wifed into the World, and the Skill immediately im-proved by *Fauſt* and *Schoeffer?* Why muſt Mankind have no *Teleſcopes* till the Year 1609, when one whom *Syrturus* would ſuſpect almoſt an *Angel* in the Shape of a *Dutchman*, inſtructed *Lipperſein* at *Middleburgh* to proceed upon them? To mention a Subject which my *Chriſtian Philoſopher* has very much liv'd upon, What is the Anatomy of *Mundinus*, if compared to our *mo-dern?* (tho *Cardan*, and other learned Men, have ſo much cried it up with their Elogies and Commen-taries.) *Baglivi* ſays truly, *'tis as far ſhort of it as a Flea is of an Elephant.* We will paſs to another In-ſtance: The *Romans* had not ſo much as a *Sun-dial* till the ſecond *Punick* War, and when they had one, they had no more than that one, in the *Forum*, above an hundred Years, tho *Pliny* ſays it never went right in all this time. Our King *Alfred* had no better ſhift than this for meaſuring his Hours, the burning of a *Candle*, marked into *twelve parts*, for which a *Lanthorn* was needful to ſecure it from the Winds of the *Win-dows*, for *Glazing* was not yet in faſhion. Dr. *Grew* obſerves, the firſt Conceit which tended to a *Watch*, was a *Draw-well*; firſt, People found the drawing of

Water

Water with a *Hand-cord* and a *Pitcher* troublesome, so they thought of a *Draught-wheel*; by and by they conceived such a Movement applicable to a *Spit*, if the motion of the Weight could be made slow enough, this was done by adding more *Wheels* and a *Flyer*, which made a *Jack*: by and by Men began to see, that if the motion were yet slower, it would serve to *measure Time* also, then instead of a *Flyer* they put a *Balance*, and thus made a *Clock*; this being so useful, Men considered how it might be made portable, by something answerable to a *Weight*, and so instead of that they put the *Spring* and the *Fuse-wheel*, which make a *Watch*. Here is the Pedigree of the noble Engine. But to what an astonishing Perfection is *Clock-work* and *Watch-work* now arrived! We will hardly allow a Gentleman of such Antiquity as *Boethius* to be the Inventor of the *Clock-work*, that hath been so mightily improved; no, *Regiomontanus*, thou shalt have the Honour of being the Instrument employed by God for the rare Invention, not more than between two and three hundred Years ago. The curious Performances of *Clock-work* cannot be related without our finding a Surprize of Pleasure in the Relations; how many *Motions* produced! How many *Designs* answer'd! The Gentleman who writes *The Artificial Clock-maker*, has with his Calculations made provision for a marvellous variety of them. What *Heylin* in his *Cosmography* reports of the Clock at *Lunden* in *Denmark*, what *Gaffarel* in his *unheard-of Curiosities* reports that he himself saw in a *Clock* at *Ligorn*, and the *Clock* which every day diverts the Spectators at *Harlem*, are notable Instances among many others. The *Repeating-Clocks* are now *common* on thousands of Tables, but how *curious!* At length Mr. *Huygens* has invented the way of applying *Pendulums* to *Watch-work*. If *Galilæo* entertained a Thought of such a thing, yet he never brought it to Perfection. We must not let Mr. *Huygens* be robb'd of his Claim, either by *Becher*, or the Academy *Del Cimento*. The first that was made in *England* was in
the

the Year 1662. The Uſes of theſe *Pendulum-Watches* cannot be ſufficiently celebrated.

But uſeful indeed will be theſe *Meaſurers of Time,* if they teach and help us to be the more wiſe *Redeemers* of it.

It was thought, that he, who when Patents for *Monopolies* were granting in *France,* begg'd for one *to demand a Shilling from every Man who wore a Watch, but had no care how he ſpent his Time,* ask'd for what would have afforded a Revenue too rich for a Subject!

If the *Mathematicks,* which have in the two laſt Centuries had ſuch wonderful Improvements, do for two hundred Years more improve in proportion to the former, who can tell what Mankind may come to! We may believe, without having *Seneca* our Author for it, *Multa venientis ævi populus ignota nobis ſciet.*

The Union between the S O U L and the B O D Y is altogether inexplicable, the *Soul* not having any *Surface* to touch the *Body,* and the *Body* not having any *Sentiment* as the *Soul.* The *Union* of the *Soul* and *Body* does conſiſt, as Monſieur *Tauvry* expreſſes it, in the *Conformity* of our *Thoughts* to our *Corporeal* Actions; but, ſays he, *for the Explication of this Conformity, we muſt have recourſe to a ſuperior Power.* Truly, *Sirs,* do what you can, you muſt quickly come to *that!*

Our *nervous Parts* are very ſenſible. *Objects* do affect our *Senſes,* and make Impreſſions on them; the *Senſes* receiving ſuch Impreſſions, the Modifications of the *Organs* produced by them terminate in the *Brain:* if they do not ſo, the *Soul* is unconcerned in them; but there is a *Law* given to the Soul by the glorious God, *who forms the Spirit of Man within him,* that in their doing ſo there ſhall be ſuch and ſuch *Thoughts* produced in the *Soul.*

'O *my Soul,* what a wondrous Being art thou! How 'capable of aſtoniſhing *Improvements!* How worthy to 'be cultivated with the beſt *Improvements!* How wor-'thy to have all poſſible Endeavours uſed for thy *Re-*'covery from the *Depravations* which thy *Fall from God*

U 2 'has

' has brought upon thee! How worthy to be *kept with*
' *all Diligence* from every thing that will bring any
' more *Wounds* upon thee! What *reaſon* is there that
' thou ſhouldſt be filled with the *Love* of God, and
' acted by the *Faith* of thy only Saviour! And if the
' *Image* of the glorious God, which has been impaired
' by *Satanick* Impreſſions on thee, be revived and re-
' ſtored in thee, what marvellous, and even eternal
' *Felicities*, art thou ſure of arriving to!'

But, O M A N, wilt thou ſtop here, and know nothing *above thy ſelf*? Among the antient *Jews* there
was a ſort of *natural Philoſophers*, who are by the *Rabbins* called חַכְמֵי הַמֶּדְקָר, *Sapientes Inquiſitionis*, or *Sapientes Scrutationis*, from their *enquiring* after *natural
Cauſes*; perhaps our Apoſtle may mean theſe, when he
ſays, 1 *Cor.* 1. 20. *Where is the Enquirer of this World?*
Jerome's Verſion favours it. Now of theſe Gentlemen
it is reported, that they denied the Exiſtence of *ſuperior Intelligences*; our *Chriſtian Philoſopher* will not be
guilty of ſuch a Stupidity.

We are now ſoaring into the *inviſible World*, a
World of *intellectual Beings*, but inviſible to ſuch *Eyes*
as ours. I do here in the firſt place moſt religiouſly
affirm, that even *my Senſes* have been convinced of ſuch
a World, by as clear, plain, full *Proofs* as ever any
Man's have had of what is moſt obvious in the *ſenſible
World*; *Proofs* which I am ready to offer in the moſt
convenient Seaſon. But then, *how glorious art thou, O
God, in thy innumerable Company of the holy Angels, and
in thy Government over thoſe alſo that have made themſelves
evil ones*! All the Wonders we have hitherto ſeen in
the *viſible Creation*, what are they, compared to thoſe
that are out of ſight, thoſe that are found among the
Angels that excel in Powers, the Hoſts of the infinite
G O D, *the Miniſters which do His Pleaſure*!

There is a *Scale of Nature*, wherein we paſs regularly and proportionably from a *Stone* to a *Man*, the
Faculties of the Creatures in their *various Claſſes* growing ſtill brighter and brighter, and more capacious,
till

till we arrive to thofe noble ones which are found in the *Soul* of M A N; and yet M A N is, as one well expreffes it, *but the Equator of the Univerfe.*

It is a juft View which Dr. *Grew* had of *the World,* when he came to this Determination: ' As there are ' feveral Orders of *animated Body* before we come to ' *Intellect,* fo it muft needs be that there are feveral ' Orders of *imbodied Intellect* before we come to *pure* ' *Mind.*'

It is likely that the Tranfition from *Human* to *per-fect* M I N D is made by a *gradual Afcent;* there may be *Angels* whofe Faculties may be as much fuperior to *ours,* as ours may be to thofe of a *Snail* or a *Worm.*

By and by we may arrive to *Minds* divefted of all *Body,* excellent *Minds,* which may enjoy the Know-ledge of Things by a more *immediate Intuition,* as well as without any Inclination to any *moral Evil.*

The higheft Perfection that any *created Mind* can arife to, is that in the *Soul* of our admirable Saviour, which is indeed *embodied;* but it is the *Soul* of the *Man* who is perfonally united to the S O N of G O D.

Anon we fee an infinite G O D; but *canft thou by fearching find out G O D? Canft thou find out the Almighty to Perfection?*

It is a good Thought, and well expreffed of an ho-neft Writer on *the Knowledge of God from the Works of Creation.* ' It is true there are fome *Footfteps* of a *Deity* ' in all the Works of Nature, but we fhould afcend ' by thefe *Footfteps* as by a *Footftool* to the *God* of the ' World, as *Solomon* by feveral Steps afcended to his ' *Throne,* and by the *Scale* of *Nature* afcend to the ' *God of Nature.*'

This is what we fhall now, tho in a more *fummary way,* a little more diftinctly proceed to.

No *Dominion over the Creatures* can be more accepta-bly, more delightfully exercifed with me than this; for me to *employ them* as often as I pleafe in *leading me to* G O D, and fo in ferving that which I propofe as the chief E N D for which I *live,* and *move,* and have my

Beings

Being ; which is, *to glorify G O D, and acknowledge Him.* When the *Creatures* were brought to our *Protoplaſt, to ſee what he would call them,* he did not exerciſe a more deſirable *Dominion* over them, in giving what *Name* he pleaſed to each of them, than I ſhall do in having them all brought to me, that I may read the *Name* of God, ſo far as it is to be ſeen in them, and be aſſiſted in my *Acknowledgments* of the Glorious-O N E.

¶. *Hear now the Concluſion of the Matter.* To en-kindle the *Diſpoſitions* and the *Reſolutions* of P I E T Y in my Brethren, is the *Intention* of all my E S S A Y S, and muſt be the *Concluſion* of them.

Atheiſm is now for ever chaſed and hiſſed out of the World, every thing in the World concurs to a Sen-tence of *Baniſhment* upon it. *Fly, thou Monſter, and hide, and let not the darkeſt Receſſes of* Africa *itſelf be able to cheriſh thee ; never dare to ſhew thyſelf in a World where every thing ſtands ready to overwhelm thee!* A B E I N G that muſt be *ſuperior* to *Matter,* even the *Creator* and *Governor* of all *Matter,* is every where ſo conſpicuous, that there can be nothing more *monſtrous* than *to deny the God that is above.* No *Syſtem* of *Atheiſm* has ever yet been offered among the Children of Men, but what may preſently be convinced of ſuch *Inconſiſtences,* that a Man muſt ridiculouſly believe *nothing certain* before he can imagine them ; it muſt be a *Syſtem* of *Things* which *cannot ſtand together !* A Bundle of *Contradictions* to themſelves, and to all *common Senſe.* I doubt it has been an *inconſiderate* thing to pay ſo much of a Compli-ment to *Atheiſm,* as to beſtow ſolemn *Treatiſes* full of learned *Arguments* for the Refutation of a *delirious Phrenzy,* which ought rather to be put out of coun-tenance with the moſt *contemptuous Indignation.* And I fear ſuch Writers as have been at the pains to put the *Objections* of *Atheiſm* into the moſt plauſible Terms, that they may have the honour of *laying a Devil when they have raiſed him,* have therein done too *unadviſedly.* However, to ſo much notice of the raving *Atheiſt* we may condeſcend while we go along, as to tell him, that

for

for a Man to queſtion the *Being* of a G O D, who requires from us an *Homage* of *Affection*, and *Wonderment*,
and Obedience to Himſelf, and a perpetual Concern
for the Welfare of the *Human Society*, for which He
has in our *Formation* evidently *ſuited* us, would be an
exalted Folly, which undergoes eſpecially two Condem-
nations; it is firſt condemned by this, that every Part
of the *Univerſe* is continually *pouring in* ſomething for
the *confuting* of it; there is not a Corner of the whole
World but what ſupplies a *Stone* towards the Infliction
of ſuch a *Death* upon the *Blaſphemy* as juſtly belongs
to it : and it has alſo this condemning of it, that Men
would ſoon become *Canibals* to one another by embracing it ; Men being utterly deſtitute of any Principle
to keep them *honeſt in the Dark*, there would be no *In-
tegrity* left in the World, but they would be as the
Fiſhes of the Sea to one another, and worſe than *the creeping Things, that have no Ruler over them.* Indeed from
every thing in the World there is this Voice more audible than the loudeſt Thunder to us ; *God hath ſpoken,
and theſe two things have I heard!* Firſt, *Believe and
adore a glorious G O D, who has made all theſe Things,
and know thou that He will bring thee into Judgment!*
And then *be careful to do nothing but what ſhall be for the
Good of the Community which the glorious G O D has made
thee a Member of.* Were what God *hath ſpoken* duly
regarded, and were theſe *two things* duly complied
with, the World would be ſoon revived into a deſirable *Garden of God*, and Mankind would be fetch'd
up into very comfortable Circumſtances; till *then* the
World continues in a wretched Condition, *full of dole-
ful Creatures,* with *wild Beaſts crying* in its *deſolate Hou-
ſes, Dragons* in its moſt *pleaſant Palaces.* And now declare, *O every thing that is reaſonable,* declare and pronounce upon it whether it be poſſible that *Maxims* abſolutely *neceſſary* to the *Subſiſtence* and *Happineſs* of
Mankind, can be *Falſities?* There is no poſſibility for
this, that *Cheats* and *Lyes* muſt be ſo *neceſſary,* that the
Ends which alone are worthy of a glorious GOD, cannot be attain'd without having *them* impoſed upon us!

Having

Having diſpatch'd the *Atheiſt*, with beſtowing on him *not many* Thoughts, yet *more* than could be deſerved by ſuch an *Idiot*; I will proceed now to propoſe two general Strokes of *Piety*, which will appear to a *Chriſtian Philoſopher* as unexceptionable as any Propoſals that ever were made to him.

Firſt, the Works of the glorious God exhibited to our View, 'tis moſt certain they do *beſpeak*, and they ſhould *excite* our *Acknowledgments of His Glories* appearing in them: the Great G O D is infinitely *gratified* in beholding the Diſplays of His own infinite *Power*, and *Wiſdom*, and *Goodneſs*, in the Works which He has made; but it is alſo a moſt acceptable Gratification to Him, when ſuch of His Works as are the *rational Beholders* of themſelves, and of the reſt, ſhall with devout Minds *acknowledge* His Perfections, which they ſee ſhining there. Never does one endued with *Reaſon* do any thing more evidently *reaſonable*, than when he makes every thing that occurs to him in the vaſt Fabrick of the World, an *Incentive* to ſome agreeable Efforts and Salleys of *Religion*. What can any Man living object againſt the *Piety* of a Mind awaken'd by the ſight of God in His Works, to ſuch Thoughts as theſe: *Verily, there is a glorious G O D! Verily, the G O D who does theſe things is worthy to be feared, worthy to be loved, worthy to be relied on! Verily, all poſſible Obedience is due to ſuch a G O D; and moſt abominable, moſt inexcuſable is the Wickedneſs of all Rebellion againſt Him!* A Mind kept under the Impreſſion of ſuch Thoughts as theſe, is an *holy* and a *noble* Mind, a *Temple* of God, a *Temple filled with the Glory of God.* There is nothing but what will afford an *Occaſion* for the *Thoughts*; the oftner a Man improves the *Occaſion*, the more does he *glorify G O D*, and anſwer the *chief End of Man*; and why ſhould he not *ſeek occaſion* for it, by viſiting for this purpoſe the ſeveral *Claſſes* of the Creatures (for *Diſcipulus in hâc Scholâ erit Peripateticus*) as he may have opportunity for ſo generous an Exerciſe! But ſince the horrid Evil of all *Sin* is to be inferred from this; *it is* a *Rebellion againſt the Laws of the glorious* GOD, *who is the Maker and the Ruler of all Worlds* ; and *it is a diſturbance of the good Order wherein the glorious Maker and Ruler of all Things has placed them all* ; how much ought a quickned *Horror of Sin* to accompany this Contemplation, and produce this moſt agreeable Reſolution, *My God, I will for ever fear to offend thy glorious Majeſty!* Nor is this all the *Improvement* which we are to make of what we ſee in the *Works of God* ; in our *improving* of them, we are to accept of the *Rebuke* which they give to our *Preſumption,* in pretending to criticize upon the *dark things* which occur in the Diſpenſations of His *Providence;* there is not any one of all the *Creatures* but what has thoſe *fine things* in the *Texture* of it, which have never yet been reached by our *Searches,* and we are as much at a loſs about the *Intent* as about the *Texture* of them; *as yet* we know not what the glorious God *intends* in His forming of thoſe *Creatures,* nor what *He has to do* in them, and with them; He therein proclaims this Expectation, *Surely they will fear me, and receive Inſtruction.* And the Point wherein we are now inſtructed is this : ' What! Shall I be ſo vain ' as to be *diſſatisfied* becauſe I do not *underſtand* what ' is done by the glorious GOD in the Works of His ' *Providence!' O my Soul, haſt thou not known, haſt thou not heard concerning the everlaſting God, the Lord, the Creator of the Ends of the Earth, that there is no ſearching of His Underſtanding?*

And then, ſecondly, the CHRIST of God muſt not be forgotten, who is *the Lord of all. I am not aſhamed of the Goſpel of CHRIST,* of which I will *affirm conſtantly,* that if the *Philoſopher* do not call it in, he *paganizes,* and leaves the fineſt and brighteſt Part of his Work *unfiniſhed.* Let *Colerus* perſuade us if he can, that in the Time of *John Frederick* the Elector of *Saxony* there was dug up a *Stone,* on which there was a Repreſentation of our *crucified Saviour;* but I cannot forbear ſaying, there is not a *Stone* any where which would not look *black* upon me, and *ſpeak* my Condemnation,

nation, if my *Philosophy* should be so *vain* as to make me lay aside my Thoughts of my *enthroned Saviour.* Let *Lambecius*, if he please, employ his Learning upon the Name of our Saviour C H R I S T, found in Letters naturally engraven at the bottom of a large *Agate-Cup*, which is to be seen among the Emperor's Curiosities; I have never drank in that *Cup*, however I can more easily believe it than I can the *Crucifixus ex Radice Crambres enatus*, or the *Imago Virginis cum Filiolo in Minerâ Ferri expressa*, and several more such things, which the Publishers of the *German Ephemerides* have mingled with their better Entertainments: but I will assert, that a glorious C H R I S T is more to be considered in the *Works of Nature* than the *Philosopher* is generally aware of; and my *CHRISTIAN Philosopher* has not fully done his Part, till He who is *the First-born of every Creature* be come into Consideration with him. *Alsted* mentions a *Siclus Judæo-Christianus*, which had on one side the Name *J E S U S*, with the Face of our *Saviour*, and on the other the Words that signify *the King Messiah comes with Peace, and God becomes a Man*; and *Leusden* says he had a couple of these *Coins* in his possession. I have nothing to say on the behalf of the *Zeal* in those *Christianized Jews*, who probably were the Authors of these *Coins*, a *Zeal* that *boil'd* into so needless an Expression of an Homage, that indeed cannot be too much expressed in the *instituted ways* of it to a Redeemer, whose *Kingdom is not of this World*: but this I will say, *all the Creatures in this World are part of His Kingdom*; there are no *Creatures* but what are His *Medals*, on every one of them the Name of J E S U S is to be found inscribed. Celebrate, O *Danbaver*, thy *Granatilla*, the *Peruvian Plant*, on which a strong Imagination finds a Representation of the *Instruments* employed in the *Sufferings* of our Saviour, and especially the *bloody Sweat* of His Agonies; were the Representation as really and lively made as has been imagined, I would subscribe to the Epigram upon it, which concludes:

Flos

Flos hic ità formâ vincit omnes Flosculos,
Ut totus optet esse Spectator Oculus.

But I will, with the Exercise of the most *solid Reason,*
by every part of the World, as well as the *Vegetables,*
be led to my Saviour.

A *View of the Creation* is to be taken, with suitable
Acknowledgments of the glorious C H R I S T, in
whom the *eternal Son of God* has personally united Himself to O N E of His *Creatures,* and becomes on *his*
account propitious to *all the rest;* our *Piety* indeed will
not be *Christianity* if H E be left unthought upon.

This is H E, of whom we are instructed, *Col.* 1.
16, 17. *All things were created by Him, and for Him;*
and He is before all things, and by Him all things consist.
It is no contemptible Thought wherewith *De Sabunde*
has entertained us: *Productio Mundi à Deo facta de Ni-*
hilo, arguit aliam productionem, summam, occultam, &
æternam in Deo, quæ est de sua propria Natura, in qua
producitur Deus de Deo, & per quam ostenditur summa
Trinitas in Deo. And certainly he that as a *Father*
does produce a *Son,* but as an *Artist* only produce an
House, has a Value for the *Son* which he has not for
the *House;* yea, we may say, if G O D had not first,
and from Eternity, been a *Father* to our *Saviour,* He
would never have exerted Himself as an *Artist* in that
Fabrick, which He has built *by the Might of His Power,*
and for the Honour of His Majesty!

The Great Sir *Francis Bacon* has a notable Passage
in his *Confession of Faith: I believe that God is so holy, as*
that it is impossible for Him to be pleased in any Creature,
tho the Work of his own Hands, without beholding of the
same in the Face of a Mediator; —— *without which it was*
impossible for Him to have descended to any Work of Crea-
tion, but He should have enjoyed the blessed and individual
Society of three Persons in the Godhead for ever; but out of
His eternal and infinite Goodness and Love purposing to be-
come a Creature, and communicate with His Creatures, He
ordained

ordained in His eternal Counsel that one Person of the God-head should be united to one Nature, and to one particular of His Creatures; that so in the Person of the Mediator the true Ladder might be fixed, whereby God might descend to His Creatures, and His Creatures ascend to Him.

It was an high Flight of *Origen*, who urges, that our *High-Priest's* having *tasted of Death*, ὑπὲρ παντὸς, F O R A L L, is to be extended even to the very *Stars*, which would otherwise have been *impure* in the sight of God; and thus are A L L T H I N G S re-stored to the *Kingdom* of the Father. Our Apostle *Paul* in a famous Passage to the *Colossians* [i. 19, 20.] may seem highly to favour this Flight. One says up-on it, ' If this be so, we need not break the Glasses ' of *Galilæo*, the *Spots* may be washed out of the *Sun*, ' and *total Nature* sanctified to God that made it.'

Yea, the sacred Scriptures plainly and often invite us to a Conception, which Dr. *Goodwin* has chosen to deliver in such Terms as these : ' The *Son of God* per-' sonally and actually existing as the Son of God with ' God, afore the World or any Creature was made, *He* ' undertaking and covenanting with God to become ' a *Man*, yea, *that Man* which He hath now taken up ' into one Person with Himself, as well for *this End*, ' as for *other Ends* more glorious ; God did in the ' Fore-knowledge of *that*, and in the Assurance of that ' *Covenant* of His, proceed to the *creating* of all things ' which He hath made ; and without the Intuition of ' *this*, or having *this* in His Eye, He would not have ' made any thing which He hath made.'

O C H R I S T I A N, *lift up now thine Eyes, and look from the place where thou art* to all Points of the Compass, and concerning *whatever thou seest*, allow that all these things were formed *for the Sake* of that Glo-rious-One, who is now *God manifest in the Flesh* of our J E S U S; 'tis on *His* Account that the eternal God-head has the *Delight* in all these things, which pre-serves them in their Being, and grants them the *Help*, in the *obtaining* whereof they *continue to this day.*

But

But were they not all made *by the Hand,* as well as *for the Sake* of that Glorious-O N E? They were verily ſo. *O my JESUS, it was that Son of God who now dwells in thee, in and by whom the Godhead exerted the Power, which could be exerted by none but an all-powerful GOD, in the creating of the World!* He is that WORD of GOD *by whom all things were made, and without whom was not any thing made that was made.*

This is not all that we have to think upon; we ſee an incomparable *Wiſdom* of GOD in His *Creatures;* one cannot but preſently infer, *What an incomprehenſible Wiſdom then in the Methods and Affairs of that Redemption, whereof the glorious GOD has laid the Plan in our JESUS!* Things which the *Angels deſire to look into.* But, O *evangelized Mind,* go on, mount up, ſoar higher, think at this rate; *the infinite Wiſdom which formed all theſe things is peculiarly ſeated in the Son of God;* He is that *reflexive Wiſdom* of the eternal *Father,* and that *Image of the inviſible God, by whom all things were created;* in *Him* there is after a peculiar manner the original *Idea* and *Archetype* of every thing that offers the infinite *Wiſdom* of God to our Admiration. Wherever we ſee the *Wiſdom* of God admirably ſhining before us, we are invited to ſuch a Thought as this; *this Glory is originally to be found in thee, O our Immanuel!* 'Tis in Him *tranſcendently.* But then 'tis impoſſible to ſtop without adding, *How glorious, how wondrous, how lovely art thou, O our Saviour!*

Nor may we lay aſide a grateful Senſe of this, that as the *Son* of God is *the Upholder of all Things in all Worlds,* thus, that it is owing to his potent *Interceſſion* that the *Sin of Man* has made no more havock on this *our World.* This *our World* has been by the *Sin of Man* ſo perverted from the *true Ends* of it, and rendred full of ſuch loathſome and hateful Regions, and ſuch *Scelerata Caſtra,* that the Revenges of God would have long ſince rendred it as a *fiery Oven,* if our bleſſed JESUS had not *interceded* for it: *O my Saviour, what would have become of me, and of all that comforts me, if thy Interpoſition had not preſerved us!* We

We will add one thing more : Tho the one G O D in His *three Subfistences* be the *Governor* as well as the *Creator* of the World, and so the *Son* of God ever had what we call the *natural Government* of the World, yet upon the *Fall* of Mankind there is a *mediatory Kingdom* that becomes expedient, that so *guilty Man,* and that which was *loft,* may be brought to God; and the singular Honour of this *mediatory Kingdom* is more *immediately* and most *agreeably* assign'd to the *Son of God,* who assumes the Man J E S U S into His own Person, and has *all Power in Heaven and Earth given to Him*; all things are now commanded and ordered by the *Son of God* in the *Man upon the Throne,* and this *to the Glory of the Father,* by whom the *mediatory Kingdom* is erected, and so conferred. This *peculiar Kingdom* thus managed by the *Son of God* in our J E S U S, will cease when the illustrious Ends of it are all accomplished, and *then* the *Son of God* no longer having such a *diftinct Kingdom* of His own, shall return to those eternal Circumstances, wherein He shall reign with the *Father* and the *Holy Spirit,* one God, blessed for ever. In the mean time, what Creatures can we behold without being obliged to some such Doxology as this; *O Son of God, incarnate and enthroned in my JESUS, this is part of thy Dominion! What a great King art thou, and what a Name haft thou above every Name, and how vaftly extended is thy Dominion! Dominion and Fear is with thee, and there is no Number of thine Armies! All the Inhabitants of the Earth, and their moft puiffant Emperors, are to be reputed as nothing before thee!*

But then at laft I am losing myself in such Thoughts as these : *Who can tell* what *Ufes* our Saviour will put all these *Creatures* to at the *Reftitution of all things,* when He comes to rescue them from the *Vanity* which as yet captivates them and incumbers them; and His raised People in the *new Heavens* will make their Visits to a *new Earth,* which they shall find flourishing in *Paradifaick* Regularities? *Lord, what thou meaneft in them, I know not now, but I shall know hereafter!* I go on, *Who can tell* how ſweetly our Saviour may *feaſt* His *choſen People* in the *Future State*, with Exhibitions of all theſe *Creatures*, in their various *Natures*, and their curious *Beauties* to them? *Lord, I hope for an eternally progreſſive Knowledge, from the Lamb of God ſucceſſively leading me to the Fountains of it!*

I recover out of my more *conjectural Prognoſtications*, with reſolving what may *at preſent* yield to a ſerious Mind a *Satisfaction*, to which this World knows none ſuperior: When in a way of *occaſional Reflection* I employ the *Creatures* as my *Teachers*, I will by the *Truths* wherein thoſe ready *Monitors* inſtruct me, be led to my glorious JESUS; I will conſider the *Truths as they are in JESUS*, and count my *Aſceticks* deficient, till I have ſome Thoughts of HIM and of His *Glories* awakened in me. To conclude, It is a good Paſſage which a little Treatiſe entitled, *Theologia Ruris*, or, *The Book of Nature*, breaks off withal, and I might make it my Concluſion: ' If we mind *Heaven* whilſt ' we live here upon *Earth*, this *Earth* will ſerve to con- ' duct us to *Heaven*, thro the Merits and Mediation ' of the *Son of God*, who was made the *Son of Man*, and ' came thence on purpoſe into this lower World to ' convey us up thither.'

I will finiſh with a Speculation, which my moſt valuable Dr. *Cheyne* has a little more largely proſecuted and cultivated.

All *intelligent compound Beings* have their whole Entertainment in theſe three Principles, the DESIRE, the OBJECT, and the SENSATION ariſing from the *Congruity* between them; this *Analogy* is preſerved full and clear thro the *Spiritual World*, yea, and thro the *material* alſo; ſo *univerſal* and *perpetual* an *Analogy* can ariſe from nothing but its *Pattern* and *Archetype* in the infinite God or Maker; and could we carry it up to the Source of it, we ſhould find the TRINITY of Perſons in the eternal GODHEAD admirably exhibited to us. In the GODHEAD we may firſt apprehend a *Deſire*, an infinitely active,

ardent,

ardent, powerful *Thought*, propofing of *Satisfaction*; let this reprefent GOD the FATHER: but it is not poffible for any Object but God Himfelf to *fatisfy Himfelf*, and fill His *Defire* of Happinefs; therefore HE Himfelf *reflected* in upon Himfelf, and contemplating His own infinite Perfections, even the *Brightnefs of His Glory*, and the *exprefs Image of His Perfon*, muft anfwer this glorious Intention; and this may reprefent to us GOD the SON. Upon this Contemplation, wherein GOD Himfelf does behold, and poffefs, and enjoy Himfelf, there cannot but arife a *Love*, a *Joy*, an *Acquiefcence* of God Himfelf within Himfelf, and worthy of a God; this may fhadow out to us the third and the laft of the Principles in this *myfterious Ternary*, that is to fay, the Holy SPIRIT. Tho thefe *three Relations* of the Godhead in itfelf, when derived analogically down to Creatures, may appear but *Modifications* of a *real Subfiftence*, yet in the fupreme Infinitude of the Divine Nature, they muft be infinitely *real* and *living* Principles. Thofe which are but *Relations*, when tranfferred to *created Beings*, are glorious *Relatives* in the infinite God. And in this View of the Holy Trinity, low as it is, it is impoffible the SON fhould be without the FATHER, or the FATHER without the SON, or both without the Holy SPIRIT; it is impoffible the SON fhould not be neceffarily and eternally begotten of the FATHER, or that the Holy SPIRIT fhould not neceffarily and eternally proceed both from Him and from the SON. Thus from what occurs throughout the whole Creation, *Reafon* forms an imperfect Idea of this incomprehenfible Myftery.

But it is time to ftop here, and indeed how can we go any further!

FINIS.